CLASSICAL
SCIENTIFIC
PAPERS

PHYSICS

CLASSICAL
SCIENTIFIC
PAPERS

PHYSICS

Facsimile reproductions
of famous scientific papers

With an introduction by
STEPHEN WRIGHT, B.Sc., A.R.C.S.

Mills & Boon Limited
50 Grafton Way London W.1

Printed in Great Britain by Jarrold and Sons Ltd, Norwich

0271 4P

Contents

Acknowledgments

For permission to reproduce the articles that make up this book we are indebted to a number of societies and individuals, to all of whom we should like to express our thanks.

The Fellows of the Royal Society and the Assistant Editor of their *Proceedings*, Mr J. G. Graddon, have been most generous in the help they have provided, as well as allowing us to include items 8, 13, 15, 17, 19 and 20 in this volume. We acknowledge with gratitude the individual permission given by Sir James Chadwick, Sir John Cockcroft and Sir Ernest Marsden, to reproduce their own articles and are deeply appreciative of the good wishes they have expressed for our project.

A number of contributions appeared originally in *The Philosophical Magazine* (1, 2, 3, 4, 5, 6, 7, 9, 10, 11, 12 and 16) and we acknowledge permission to reproduce them given by Messrs Taylor and Francis. Among those to whom we wish again to express our thanks are Sir Ernest Marsden (item 10) and Mrs A. H. Compton for allowing us to reproduce her late husband's article (16).

For item 18 we wish also to thank Mrs Compton, as well as Dr Doan and the National Academy of Sciences.

We acknowledge permission given by Messrs Edward Arnold & Sons for allowing us to reproduce a chapter from F. W. Aston's *Mass Spectra and Isotopes* (21) and by the Editors of *Nature* for Sir James Chadwick's letter (14).

We are also very grateful to Mr John Jarrold of Messrs Jarrold & Sons, Ltd, Norwich, whose enthusiasm and advice have been invaluable in the production of this book.

Foreword

There is a certain magic in seeing an original document which has made history, whether it is a copy of Magna Carta or a first edition of Newton's *De Motu Corporum*. In science the effect can be particularly dramatic, because a relatively short paper appearing in a learned journal can influence the whole subsequent course of research and thence the shape of world civilisation. One has only to consider the work on the structure of the atom to see how this has happened. Yet it is not easy to come by these papers. Few universities and even fewer schools will possess a complete set over the last eighty years of, for example, the *Proceedings of The Royal Society* or of *The Philosophical Magazine*. Even if they do, the papers which are relevant are widely dispersed amongst a mass of other scientific material and are not easy of access.

For this reason the view has been expressed that it would be valuable for university students and sixth forms to be able to obtain reproductions of selected scientific papers which have appeared earlier in learned journals. The main selection here was made at a Ministry of Education Conference on Modern Chemistry and Physics held in Oxford, to which a number of papers have been added to complete the pattern. The papers have been reproduced facsimile so that the modern reader can share something of the excitement felt, for instance, by contemporaries when they read the 'Structure of the Atom' by Rutherford in *The Philosophical Magazine*.

Introduction

An introduction of this kind cannot include a comprehensive account of the history of science, however desirable that might be. It is rather an attempt to set these Scientific Papers into some kind of perspective so that the explosion that occurred in scientific activity in the few decades following 1890 can be appreciated.

The two ideas which are basic to an understanding of the significance of the papers are the atomic theory and the electromagnetic field and it is a measure of the rate of advance that the atom and the field had been firmly established for barely twenty years before the scientific world was asked to give up fundamental parts of each concept. The miracle is that the experimental evidence was so readily accepted, leading, as it did, to an unconventional and contradictory picture of the physical world.

The notion of the atom is first fully recorded by the poet Lucretius (95–55 B.C.), who obtained his physics from Democritus. It is thus Democritus to whom we owe this concept.

> Know, too, that bodies in their frame consist,
> Part, of primordial atoms uncombined,
> And part combined and blending; these alone
> Pervious and rare; while those so solid formed
> No force create can sever, or dissolve.   (*line 535*)

> But what more obvious than that bounds exist
> To matter decompounding. . . .   (*line 614*)

To account for the nature of fluids Democritus assumed the atoms to be less closely packed in the rarer media.

> . . . In created things exists,
> Search where thou wilt, an incorporeal void   (*line 375*)

and a little later

> Were space like this vouchsafed not, naught could move,
> Corporeal forms would still resist, and strive
> With forms corporeal, nor consent to yield.   (*line 381*)[1]

Nothing exists except atoms and space. Between some atoms there is an affinity and various substances may therefore be formed by combination. But,

> . . . For seeds these are
> That through the boundless void for ever stray,
> Of social bond abhorrent. . . .
>
> *(line 114)*[2]

And these are the specks of dust to be seen when light is scattered from them in a room across which there is a beam of sunlight.

The 'atoms' are supposed to 'fall' through space under some gravitational attraction. Lucretius was acute enough to observe that the heavy and light particles will move together and, in order that combination can take place, some must veer and collide. Once the atoms are in each other's sphere of influence, they ceaselessly jostle each other and to withstand such conditions they must be hard.

Because the creation of bodies appeared to take place by chance and there was no room for a Creator in the scheme of Democritus, his views incurred the odium of medieval Schoolmen. Aristotle's writings were the standard text and his authority was undisputed.

Francis Bacon was a prime mover in the attempt to challenge this authority and to verify the fruits of reasoning with experiment.

Again, the reverence for antiquity, and the authority of men who have been esteemed great in philosophy, and general unanimity, have retarded men from advancing in science and almost enchanted them.[3]

Also,

The evil, however, has been wonderfully increased by an opinion, or inveterate conceit, which is both vainglorious and prejudicial, namely, that the dignity of the human mind is lowered by long and frequent intercourse with experiments. . . .[4]

The way was open for Galileo, Kepler, Newton and the rest. However, the atom is what concerns us and a quotation from Robert Boyle will show that the atomic idea had progressed very little in substance. But it was at least discussed and there existed a body of men who were prepared to experiment.

1. Local motion in various parts of the universal matter tends in different ways. It will follow that matters must be divided into distinct parts.
2. These parts, each being finite, must be of some bigness or size.
3. Each part must have a determinate shape.
4. Some parts of the matter will be arrested in their motion by their mutual implication (connexions or actions) and will be in a state of rest in the popular sense of the word.

. . .

xiv

7. Corpuscles are, in great numbers, associated together to form a mass or body, and give to it a texture.

8. Because of irregularities of figure of the corpuscles, almost all solid and all gross fluid bodies have pores in them.

. . .

10. (a) Durable aggregations of simple corpuscles constitute primary concretions, or elements (i.e. gold, phosphorus, tin, etc.).

(b) The elements may be mingled together to form compound bodies.

(c) Compound bodies may be mingled to make decompounded bodies and so afford a way whereby nature varies matter, which we will call mixture or composition.[5]

Newton supposed the atoms of gases to consist of infinitely hard spheres, capable of mutual repulsion.

Facts were now required to make the atomic nature of matter an unavoidable deduction and it was necessary to show that atoms of different elements have different weights as well as different chemical properties. The scientific history of the period immediately preceding that in which this evidence was gathered was dominated by phlogiston, 'the fire-material' which was supposed to escape from a body during combustion. By weighing mercury before and after heating it gently, Lavoisier demonstrated that it gained weight and that the weight gained by the substance equalled the weight lost by the air. He also showed that the missing portion of the air was oxygen. The phlogistonists tried to modify their ideas to accommodate new facts and in the attempt drew from Lavoisier the following characteristic comment:

Sometimes this principle (phlogiston) is a principle of weight and sometimes it is not; sometimes it is free fire, sometimes it is fire combined with the earthly element; sometimes it passes through the pores of vessels, sometimes they are impenetrable to it; it explains both causticity and non-causticity, transparency and opacity, colours and lack of colours. It is a veritable Proteus which changes form at every instant.[6]

The success of this precise quantitative series of investigations seems to have stimulated others. Berzelius in 1818 published an analysis of nearly 2000 elements and compounds to test the law of multiple proportions, and similar work was performed, notably by Stas, on behalf of the law of constant proportions. Both these laws are a consequence of Dalton's atomic theory (1808).[7] Once the distinction between atoms and molecules had been recognised (Avogadro (1811) and Gay-Lussac (1809) had, in effect, shown that under the same conditions equal volumes of gas contain equal numbers of particles) it was possible to measure atomic weights and not merely combining weights. Mendeléeff's Table followed in 1869, with its profound consequences for checking the atomic weights of known elements and stimulating a search for new ones. When some of these were discovered (e.g.

gallium, scandium and germanium) very little doubt could remain as to the correctness of the atomic theory.

Although Prout's hypothesis suggesting that matter was ultimately constituted from hydrogen had been put forward in 1816, the atom itself remained almost untouched. Indeed, it may be said that scientists were further from the truth than was Democritus. Dalton assumed that gases, for example, consisted of a collection of hard spheres surrounded by an atmosphere of heat. Gases could be compressed because the atmosphere round each nucleus was of variable density and the atoms were repelled with increasing force as they were pressed together. Gases were, therefore, a static collection of Newtonian atoms. It is unfair to quibble, however, over the technical incorrectness of Dalton's view that atoms of an element have the same mass and that atoms of different elements have different masses.

A further note must be added to bring the state of the atomic theory to the point it had reached towards the end of the last century. On the basis of experiment, Rumford (1798) and Davy (1800) rendered the 'Caloric' theory of heat untenable. To replace it a dynamic theory was conceived in which the atoms of a substance receive kinetic energy when heated, i.e. heat energy is simply the mechanical energy of particles. In determining the mechanical equivalent of heat by a series of experiments (1843–9), Joule made the dynamic idea very attractive. Mathematical physicists, notably Herapath (1816), Waterson (1846), Clausius (1858), Maxwell (1859) and Boltzmann (1897) applied the idea to gases and, although some simplifying assumptions had to be made, deduced the gas laws and obtained correct values for (Cp/Cv), etc. In addition, Maxwell obtained a distribution curve showing the velocity spread of the particles. To do this he had to modify the billiard ball atom to one which repelled its neighbours with a force inversely proportional to the fifth power of the distance, but the curve was correct, as Stern finally showed in a direct method in 1920. Although we are dealing in the vast majority of cases with molecules and not atoms, the work on the kinetic theory of gases demonstrated that it was correct to view matter as a collection of particles in constant motion and what, at first, had been a puzzling chance observation in 1828 by an English naturalist, Brown, now fitted perfectly into the scheme of things. His pollen grains were merely subject to uneven bombardment by the water molecules in which they were suspended.

In the second half of the nineteenth century a revolution in physics took place, usually referred to as the decline of the mechanical view. On this view every physical phenomenon could be interpreted on the basis of the laws governing the interactions of the particles which comprise matter. Taking the simplest case, any two particles will experience a force inversely proportional to the square of the distance separating them, and along a line joining their centres. Such an idea had had very notable successes in the persuasive hands of Kepler, Newton and Galileo and, once the active principle of heat was recognised as mechanical energy instead of caloric, it was possible to predict the behaviour of a gas under given conditions with considerable precision. All that was required was the application of simple dynamics.[8]

Initial studies of electricity and magnetism supported the mechanical hypothesis. Coulomb's inverse square law was shown to hold for magnetic poles and electrostatically charged spheres. Under the weight of evidence adduced by Young (1801), Fresnel (1813) and Foucault (1850), light was recognised as a transverse wave which required a medium, the aether, in which to travel. Accepting the existence of this fluid, it was quite possible to account for all the known optical phenomena in terms of mechanics. Similar success was achieved in the field of acoustics.

Then the difficulties of this viewpoint began to accumulate. The nature of the aether, which must certainly have some very remarkable facets, was a stumbling block of which Huygens himself was very well aware. It is interesting and instructive to follow his arguments as recorded in *A Treatise on Light* (1690). The advantage of the aether hypothesis was that the difficulties were concentrated in one entity. Newton's light corpuscles had to be of many different kinds to account for the large variety of observed colours and it was unsatisfactory to be forced to invent so many distinct particles. Experiments performed by Oersted (1820) indicated that the force experienced by a magnetic needle pivoted at the centre of a coil in which a steady current flowed was perpendicular to the plane of the coil; therefore the force between a small current element and the needle certainly did not lie on a line joining the two. This flaw in the mechanical view was more searchingly exposed in 1876 by Rowland, who rotated two partially charged discs about a common axis and placed a magnetic needle at the centre of the apparatus. Not only was the force found to be perpendicular to the planes of the circles, but it depended upon the velocity of the charges as well as on their magnitude. Only a much altered mechanical system could incorporate these new facts and the alteration could only be made at the expense of the cardinal virtue of simplicity. The mechanical view had to be abandoned.

The great idea of field is due to Michael Faraday (1791–1867). It began with the almost tangible lines of force he imagined to stretch between two charged bodies or across the gap between the poles of adjacent magnets. Faraday endowed the lines with properties akin to elasticity and mutual repulsion so that forces, somehow transmitted along them, had magnitudes and directions similar to those actually observed. They proved significant in another respect too. The long search for proof of Faraday's faith that magnetism and electricity were reciprocally linked culminated in 1831 when he discovered electromagnetic induction. He found it convenient and illuminating to express his findings in terms of the changes in the number of lines of force which occur when a magnet is moved or a current decays in a circuit. In addition, if the lines are cut by a conductor, an electro-motive force is induced but when the conductor and lines are at rest with respect to each other this does not happen.

Once the pattern of these lines had been established their source could be ignored. A striking example of the fruitfulness of this viewpoint is the well-known one of the solenoid and bar magnet. The external effect of each on a compass needle can be the same under the right conditions and this is predicted by the congruence of their fields, whereas the objects from which the fields emanate are different.

Now suppose the parallel plates of a capacitor are charged and then shorted with a loop wire. The varying current in the loop generates a changing magnetic field and it is implausible to suppose that a gap will occur in the magnetic field in the region of the capacitor. The changing electric field between the capacitor plates gives rise to magnetic effects similar to those caused by the current. Thus reduced to their essentials, the laws of electromagnetic induction are concerned with changing electric and magnetic fields and a flow of current in a circuit is a secondary effect. Maxwell's great achievement was to construct equations to describe the variation of these fields in space, which enable us to predict the behaviour of an electromagnetic wave as it spreads out from its source.[9] He disliked the idea of action at a distance and visualised the source of the electromagnetic waves causing a disturbance in the immediate vicinity, which was then transmitted to the next point and so on. From the equations it turned out that the velocity of the wave was equal to the ratio of the electrostatic to the electromagnetic units and measurements of these gave a value of $3 \cdot 1 \times 10^{10}$ cm./sec. This was in such striking agreement with the value of the velocity of light determined by Fizeau (1849), $3 \cdot 15 \times 10^{10}$ cm./sec., that other evidence of the electromagnetic nature of light waves was sought. The search ended with the experiments of Hertz[10] who demonstrated refraction, interference, diffraction, etc. and obtained a value for the velocity of his electromagnetic waves of between about 2 and $4 \cdot 5 \times 10^{10}$ cm./sec.

To sum up, a quotation from the book by Einstein and Infeld[8] is relevant:

In the beginning, the field concept was no more than a means of facilitating the understanding of phenomena from the mechanical point of view. In the new field language it is the description of the field between two charges, and not the charges themselves which is essential for an understanding of their action. The recognition of the new concept grew steadily, until substance was overshadowed by the field. It was realised that something of great importance had happened in physics. A new reality was created, a new concept for which there was no place in the mechanical description. Slowly and by a struggle the field concept established for itself a leading place in physics and has remained one of the basic physical concepts. The electromagnetic field is, for the modern physicist, as real as the chair on which he sits.

Thus physics in 1890 had atoms and it had fields. The latter were successful in the fundamental sense that two branches of the subject—light and electromagnetism—had been fused into one. A number of problems still remained, e.g. as to the nature of the atoms and the bond which exists between them when molecules are formed and so on, but physicists were not too dissatisfied with the deeper understanding they had gained. Few of them can have had an inkling of the scientific upheaval which was to take place so soon.

[1] Lucretius, *On the Nature of Things*, Book I.

[2] Lucretius, *ibid.*, Book II.

[3] Francis Bacon, *Novum Organum*, LXXXIV.

[4] Francis Bacon, *ibid.*, LXXXIII.

[5] Hon. Robert Boyle, *Experiments and Notes about the Mechanical Origin of Production of Particular Qualities*, vol. 4, 292.

[6] A. L. Lavoisier, 'Réflexions sur le phlogistique' (œuvres, vol. 2, 640). Quoted by L. S. More in *The Life and Works of the Hon. Robert Boyle*.

[7] For the claims of William Higgins as originator of the atomic theory, see *The Story of Atomic Energy* by F. Soddy.

[8] For more extended and rounded discussion of this topic see *The Evolution of Physics* by A. Einstein and L. Infeld (Cambridge University Press), or *Turning Points in Physics*, chapter 1 by R. J. Blin-Stoyle (North Holland University Publishing Company, Amsterdam).

[9] See *Clerk Maxwell and Modern Science*, chapter 2 by R. E. Peierls, edited by C. Domb (University of London Press).

[10] See *Electric Waves* by H. Hertz, translated by D. E. Jones (Dover Publications).

Group I

RADIOACTIVITY

In the nineteenth century the astonishing progress of chemical science rested on the immutable character of the elements. When, therefore, the young Professor of Physics in Montreal proposed that, after all, transmutation was not only possible but was actually in continuous progress, he was clearly in need of plenty of evidence to support this most unorthodox hypothesis.[1]

These papers record some of that evidence. They illustrate, too, Rutherford's uncanny knack of going to the heart of a problem and designing experiments which showed directly and unambiguously the answer to the question he was asking. In this respect, the paper by Rutherford and Royds is a real classic.

The diagrams given below, showing the three naturally occurring radioactive series, will help the reader to follow the first paper.

URANIUM SERIES

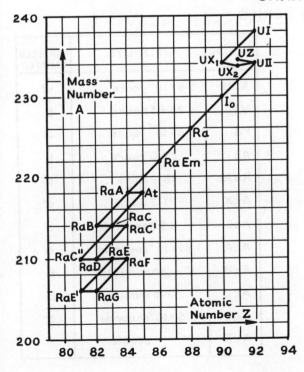

NUCLIDE	HALF-LIFE	PARTICLE EMITTED
UI	$4 \cdot 50 \times 10^{9}$ years	α
UX$_1$	$24 \cdot 1$ days	β
UX$_2$	$1 \cdot 18$ minutes	β
UII	$2 \cdot 5 \times 10^{5}$ years	α
I$_0$	$8 \cdot 0 \times 10^{4}$ years	α
Ra	1622 years	α
RaEm	$3 \cdot 825$ days	α
RaA	$3 \cdot 05$ minutes	α
RaB	$26 \cdot 8$ minutes	β
RaC	$19 \cdot 7$ minutes	β
RaC'	$1 \cdot 6 \times 10^{-4}$ seconds	α
RaD	22 years	β
RaE	$5 \cdot 0$ days	β
RaF	138 days	α
RaG	stable	

[1] Obituary notice of Lord Rutherford in *The Times*, October 1937.

THORIUM SERIES

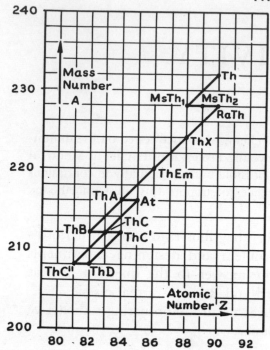

NUCLIDE	HALF-LIFE	PARTICLE EMITTED
Th	1.39×10^{10} years	α
MsTh$_1$	6.7 years	β
MsTh$_2$	6.13 hours	β
RaTh	1.9 years	α
ThX	3.64 days	α
ThEm	54.5 seconds	α
ThA	0.16 seconds	α
ThB	10.6 hours	β
ThC	60.5 minutes	β
ThC'	3×10^{-7} seconds	α
ThD	stable	

ACTINIUM SERIES

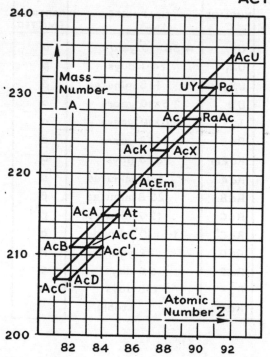

NUCLIDE	HALF-LIFE	PARTICLE EMITTED
AcU	8.8×10^8 years	α
UY	25.65 hours	β
Pa	3.4×10^4 years	α
Ac	22.0 years	β
RaAc	18.9 days	α
AcX	11.2 days	α
AcEm	3.92 seconds	α
AcA	1.83×10^{-3} seconds	α
AcB	36 minutes	β
AcC	2.16 minutes	β
AcC'	5×10^{-3} seconds	α
AcD	stable	

XLI. *The Cause and Nature of Radioactivity.*—Part I. *By* E. RUTHERFORD, *M.A., D.Sc., Macdonald Professor of Physics, and* F. SODDY, *B.A.* (*Oxon.*), *Demonstrator in Chemistry, McGill University, Montreal* *.

CONTENTS.

I. *Introduction.*

THE following papers give the results of a detailed investigation of the radioactivity of thorium compounds which has thrown light on the questions connected

* Communicated by the Authors. Accounts of these researches, during the progress of the investigation, have already been given to the London Chemical Society.

with the source and maintenance of the energy dissipated by radioactive substances. Radioactivity is shown to be accompanied by chemical changes in which new types of matter are being continuously produced. These reaction products are at first radioactive, the activity diminishing regularly from the moment of formation. Their continuous production maintains the radioactivity of the matter producing them at a definite equilibrium-value. The conclusion is drawn that these chemical changes must be sub-atomic in character.

The present researches had as their starting-point the facts that had come to light with regard to thorium radioactivity (Rutherford, Phil. Mag. 1900, vol. xlix. pp. 1 & 161). Besides being radioactive in the same sense as the uranium compounds, the compounds of thorium continuously emit into the surrounding atmosphere a gas which possesses the property of temporary radioactivity. This "emanation," as it has been named, is the source of rays, which ionize gases and darken the photographic film *.

The most striking property of the thorium emanation is its power of exciting radioactivity on all surfaces with which it comes into contact. A substance after being exposed for some time in the presence of the emanation behaves as if it were covered with an invisible layer of an intensely active material. If the thoria is exposed in a strong electric field, the excited radioactivity is entirely confined to the negatively charged surface. In this way it is possible to concentrate the excited radioactivity on a very small area. The excited radioactivity can be removed by rubbing or by the action of acids, as, for example, sulphuric, hydrochloric, and hydrofluoric acids. If the acids be then evaporated, the radioactivity remains on the dish.

The emanating power of thorium compounds is independent of the surrounding atmosphere, and the excited activity it produces is independent of the nature of the substance on which it is manifested. These properties made it appear that both phenomena were caused by minute quantities of special kinds of matter in the radioactive state, produced by the thorium compound.

The next consideration in regard to these examples of radioactivity, is that the activity in each case diminishes regularly with the lapse of time, the intensity of radiation at each instant being proportional to the amount of energy remaining to be radiated. For the emanation a period of

---

* If thorium oxide be exposed to a white heat its power of giving an emanation is to a large extent destroyed. Thoria that has been so treated is referred to throughout as " de-emanated."

one minute, and for the excited activity a period of eleven hours, causes the activity to fall to half its value.

These actions—(1) the production of radioactive material, and (2) the dissipation of its available energy by radiation—which are exhibited by thorium compounds in the secondary effects of emanating power and excited radioactivity, are in reality taking place in all manifestations of radioactivity. The constant radioactivity of the radioactive elements is the result of an equilibrium between these two opposing processes.

II. *The Experimental Methods of investigating Radioactivity.*

Two methods are used for the measurement of radioactivity, the electrical and the photographic. The photographic method is of a qualitative rather than a quantitative character; its effects are cumulative with time, and as a rule long exposures are necessary when the radioactivity of a feeble agent like thoria is to be demonstrated. In addition, Russell has shown that the darkening of a photographic plate is brought about also by agents of a totally different character from those under consideration, and, moreover, under very general conditions. Sir William Crookes (Proc. Roy. Soc. (1900) lxvi. p. 409) has sounded a timely note of warning against putting too much confidence in the indications of the photographic method of measuring radioactivity. The uncertainty of an effect produced by cumulative action over long periods of time quite precludes its use for work of anything but a qualitative character.

But the most important objection to the photographic method is that certain types of rays from radioactive substances, which ionize gases strongly, produce little if any effect on the sensitive film. In the case of uranium, these protographically inactive rays form by far the greatest part of the total radiation, and much of the previous work on uranium by the photographic method must be interpreted differently (Soddy, Proc. Chem. Soc. 1902, p. 121).

On the other hand, it is possible to compare intensities of radiation by the electrical method with greater rapidity and with an error not exceeding 1 or 2 per cent. These methods are based on the property generally possessed by all radiations of the kind in question, of rendering a gas capable of discharging both positive and negative electricity. These, as will be shown, are capable of great refinement and certainty. An ordinary quadrant electrometer is capable of detecting and measuring a difference of potential of at least 10^{-2} volts. With special instruments, this sensitiveness may be increased a hundredfold. An average value for the capacity of the electrometer and connexions is 3×10^{-5} microfarads; and when this is charged up to 10^{-2} volts, a quantity of electricity corresponding to 3×10^{-13} coulombs is stored up. Now in the electrolysis of water one gram of hydrogen carries a charge of 10^5 coulombs. Assuming, for the sake of example, that the conduction of electricity in gases is analogous to that in liquids, this amount of electricity corresponds to the transport of a mass of 3×10^{-18} grams of hydrogen; that is, a quantity of the order of 10^{-12} times that detected by the balance. For a more delicate instrument, this amount would produce a large effect.

The examples of radium in pitchblende and of the thorium-excited radioactivity make it certain that comparatively large ionization effects are produced by quantities of matter beyond the range of the balance or spectroscope.

The electrometer also affords the means of recognizing and differentiating between the emanations and radiations of different chemical substances. By the rate of decay the emanation from thorium, for example, can be instantly distinguished from that produced by radium; and although a difference in the rate of decay does not of itself argue a fundamental difference of nature, the identity of the rate of decay furnishes at least strong presumption of identity of nature.

Radiations, on the other hand, can be compared by means of their penetration powers (Rutherford, Phil. Mag. 1899, vol. xlvii. p. 122). If the rays from various radioactive substances are made to pass through successive layers of aluminium-foil, each additional layer of foil cuts down the radiation to a fraction of its former value, and a curve can be plotted with the thickness of metal penetrated as abscissæ, and the intensity of the rays after penetration as ordinates, expressing at a glance the penetration power of the rays under examination. The curves so obtained are quite different for different radioactive substances. The radiations from uranium, radium, thorium, each give distinct and characteristic curves, whilst that of the last-named again is quite different from that given by the excited radioactivity produced by the thorium emanation. It has been recently found (Rutherford and Grier, *Phys. Zeit.* 1902, p. 385) that thorium compounds, in addition to a type of easily absorbed Röntgen-rays, non-deviable in the magnetic field, emit also rays of a very penetrating character deviable in the magnetic field. The latter are therefore similar to cathode-rays, which are known to consist of material particles travelling with a velocity approaching that of light. But thorium, in comparison with uranium and radium, emits a much smaller proportion of deviable radiation. The determination of the proportion between the deviable and non-deviable rays affords a new means of investigating thorium radioactivity.

The electrometer thus supplies the study of radioactivity with methods of quantitative and qualitative investigation, and there is therefore no reason why the cause and nature of the phenomenon should not be the subject of chemical investigation.

Fig. 1 shows the general arrangement. From 0·5 to 0·1 gram of the compound to be tested, reduced to fine powder, is uniformly sifted over a platinum plate 36 sq. cms. in area.

Fig. 1.

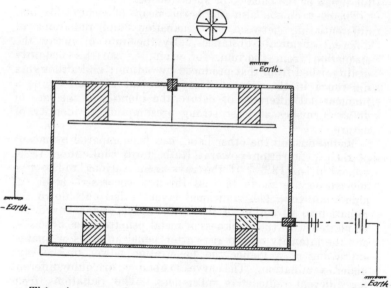

This plate was placed on a large metal plate connected to one pole of a battery of 300 volts, the other pole of which was earthed. An insulated parallel plate was placed about 6 cm. above it, and the whole apparatus inclosed in a metal box connected to earth, to prevent electrostatic disturbance. The shaded portions in the figure represented insulators. A door was made in the apparatus so that the plate could be rapidly placed in position or removed. Both pairs of quadrants are first connected to earth. On connecting the one pair with the apparatus, the deflexion of the needle from zero increases uniformly with time, and the time taken to pass over 100 divisions of the scale is taken by a stop-watch. The *rate* of movement is a measure of the ionization-current between the plates. The ratio of the currents for different substances is a comparative measure of their radioactivity.

With this apparatus ·5 gr. of thorium oxide produces a current of $1·1 \times 10^{-11}$ amperes, which, with the electrometer used, working at average sensitiveness, corresponds to 100 divisions of the scale in 36 seconds. In certain cases a special modification of the Dolezalek electrometer was employed which is 100 times more sensitive. With this instrument the radioactivity of 1 milligram of thoria produces a measurable effect. If the substance gives off an emanation, the current between the plates increases with time. Under these conditions, when the thorium compound is exposed in thin layers with a maximum of radiating surface, all but one or two per cent. of the total effect is due to the straight-line radiation. Even when the effect due to the emanation has attained a maximum, this constitutes a very small fraction of the whole. This effect, however, may to a large extent be eliminated by taking the current between the electrodes immediately after the material is placed in the testing-apparatus. It may be completely eliminated by passing a current of air between the electrodes to remove the emanation as fast as it is formed.

The current between the plates observed with the electrometer at first increases with the voltage, but a stage is very soon reached when there is a very small increase for a large additional voltage. A P.D. of 300 volts was sufficient to obtain the maximum current, so that all the ions reached the electrodes before any appreciable recombination occurred.

It must, however, at once be pointed out that it is difficult to make any absolute measure of radioactivity. The radiation from thorium is half absorbed by a thickness of aluminium of ·0004 cm. ; and since thorium oxide is far denser than aluminium, it is probable that the radiation in this case is confined to a surface-layer only ·0001 cm. deep. It is obvious that different preparations, each containing the same percentage of thorium but with different densities and different states of division, will not give the same intensity of radiation. In comparing two different specimens of the same compound, it is important that the final steps in their preparation should be the same in each case. As a rule absolute measurements of this kind have been avoided. It is possible, however, to trace with great accuracy the *change* of radioactivity of any preparation with time by leaving it undisturbed on its original plate, and comparing it with a similarly undisturbed constant comparison sample. Most of the investigations have been carried out by this method.

III. *The Separation of a Radioactive Constituent from Thorium Compounds.*

During an investigation of the emanating power of thorium compounds, to be described later, evidence was obtained of the separation of an intensely radioactive constituent by chemical methods. It had been noticed that in certain cases thorium hydroxide, precipitated from dilute solutions of thorium nitrate by ammonia, possessed an abnormally low emanating power. This led naturally to an examination being made of the filtrates and washings obtained during the process. It was found that the filtrates invariably possessed emanating power, although from the nature of their production they are chemically free from thorium. If the filtrate is evaporated to dryness, and the ammonium salts removed by ignition, the small residues obtained exhibit radioactivity also, to an extent very much greater than that possessed by the same weight of thorium. As a rule these residues were of the order of one-thousandth part by weight of the thorium salt originally taken, and were many hundred, in some cases over a thousand, times more active than an equal weight of thoria. The separation of an active constituent from thorium by this method is not all dependent on the purity of the salt used. By the kindness of Dr. Knöfler, of Berlin, who, in the friendliest manner, presented us with a large specimen of his purest thorium nitrate, we were enabled to test this point. This specimen, which had been purified by a great many processes, did not contain any of the impurities found in the commercial salt before used. But its radioactivity and emanating power were at least as great, and the residues from the filtrates after precipitation by ammonia were no less active than those before obtained. These residues are free from thorium, or at most contain only the merest traces, and when redissolved in nitric acid do not appear to give any characteristic reaction.

An examination of the penetrating power of the rays from the radioactive residue, showed that the radiations emitted were in every respect identical with the ordinary thorium radiation. In another experiment the nature of the emanation from a similar intensely active thorium-free residue was submitted to examination. The rate of decay was quite indistinguishable from that of the ordinary thorium emanation; that is, substances chemically free from thorium have been prepared possessing thorium radioactivity in an intense degree.

The thorium hydroxide which had been submitted to the above process was found to be less than half as radioactive as the same weight of thorium oxide. It thus appeared that a constituent responsible for the radioactivity of thorium had been obtained, which possessed distinct chemical properties and an activity of the order of at least a thousand times as great as the material from which it had been separated.

Sir William Crookes (Proc. Roy. Soc. 1900, lxvi. p. 409) succeeded in separating a radioactive constituent of great activity and distinct chemical nature from uranium, and gave the name UrX to this substance. For the present, until more is known of its real nature, it will be convenient to name the active constituent of thorium ThX, similarly. Like UrX, however, ThX does not answer to any definite analytical reactions, but makes its appearance with precipitates formed in its solution even when no question of insolubility is involved. This accords with the view that it is present in infinitesimal quantity, and possesses correspondingly great activity. Even in the case of the most active preparations, these probably are composed of some ThX associated with accidental admixtures large in proportion.

These results receive confirmation from observations made on a different method of separating ThX. The experiment was tried of washing thoria with water repeatedly, and seeing if the radioactivity was thereby affected. In this way it was found that the filtered washings, on concentration, deposited small amounts of material with an activity often of the order of a thousand times greater than that of the original sample. In one experiment, 290 grams of thoria were shaken for a long time with nine quantities, each of 2 litres of distilled water. The first washing, containing thorium sulphate present as an impurity, was rejected, the rest concentrated to different stages and filtered at each stage. One of the residues so obtained weighed 6·4 mg., and was equivalent in radioactivity to 11·3 grams of the original thoria, and was therefore no less than 1800 times more radioactive. It was examined chemically, and gave, after conversion into sulphate, the characteristic reaction of thorium sulphate, being precipitated from its solution in cold water by warming. *No other substance than thorium could be detected by chemical analysis,* although of course the quantity was too small for a minute examination. The penetrating power of the radiation from this substance again established its identity with the ordinary thorium radiation.

Phil. Mag. S. 6. Vol. 4. No. 21. *Sept.* 1902.   2 C

In another experiment, a small quantity of thoria was shaken many times with large quantities of water. In this case, the radioactivity of the residue was examined and found to be about 20 per cent. less radioactive than the original sample.

The influence of Time on the activity of Thorium and ThX.—The preparations employed in our previous experiments were allowed to stand over during the Christmas vacation. On examining them about three weeks later it was found that the thorium hydroxide, which had originally possessed only about 36 per cent. of its normal activity, had almost completely recovered the usual value. The active residues, on the other hand, prepared by both methods, had almost completely lost their original activity. The chemical separation effected was thus not permanent in character. At this time M. Becquerel's paper (*Comptes Rendus*, cxxxiii. p. 977, Dec. 9th, 1901) came to hand, in which he shows that the same phenomena of recovery and decay are presented by uranium after it has been partially separated from its active constituent by chemical treatment.

A long series of observations was at once started to determine—

(1) The rate of recovery of the activity of thorium rendered less active by removal of ThX ;

(2) The rate of decay of the activity of the separated ThX ;

in order to see how the two processes were connected. The results led to the view that may at once be stated. The radioactivity of thorium at any time is the resultant of two opposing processes—

(1) The production of fresh radioactive material at a constant rate by the thorium compound ;

(2) The decay of the radiating power of the active material with time.

The normal or constant radioactivity possessed by thorium is an equilibrium value, where the rate of increase of radioactivity due to the production of fresh active material is balanced by the rate of decay of radioactivity of that already formed. It is the purpose of the present paper to substantiate and develope this hypothesis.

IV. *The Rates of Recovery and Decay of Thorium Radioactivity.*

A quantity of the pure thorium nitrate was separated from ThX in the manner described by several precipitations with ammonia. The radioactivity of the hydroxide so obtained was tested at regular intervals to determine the rate of recovery of its activity. For this purpose the original specimen of ·5 gram was left undisturbed throughout the whole series of measurements on the plate over which it had been sifted, and was compared always with ·5 gram of ordinary de-emanated thorium oxide spread similarly on a second plate and also left undisturbed. The emanation from the hydroxide was prevented from interfering with the results by a special arrangement for drawing a current of air over it during the measurements.

The active filtrate from the preparation was concentrated and made up to 100 c.c. volume. One quarter was evaporated to dryness and the ammonium nitrate expelled by ignition in a platinum dish, and the radioactivity of the residue tested at the same intervals as the hydroxide to determine the rate of decay of its activity. The comparison in this case was a standard sample of uranium oxide kept undisturbed on a metal plate, which repeated work has shown to be a perfectly constant source of radiation. The remainder of the filtrate was used for other experiments.

The following table gives an example of one of a numerous series of observations made with different preparations at different times. The maximum value obtained by the hydroxide and the original value of the ThX are taken as 100 :—

Time in days.	Activity of Hydroxide.	Activity of ThX.
0	44	100
1	37	117
2	48	100
3	54	88
4	62	72
5	68	
6	71	53
8	78	
9	...	29·5
10	83	25·2
13	...	15·2
15	...	11·1
17	96·5	
21	99	
28	100	

Fig. 2 shows the curves obtained by plotting the radioactivities as ordinates, and the time in days as abscissæ. Curve II. illustrates the rate of recovery of the activity of thorium, curve I. the rate of decay of activity of ThX. It

2 C 2

will be seen that neither of the curves is regular for the first two days. The activity of the hydroxide at first actually

Fig. 2.

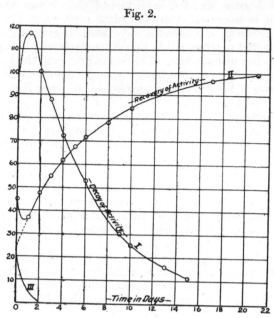

diminished and was at the same value after two days as when first prepared. The activity of the ThX, on the other hand, at first increases and does not begin to fall below the original value till after the lapse of two days (compare section IX.). These results cannot be ascribed to errors of measurement, for they have been regularly observed whenever similar preparations have been tested. The activity of the residue obtained from thorium oxide by the second method of washing decayed very similarly to that of ThX, as shown by the above curve.

If for present purposes the initial periods of the curve are disregarded and the later portions only considered, it will be seen at once that the time taken for the hydroxide to recover one half of its lost activity is about equal to the time taken by the ThX to lose half its activity, viz., in each case about 4 days, and speaking generally the percentage proportion of the lost activity regained by the hydroxide over any given interval is approximately equal to the percentage proportion of the activity lost by the ThX during the same interval. If the recovery curve is produced backwards in the normal direction to cut the vertical axis, it will be seen to do so at a minimum of about 25 per cent., and the above result holds even more accurately if the recovery is assumed to start from this constant minimum, as, indeed, it has been shown to do under suitable conditions (section IX., fig. 4).

This is brought out by fig. 3, which represents the recovery

Fig. 3.

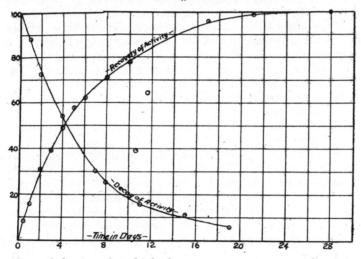

curve of thorium in which the percentage amounts of activity recovered, reckoned from this 25 per cent. minimum, are plotted as ordinates. In the same figure the decay curve after the second day is shown on the same scale.

The activity of ThX decreases very approximately in a geometrical progression with the time, *i. e.* if I_0 represent the initial activity and I_t the activity after time t,

$$\frac{I_t}{I_0} = e^{-\lambda t}, \quad . \quad . \quad . \quad . \quad . \quad . \quad . \quad (1)$$

where λ is a constant and e the base of natural logarithms.

The experimental curve obtained with the hydroxide for the rate of rise of its activity from a minimum to a maximum value will therefore be approximately expressed by the equation

$$\frac{I_t}{I_0} = 1 - e^{-\lambda t}, \quad . \quad . \quad . \quad . \quad . \quad (2)$$

where I_0 represents the amount of activity recovered when the maximum is reached, and I_t the activity recovered after time t, λ *being the same constant as before.*

Now this last equation has been theoretically developed in other places (compare Rutherford, Phil. Mag. 1900, pp. 10 and 181) to express the rise of activity to a constant maximum of a system consisting of radiating particles in which

(1) The rate of supply of fresh radiating particles is constant.

(2) The activity of each particle dies down geometrically with the time according to equation (1).

It therefore follows that if the initial irregularities of the curves are disregarded and the residual activity of thorium is assumed to possess a *constant* value, the experimental curve obtained for the recovery of activity will be explained if two processes are supposed to be taking place :

(1) That the active constituent ThX is being produced at a constant rate;

(2) That the activity of the ThX decays geometrically with time.

Without at first going into the difficult questions connected with the initial irregularities and the residual activity, the main result that follows from the curves given can be put to experimental test very simply. The primary conception is that the major part of the radioactivity of thorium is not due to the thorium at all, but to the presence of a non-thorium substance in minute amount which is being continuously produced.

V. *Chemical Properties of ThX.*

The fact that thorium on precipitation from its solutions by ammonia leaves the major part of its activity in the filtrate does not of itself prove that a material *constituent* responsible for this activity has been chemically separated. It is possible that the matter constituting the non-thorium part of the solution is rendered temporarily radioactive by its association with thorium, and this property is retained through the processes of precipitation, evaporation, and ignition, and manifests itself finally on the residue remaining.

This view, however, can be shown to be quite untenable, for upon it any precipitate capable of removing thorium completely from its solution should yield active residues similar to those obtained from ammonia. Quite the reverse, however, holds.

When thorium nitrate is precipitated by sodium or ammonium carbonate, the residue from the filtrate by evaporation and ignition is free from activity, and the thorium carbonate possesses the normal value for its activity.

The same holds true when oxalic acid is used as the

precipitant. This reagent even in strongly acid solution precipitates almost all of the thorium. When the filtrate is rendered alkaline by ammonia, filtered, evaporated, and ignited, the residue obtained is inactive.

In the case where sodium phosphate is used as the precipitant in ordinary acid solution, the part that comes down is more or less free from ThX. On making the solution alkaline with ammonia, the remainder of the thorium is precipitated as phosphate, and carries with it the whole of the active constituent, so that the residue from the filtrate is again inactive.

In fact ammonia is the only reagent of those tried capable of separating ThX from thorium.

The result of Sir William Crookes with uranium, which we have confirmed working with the electrical method, may be here mentioned. UrX is completely precipitated by ammonia together with uranium, and the residue obtained by the evaporation of the filtrate is quite inactive.

There can thus be no question that both ThX and UrX are distinct types of matter with definite chemical properties. Any hypothesis that attempts to account for the recovery of activity of thorium and uranium with time must of necessity start from this primary conception.

VI. *The Continuous Production of* **ThX**.

If the recovery of the activity of thorium with time is due to the production of ThX, it should be possible to obtain experimental evidence of the process. The first point to be ascertained is how far the removal of ThX by the method given reduces the total radioactivity of thorium. A preliminary trial showed that the most favourable conditions for the separation are by precipitating in hot dilute solutions by dilute ammonia. A quantity of 5 grams of thorium nitrate, as obtained from the maker, was so precipitated by ammonia, the precipitate being redissolved in nitric acid and reprecipitated under the same conditions successively *without lapse of time.*

The removal of ThX was followed by measuring the activity of the residues obtained from the successive filtrates. The activity of the ThX from the first filtrate was equivalent to 4·25 grams of thoria, from the second to 0·33 gram, and from the third to 0·07 gram. It will be seen that by two precipitations practically the whole of the ThX is removed. The radioactivity of the separated hydroxide was 48 per cent. of that of the standard de-emanated sample of thoria.

Rate of production of ThX.—A quantity of thorium nitrate solution that had been freed from ThX about a month before, was again subjected to the same process. The activity of the residue from the filtrate in an experiment in which 10 grams of this nitrate had been employed was equivalent to 8·3 grams of thorium oxide. This experiment was performed on the same day as the one recorded above, in which 5 grams of new nitrate had been employed, and it will be seen that there is no difference in the activity of the filtrate in the two cases. In one month the activity of the ThX in a thorium compound again possesses its maximum value.

If a period of 24 hours is allowed to elapse between the successive precipitations, the activity of the ThX formed during that time corresponds to about one-sixth of the maximum activity of the total thorium employed. In three hours the activity of the amount produced is about one-thirtieth. The rate of production of ThX worked out from those figures well agrees with the form of the curve obtained for the recovery of activity of thorium, if the latter is taken to express the continuous production of ThX at a constant rate and the diminution of the activity of the product in geometrical progression with the time.

By using the sensitive electrometer, the course of production of ThX can be followed after extremely short intervals. Working with 10 grams of thorium nitrate, the amount produced in the minimum time taken to carry out the successive precipitations is as much as can be conveniently measured. If any interval is allowed to lapse the effect is beyond the range of the instrument, unless the sensitiveness is reduced to a fraction of its ordinary value by the introduction of capacities into the system. Capacities of ·01 and ·02 microfarad, which reduce the sensitiveness to less than one two-hundredth of the normal, were frequently employed in dealing with these active residues.

The process of the production of ThX is continuous, and no alteration was observed in the amount produced in a given time after repeated separations. In an experiment carried out for another purpose (section IX.) after 23 successive precipitations extending over 9 days, the amount formed during the last interval was as far as could be judged no less than what occurred at the beginning of the process.

The phenomenon of radioactivity, by means of the electrometer as its measuring instrument, thus enables us to detect and measure changes occurring in matter after a few minutes interval, which have never yet been detected by the balance or suspected of taking place.

VII. *Influence of Conditions on the Changes occurring in Thorium.*

It has been shown that in thorium compounds the decay of radioactivity with time is balanced by a continuous production of fresh active material. The change which produces this material must be chemical in nature, for the products of the action are different in chemical properties from the thorium from which they are produced. The first step in the study of the nature of this change is to examine the effects of conditions upon its rate.

Effect of conditions on the rate of decay.—Since the activity of the products affords the means of measuring the amount of change, the influence of conditions on the rate of decay must be first found. It was observed that, like all other types of temporary radioactivity, the rate of decay is unaltered by any known agency. It is unaffected by ignition and chemical treatment, and the material responsible for it can be dissolved in acids and re-obtained by the evaporation of the solution, without affecting the activity. The following experiment shows that the activity decays at the same rate in solutions as in the solid state. The remainder of the solution that had been used to determine the decay curve of ThX (fig. 2) was allowed to stand, and at the end of 12 days a second quarter was evaporated to dryness and ignited, and its activity compared with that of the first which had been left since evaporation upon its original platinum dish. The activities of the two specimens so compared with each other were the same, showing that in spite of the very different conditions the two fractions had decayed at equal rates. After 19 days a third quarter was evaporated, and the activity, now very small, was indistinguishable from that of the fraction first evaporated. Re-solution of the residues after the activity had decayed does not at all regenerate it. The activity of ThX thus decays at a rate independent of the chemical and physical condition of the molecule.

Thus the rate of recovery of activity under different conditions in thorium compounds affords a direct measure of the rate of production of ThX under these conditions. The following experiments were performed :—

One part of thorium hydroxide newly separated from ThX was sealed up in a vacuum obtained by a good Töpler pump, and the other part exposed to air. On comparing the samples 12 days later no difference could be detected between them either in their radioactivity or emanating power.

In the next experiment a quantity of hydroxide freed from

ThX was divided into two equal parts; one was exposed for 20 hours to the heat of a Bunsen burner in a platinum crucible, and then compared with the other. No difference in the activities was observed. In a second experiment, one half was ignited for 20 minutes on the blast, and then compared with the other with the same result. The difference of temperature and the conversion of thorium hydroxide into oxide thus exercised no influence on the activity.

Some experiments that were designed to test in as drastic a manner as possible the effect of the chemical condition of the molecule on the rate of production of ThX brought to light small differences, but these are almost certainly to be accounted for in another way. It will be shown later (section IX.) that about 21 per cent. of the normal radioactivity of thorium oxide under ordinary conditions consists of a secondary activity excited on the mass of the material. This portion is of course a variable, and since it is divided among the total amount of matter present, the conditions of aggregation, &c., will affect the value of this part. This effect of excited radioactivity in thorium makes a certain answer to the question difficult, and on this account the conclusion that the rate of production of ThX is independent of the molecular conditions is not final. The following experiment, however, makes it extremely probable.

A quantity of thorium nitrate as obtained from the maker was converted into oxide in a platinum crucible by treatment with sulphuric acid and ignition to a white heat. The de-emanated oxide so obtained was spread on a plate, and any change in radioactivity with time, which under these circumstances could certainly be detected, was looked for during the first week from preparation. None whatever was observed, whereas if the rate of production of ThX in thorium nitrate is different from that in the oxide, the equilibrium point, at which the decay and increase of activity balance each other, will be altered in consequence. There should have therefore occurred a logarithmic rise or fall from the old to the new value. As, however, the radioactivity remained constant, it appears very probable that the changes involved are independent of the molecular condition.

It will be seen that the assumption is here made that the proportion of excited radioactivity in the two compounds is the same, and for this reason compounds were chosen which possess but low emanating power. (Compare section IX. last paragraph.)

Uranium is a far simpler example of a radioactive element than thorium, as the phenomena of excited radioactivity and emanating power are here absent. The separation of UrX and the recovery of the activity of the uranium with time appear, however, analogous to these processes in thorium, and the rate of recovery and decay of uranium activity are at present under investigation. It is proposed to test the influence of conditions on the rate of change more thoroughly in the case of uranium, as here secondary changes do not interfere.

VIII. *The Cause and Nature of Radioactivity.*

The foregoing conclusions enable a great generalization to be made in the subject of radioactivity. Energy considerations require that the intensity of radiation from any source should die down with time unless there is a constant supply of energy to replace that dissipated. This has been found to hold true in the case of all known types of radioactivity with the exception of the "naturally" radioactive elements—to take the best established cases, thorium, uranium, and radium. It will be shown later that the radioactivity of the emanation produced by thorium compounds decays geometrically with the time under all conditions, and is not affected by the most drastic chemical and physical treatment. The same has been shown by one of us (Phil. Mag. 1900, p. 161) to hold for the excited radioactivity produced by the thorium emanation. This decays at the same rate whether on the wire on which it is originally deposited, or in solution of hydrochloric or nitric acid. The excited radioactivity produced by the radium emanation appears analogous. All these examples satisfy energy considerations. In the case of the three naturally occurring radioactive elements, however, it is obvious that there must be a continuous replacement of the dissipated energy, and no satisfactory explanation has yet been put forward.

The nature of the process becomes clear in the light of the foregoing results. The material constituent responsible for the radioactivity, when it is separated from the thorium which produces it, then behaves in the same way as the other types of radioactivity cited. Its activity decays geometrically with the time, and the rate of decay is independent of the molecular conditions. The normal radioactivity is, however, maintained at a constant value by a chemical change which produces fresh radioactive material at a rate also independent of the conditions. The energy required to maintain the radiations will be accounted for if we suppose that the energy of the system after the change has occurred is less than it was before.

The work of Crookes and Becquerel on the separation of UrX and the recovery of the activity of the uranium with time, makes it appear extremely probable that the same explanation holds true for this element. The work of M. and Mme. Curie, the discoverers of radium, goes to show that this body easily suffers a temporary decrease of its activity by chemical treatment, the normal value being regained after the lapse of time, and this can be well interpreted on the new view. All known types of radioactivity can thus be brought under the same category.

IX. *The Initial Portions of the Curves of Decay and Recovery.*

The curves of the recovery and decay of the activities of thorium and ThX with time suggested the explanation that the radioactivity of thorium was being maintained by the production of ThX at a constant rate. Before this can be considered rigidly established, two outstanding points remain to be cleared up. 1. What is the meaning of the early portion of the curves? The recovery curve drops before it rises, and the decay curve rises before it drops. 2. Why does not the removal of ThX render thorium completely inactive? A large proportion of the original radioactivity is not affected by the removal of ThX.

A study of the curves (fig. 2) shows that in each case a double action is probably at work. It may be supposed that the normal decay and recovery are taking place, but are being masked by a simultaneous rise and decay from other causes. From what is known of thorium radioactivity, it was surmised that an action might be taking place similar to that effected by the emanation of exciting radioactivity on surrounding inactive matter. It will be shown later that the ThX, and not thorium, is the cause of the emanating power of thorium compounds. On this view, the residual activity of thorium might consist in whole or in part of a secondary or excited radioactivity produced on the whole mass of the thorium compound by its association with the ThX. The drop in the recovery-curve on this view would be due to the decay of this excited radioactivity proceeding simultaneously with, and at first reversing the effect of the regeneration of ThX. The rise of the decay-curve would be the increase due to the ThX exciting activity on the matter with which it is associated, the increase from this cause being greater than the decrease due to the decay of the activity of the ThX. It is easy to put this hypothesis to experimental test. If the ThX is removed from the thorium as soon as it is formed over a sufficient period, the former will be prevented from exciting activity on the latter, and that already excited will decay spontaneously. The experiment was therefore performed. A quantity of nitrate was precipitated as hydroxide in the usual way to remove ThX, the precipitate redissolved in nitric acid, and again precipitated after a certain interval. From time to time a portion of the hydroxide was removed and its radioactivity tested. In this way the thorium was precipitated in all 23 times in a period of 9 days, and the radioactivity reduced to a constant minimum. The following table shows the results :—

	Activity of Hydroxide. per cent.
After first precipitation	46
After precipitations at three intervals of 24 hours	39
At three more intervals each of 24 hours, and three more each of 8 hours	22
At three more each of 8 hours	24
At six more each of 4 hours	25

The constant minimum thus attained—about 25 per cent. of the original activity—is thus about 21 per cent. below that obtained by two successive precipitations without interval, which has been shown to remove all the ThX separable by the process. The rate of recovery of this 23 times precipitated hydroxide was then measured (fig. 4). It will be

Fig. 4.

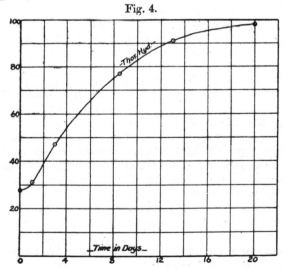

seen that it is now quite normal, and the initial drop characteristic of the ordinary curve is quite absent. It is in fact almost identical with the ordinary curve (fig. 2) that has been produced back to cut the vertical axis, and there is thus no doubt that there is a residual activity of thorium unconnected apparently with ThX, and constituting about one fourth of the whole.

The decay-curves of several of the fractions of ThX separated in this experiment after varying intervals of time were taken for the first few days. All of them showed the initial rise of about 15 per cent. at the end of 18 hours, and then a normal decay to zero. The position is thus proved that the initial irregularities are caused by the secondary radiation excited by ThX upon the surrounding matter. By suitably choosing the conditions the recovery-curve can be made to rise normally from a constant minimum, and the decay-curve be shown to consist of two curves, the first the rate of production of excited radioactivity, and the second the rate of decay of the activity as a whole.

So far nothing has been stated as to whether the excited radioactivity which contributes about 21 per cent. of the total activity of thorium is the same or different from the known type produced by the thorium emanation. All that has been assumed is that it should follow the same general law ; *i. e.* the effect will increase with the time of action of the exciting cause, and decrease with time after the cause is removed. If the rate of rise of the excited activity be worked out from the curves given (fig. 5) it will be found to agree with that of the ordinary excited activity, *i. e.* it rises to half value in about 12 hours. Curve 1 is the observed decay-curve for ThX ; curve 2 is the theoretical curve, assuming that it decreases geometrically with time and falls to half value in four days. Curve 3 is obtained by plotting the difference between these two, and therefore constitutes the curve of excited activity. Curve 4 is the experimental curve obtained for the rise of the excited radioactivity from the thorium emanation when the exciting cause is constant. But the exciting cause (ThX) in the present case is not constant, but is itself falling to half value in 4 days, and hence the difference curve, at first almost on the other, drops away from it as time goes on, and finally decays to zero. There is thus no reason to doubt that the effect is the same as that produced by the thorium emanation, which is itself a secondary effect of ThX. Curve 3 (fig. 2) represents a similar difference curve for *the decay* of excited activity, plotted from *the recovery curve* of thorium.

Since this effect of excited activity is caused by the emanation, it seemed reasonable to suppose that it will be greater, the less the emanation succeeds in escaping in the radioactive state, and therefore that de-emanated compounds should

Fig. 5.

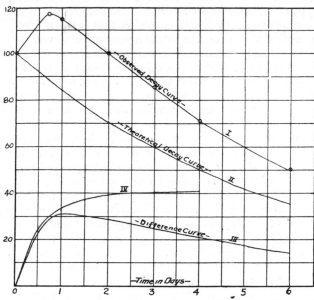

possess a greater proportion of excited radioactivity than those with high emanating power. This conclusion was tested by converting a specimen of thorium carbonate with an emanating power five times that of ordinary thoria, into oxide and de-emanating by intense ignition. The energy that before escaped in the form of emanation is now, all but a few per cent., prevented from escaping. The radioactivity of the oxide so prepared rose in the first three days about thirty per cent. of its original amount, and there thus seem to be grounds for the view that the excited radioactivity will contribute a much greater effect in a non-emanating thorium compound than in one possessing great emanating power.

Additional confirmation of this view is to be found in the nature of the radiations emitted by the two classes of compounds (Section XI.).

X. *The Non-separable Radioactivity of Thorium.*

It has not yet been found possible by any means to free thorium from its residual activity, and the place of this part in the scheme of radioactivity of thorium remains to be considered. Disregarding the view that it is a separate phenomenon, and not connected with the major part of the activity, two hypotheses can be brought forward capable of experimental test, and in accordance with the views advanced on the nature of radioactivity, to account for the existence of this part. First, if there was a second type of excited activity produced by ThX similar to that known, but with a very slow rate of decay, it would account for the existence of the non-separable activity. If this is true it will not be found possible to free thorium from this activity by chemical means, but the continuous removal of ThX over a very long period would, as in the above case, cause its spontaneous decay.

Secondly, if the change which gives rise to ThX produces a second type of matter at the same time, *i. e.* if it is of the type of a decomposition rather than a depolymerization, the second type would also in all probability be radioactive, and would cause the residual activity. On this view the second type of matter should also be amenable to separation by chemical means, although it is certain from the failure of the methods already tried that it resembles thorium much more closely than ThX. But until it is separated from the thorium producing it, its activity will not decay spontaneously. Thus what has already been shown to hold for ThX will be true for the second constituent if methods are found to remove it from the thorium.

It has been shown (Soddy, *loc. cit.*) that uranium also possesses a non-separable radioactivity extremely analogous to that possessed by thorium, and whatever view is taken of the one will in all probability hold also for the other. This consideration makes the second hypothesis, that the residual activity is caused by a second non-thorium type of matter produced in the original change, the more probable of the two.

XI. *The Nature of the Radiations from Thorium and ThX.*

From the view of radioactivity put forward it necessarily follows that the total radioactivity of thorium is altered neither in character nor amount by chemical treatment. With regard to the first, the amount of activity, it has been pointed out that the intensity of radiations *emitted* do not furnish alone a measure of the activity. The absorption in the mass of material must be considered also. The radiations of thorium oxide are derived from a very dense powder; those from ThX, on the other hand, have only to penetrate a very thin film of material. The difficulty can be overcome to some extent by taking for the comparison the radioactivity of a thin film of a soluble thorium salt produced by evaporating a solution to dryness over a large metal plate. Compared in this way, the radioactivity of ThX when first separated almost exactly equals the activity of the nitrate from which it is produced, while the hydroxide retains about two-fifths of this amount. The total activity of the products is therefore greater than that of the original salt; but this is to be expected, for it is certain that more absorption takes place in the nitrate than in the products into which it is separated.

Similar difficulties stand in the way of an answer to the second question, whether the nature of the radiations is affected by chemical treatment, for it has been experimentally observed that the penetrating power of these radiations decreases with the thickness of material traversed. The character of the radiations from ThX and thorium have, however, been compared by the method of penetration power. A large number of comparisons justifies the view that the character of thorium radioactivity is unaltered by chemical treatment and the separation of ThX, although the different types are unequally distributed among the separated products.

Determinations of the proportion of rays deviable by the magnetic field in thorium and ThX throws fresh light on the question. The general result is that ThX gives out both deviable and non-deviable rays, and the same applies to the excited activity produced by ThX. But in the experiment in which the excited radiation was allowed to spontaneously decay, by removing ThX as formed, the thorium compound obtained after 23 precipitations was found to be quite free from deviable radiation. This is one of the most striking resemblances between the non-separable radioactivities of uranium and thorium, and warrants the question whether the primary radiation of ThX is not, like that of UrX, composed entirely of cathode-rays. There is, however, no means of deciding this point owing to the excited radiation which always accompanies the primary radiation of ThX, and which itself comprises both types of rays.

Finally, it may be mentioned that the proportion of deviable and non-deviable radiation is different for different compounds of thorium. The nitrate and ignited oxide, compounds which hardly possess any emanating power, have a higher proportion of deviable radiation than compounds with great emanating power. This is indirect evidence of the correctness of the view already put forward (Section IX.), that when the emanation is prevented from escaping it augments the proportion of excited radioactivity of the compound.

Phil. Mag. S. 6. Vol. 4. No. 21. *Sept.* 1902.　　2 D

XII. *Summary of Results.*

The foregoing experimental results may be briefly summarized. The major part of the radioactivity of thorium—ordinarily about 54 per cent.—is due to a non-thorium type of matter, ThX, possessing distinct chemical properties, which is temporarily radioactive, its activity falling to half value in about four days. The constant radioactivity of thorium is maintained by the production of this material at a constant rate. Both the rate of production of the new material and the rate of decay of its activity appear to be independent of the physical and chemical condition of the system.

The ThX further possesses the property of exciting radioactivity on surrounding inactive matter, and about 21 per cent. of the total activity under ordinary circumstances is derived from this source. Its rate of decay and other considerations make it appear probable that it is the same as the excited radioactivity produced by the thorium emanation, which is in turn produced by ThX. There is evidence that, if from any cause the emanation is prevented from escaping in the radioactive state, the energy of its radiation goes to augment the proportion of excited radioactivity in the compound.

Thorium can be freed by suitable means from both ThX and the excited radioactivity which the latter produces, and then possesses an activity about 25 per cent. of its original value, below which it has not been reduced. This residual radiation consists entirely of rays non-deviable by the magnetic field, whereas the other two components comprise both deviable and non-deviable radiation. Most probably this residual activity is caused by a second non-thorium type of matter produced in the same change as ThX, and it should therefore prove possible to separate it by chemical methods.

XIII. *General Theoretical Considerations.*

Turning from the experimental results to their theoretical interpretation, it is necessary to first consider the generally accepted view of the nature of radioactivity. It is well established that this property is the function of the atom and not of the molecule. Uranium and thorium, to take the most definite cases, possess the property in whatever molecular condition they occur, and the former also in the elementary state. So far as the radioactivity of different compounds of different density and states of division can be compared together, the intensity of the radiation appears to depend only on the quantity of active element present. It is not at all dependent on the source from which the element is derived, or the process of purification to which it has been subjected, provided sufficient time is allowed for the equilibrium point to be reached. It is not possible to explain the phenomena by the existence of impurities associated with the radioactive elements, even if any advantage could be derived from the assumption. For these impurities must necessarily be present always to the same extent in different specimens derived from the most widely different sources, and, moreover, they must persist *in unaltered amount* after the most refined processes of purification. This is contrary to the accepted meaning of the term impurity.

All the most prominent workers in this subject are agreed in considering radioactivity an atomic phenomenon. M. and Mme. Curie, the pioneers in the chemistry of the subject, have recently put forward their views (*Comptes Rendus,* cxxxiv. 1902, p. 85). They state that this idea underlies their whole work from the beginning and created their methods of research. M. Becquerel, the original discoverer of the property for uranium, in his announcement of the recovery of the activity of the same element after the active constituent had been removed by chemical treatment, points out the significance of the fact that uranium is giving out cathode-rays. These, according to the hypothesis of Sir William Crookes and Prof. J. J. Thomson, are *material* particles of mass one thousandth of the hydrogen atom.

Since, therefore, radioactivity is at once an atomic phenomenon and accompanied by chemical changes in which new types of matter are produced, these changes must be occurring within the atom, and the radioactive elements must be undergoing spontaneous transformation. The results that have so far been obtained, which indicate that the velocity of this reaction is unaffected by the conditions, makes it clear that the changes in question are different in character from any that have been before dealt with in chemistry. It is apparent that we are dealing with phenomena outside the sphere of known atomic forces. Radioactivity may therefore be considered as a manifestation of subatomic chemical change.

The changes brought to knowledge by radioactivity, although undeniably material and chemical in nature, are of a different order of magnitude from any that have before been dealt with in chemistry. The course of the production of new matter which can be recognized by the electrometer, by means of the property of radioactivity, after the lapse of a few hours or even minutes, might conceivably require geological epochs to attain to quantities recognized by the

2 D 2

balance. However the well-defined chemical properties of both ThX and UrX are not in accordance with the view that the actual amounts involved are of this extreme order of minuteness. On the other hand, the existence of radioactive elements at all in the earth's crust is an *à priori* argument against the magnitude of the change being anything but small.

Radioactivity as a new property of matter capable of exact quantitative determination thus possesses an interest apart from the peculiar properties and powers which the radiations themselves exhibit. Mme. Curie, who isolated from pitch-blende a new substance, radium, which possessed distinct chemical properties and spectroscopic lines, used the property as a means of chemical analysis. An exact parallel is to be found in Bunsen's discovery and separation of cæsium and rubidium by means of the spectroscope.

The present results show that radioactivity can also be used to follow *chemical changes occurring in matter*. The properties of matter that fulfil the necessary conditions for the study of chemical change without disturbance to the reacting system are few in number. It seems not unreasonable to hope, in the light of the foregoing results, that radioactivity, being such a property, affords the means of obtaining information of the processes occurring within the chemical atom, in the same way as the rotation of the plane of polarization and other physical properties have been used in chemistry for the investigation of the course of molecular change.

Macdonald Physics Building,
Macdonald Chemistry and Mining Building,
McGill University, Montreal.

THE

LONDON, EDINBURGH, AND DUBLIN

PHILOSOPHICAL MAGAZINE

AND

JOURNAL OF SCIENCE.

———•———

[SIXTH SERIES.]

FEBRUARY 1903.

XV. *The Magnetic and Electric Deviation of the easily absorbed Rays from Radium.* By E. RUTHERFORD, *M.A., D.Sc., Macdonald Professor of Physics, McGill University, Montreal*.*

RADIUM gives out three distinct types of radiation:—
(1) The α rays, which are very easily absorbed by thin layers of matter, and which give rise to the greater portion of the ionization of the gas observed under the usual experimental conditions.

(2) The β rays, which consist of negatively charged particles projected with high velocity, and which are similar in all respects to cathode rays produced in a vacuum-tube.

(3) The γ rays, which are non-deviable by a magnetic field, and which are of a very penetrating character.

These rays differ very widely in their power of penetrating matter. The following approximate numbers, which show the thickness of aluminium traversed before the intensity is reduced to one-half, illustrate this difference.

Radiation.	Thickness of Aluminium.
α rays	·0005 cm.
β rays	·05 cm.
γ rays	8 cms.

In this paper an account will be given of some experiments which show that the α rays are deviable by a strong magnetic and electric field. The deviation is in the opposite sense to

* Communicated by the Author.

that of the cathode rays, so that the radiations must consist of positively charged bodies projected with great velocity. In a previous paper * I have given an account of the indirect experimental evidence in support of the view that the α rays consist of projected charged particles. Preliminary experiments undertaken to settle this question during the past two years gave negative results. The magnetic deviation, even in a strong magnetic field, is so small that very special methods are necessary to detect and measure it. The smallness of the magnetic deviation of the α rays, compared with that of the cathode rays in a vacuum-tube, may be judged from the fact that the α rays, projected at right angles to a magnetic field of strength 10,000 c.g.s. units, describe the arc of a circle of radius about 39 cms., while under the same conditions the cathode rays would describe a circle of radius about ·01 cm.

In the early experiments radium of activity 1000 was used, but this did not give out strong enough rays to push the experiment to the necessary limit. The general method employed was to pass the rays through narrow slits and to observe whether the rate of discharge, due to the issuing rays, was altered by the application of a magnetic field. When, however, the rays were sent through sufficiently narrow slits to detect a small deviation of the rays, the rate of discharge of the issuing rays became too small to measure, even with a sensitive electrometer.

I have recently obtained a sample of radium † of activity 19,000, and using an electroscope instead of an electrometer, I have been able to extend the experiments, and to show that the α rays are all deviated by a strong magnetic field.

Magnetic Deviation of the Rays.

Fig. 1 A shows the general arrangement of the experiment. The rays from a thin layer of radium passed upwards through a number of narrow slits, G, in parallel, and then through a thin layer of aluminium foil ·00034 cm. thick into the testing vessel V. The ionization produced by the rays in the testing vessel was measured by the rate of movement of the leaves of a gold-leaf electroscope B. This was arranged after the manner of C. T. R. Wilson in his experiments on

---

* Phil. Mag. Jan. 1903, p. 113. It was long ago suggested by Strutt (Phil. Trans. Roy. Soc. 1900) that the α rays consist of positively charged particles projected from the active substance. The same idea has lately been advanced by Sir Wm. Crookes (Proc. Roy. Soc. 1900),

† The sample of radium of greater activity than that usually sold was obtained from the Société Centrale de Produits Chimiques, through the kindness of M. P. Curie.

the spontaneous ionization of air. The gold-leaf system was insulated inside the vessel by a sulphur bead C, and could be

Fig. 1 A.

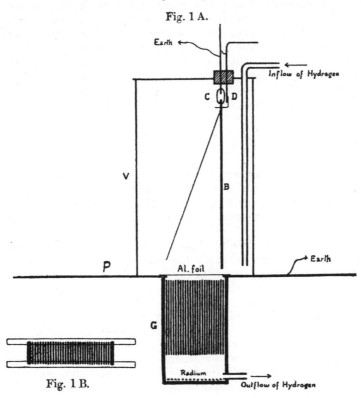

Fig. 1 B.

charged by means of a movable wire D, which was afterwards earthed. The rate of movement of the gold-leaf was observed by means of a microscope through small mica windows in the testing vessel.

In order to increase the ionization in the testing vessel, the rays passed through 20 to 25 slits of equal width, placed side by side. This was arranged by cutting grooves at regular intervals in side-plates into which brass plates were slipped. A cross section of the system of metal plates and air-spaces is shown in fig. 1 B.

The width of the slit varied in different experiments between ·042 and ·1 cm.

The magnetic field was applied perpendicular to the plane of the paper and parallel to the plane of the slits.

The testing vessel and system of plates were waxed to a lead

N 2

plate P so that the rays entered the vessel V only through the aluminium foil.

It is necessary in these experiments to have a steady stream of gas passing downwards between the plates in order to prevent the diffusion of the emanation from the radium upwards into the testing vessel. The presence in the testing vessel of a small amount of this emanation, which is always given out by radium, would produce large ionization effects and completely mask the effect to be observed.

For this purpose a steady current of dry electrolytic hydrogen of 2 c.c. per second was passed into the testing vessel, streamed through the porous aluminium foil, and passed between the plates, carrying with it the emanation from the apparatus.

The use of a stream of hydrogen instead of air greatly simplifies the experiment, for it *increases* at once the ionization current due to the α rays in the testing vessel, and (at the same time) greatly *diminishes* that due to the β and γ rays.

This follows at once from the fact that the α rays are much more readily absorbed in air than in hydrogen, while the rate of production of ions due to the β and γ rays is much less in hydrogen than in air. The intensity of the α rays after passing between the plates is consequently greater when hydrogen is used; and since the rays pass through a sufficient distance of hydrogen in the testing vessel to be largely absorbed, the total amount of ionization produced by them in hydrogen is greater than in air.

With the largest electromagnet in the laboratory I was only able to deviate about 30 per cent. of the α rays. Through the kindness of Professor Owens, of the Electrical Engineering Department, I was, however, enabled to make use of the upper part of the field-magnet of a 30 kilowatt Elison dynamo. Suitable pole-pieces are at present being made for the purpose of obtaining a strong magnetic field over a considerable area; but with rough pole-pieces I have been enabled to obtain a sufficiently strong field to completely deviate the α rays.

The following is an example of an observation on the magnetic deviation : —

Pole-pieces $1\cdot90 \times 2\cdot50$ cms.

Strength of field between pole-pieces 8370 units.

Apparatus of 25 parallel plates of length $3\cdot70$ cms., width $\cdot70$ cm., with an average air-space between plates of $\cdot042$ cm.

Distance of radium below plates $1\cdot4$ cm.

	Rate of Discharge of Electroscope in volts per minute.
(1) Without magnetic field	8·33
(2) With magnetic field	1·72
(3) Radium covered with thin layer of mica to absorb all α rays ...	0·93
(4) Radium covered with mica and magnetic field applied	0 92

The mica plate, ·01 cm. thick, was of sufficient thickness to completely absorb all the α rays, but allowed the β and γ rays to pass through without appreciable absorption. The difference between (1) and (3), 7·40 volts per minute, gives the rate of discharge due to the α rays alone; the difference between (2) and (3), 0·79 volt per minute, that due to the α rays not deviated by the magnetic field employed.

The amount of α rays not deviated by the field is thus about 11 per cent. of the total. The small difference between (2) and (4) includes the small ionization due to the β rays, for they would have been completely deviated by the magnetic field. It is probable that the ionization due to the β rays without a magnetic field was actually stronger than this; but the residual magnetic field, when the current was broken, was large enough to deviate them completely before reaching the testing vessel. (4) comprises the effect of the γ rays together with the natural leak of the electroscope in hydrogen.

In this experiment there was a good deal of stray magnetic field acting on the rays before reaching the pole-pieces. The distribution of this field at different portions of the apparatus is shown graphically in fig. 2.

Fig. 2.

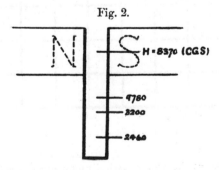

The following table shows the rate of discharge due to the α rays for different strengths of the magnetic field. The maximum value with no magnetic field is taken as 100. These results are shown graphically in fig. 3.

Magnetic field between pole-pieces.			Rate of discharge due to a rays.
0			100
3720	C.G.S. units		66
4840	,,	,,	50
6500	,,	,,	33
7360	,,	,,	23
8370	,,	,,	11

The curve (fig. 3) shows that the amount deviated is approximately proportional to the magnetic field.

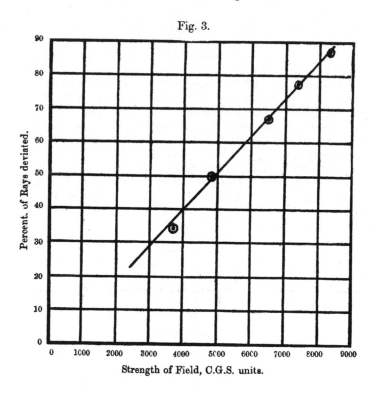

Fig. 3.

With another apparatus, with a mean air space of ·055 cm., the rays were *completely* deviated by a uniform magnetic field of strength 8400 units extending over the length of the plates, a distance of 4·5 cms.

Direction of the Deviation of the Rays.

In order to determine the direction of the deviation, the rays were passed through slits of 1 mm. width. Each slit was about half covered by a brass plate in which air-spaces were cut to correspond accurately with the system of parallel plates. Fig. 4 represents an enlarged section of three of the

Fig. 4.

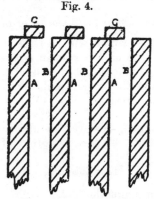

plates, with the metal plate C half covering the slit AB. If a magnetic field is applied, not sufficiently great to deviate all the rays, the rate of discharge in the testing vessel when the rays are deviated in the direction from A to B should be much greater than when the magnetic field is reversed, *i. e.* when the rays are deviated from B to A. This was found to be the case, for while the rate of discharge was not much diminished by the application of the field in one direction, it was reduced to about one quarter of its value by reversal of the field.

In this way it was found that the direction of deviation in a magnetic field was *opposite* in sense to the cathode rays, *i. e.*, the rays consisted of positively charged particles.

Electrostatic Deviation of the Rays.

The apparatus was similar to that employed for the magnetic deviation of the rays with the exception that the brass sides, which held the plates in position, were replaced by ebonite.

Twenty-five plates were used of length 4·50 cms., width 1·5 cm., and average air-space of ·055 cm. The radium was ·85 cm. below the plates. Alternate plates were connected together and charged by means of a battery of small accumulators to a potential-difference of 600 volts. A current of hydrogen was used as in the case of the magnetic experiment.

With a P.D. of 600 volts, a consistent difference * of 7 per cent. was observed in the rate of discharge due to the α rays with the electric field off and on.   A larger potential-difference could not be used as a spark passed between the plates in the presence of radium.

The amount of deviation in this experiment was too small to determine the direction of deviation by the electric field.

Determination of the Velocity of the Rays.

It is difficult to determine with certainty the value of the curvature of the path of the rays in a given magnetic field from the percentage amount of rays deviated, on account of the fact that some of the rays which strike the sides of the parallel plates are deviated so as to pass into the testing vessel.

From data obtained, however, by observing the value of the magnetic field for *complete deviation* of the rays, it was deduced that

$$H\rho = 390,000,$$

where H = value of magnetic field,
   ρ = radius of curvature of path of the rays.
This gives the higher limit of the value $H\rho$.

By using the usual equations of the deviation of a moving charged body it was deduced that the velocity V of the rays was given by

$$V = 2 \cdot 5 \times 10^9 \text{ cms. per sec.,}$$

and that the value $\frac{e}{m}$, the ratio of the charge of the carrier to its mass, was given by

$$\frac{e}{m} = 6 \times 10^3.$$

These results are only rough approximations and merely indicate the order of the values of these quantities, as the electric deviations observed were too small for accurate observations.   The experiments are being continued with special apparatus, and it is hoped that much larger electro-static deviations will be obtained, and in consequence a more accurate determination of the constants † of the rays.

---

* In later experiments, which are not yet completed, I have been able to deviate about 45 per cent. of the α rays in a strong electric field.

† The α rays are complex, and probably consist of particles projected with velocities lying between certain limits; for the radiations include the α radiations from the emanation and excited activity which are distributed throughout the radium compound.

The α rays from radium are thus very similar to the *Canal Strahlen* observed by Goldstein, which have been shown by Wien to be positively charged bodies moving with a high velocity. The velocity of the α rays is, however, considerably greater than that observed for the *Canal Strahlen*.

General Considerations.

The radiations from uranium, thorium, and radium, and also the radiations from the emanations and excited bodies, all include a large proportion of α rays. These rays do not differ much in penetrating power, and it is probable that *in all cases* the α radiations from them are charged particles projected with great velocities.

In a previous paper* it has been shown that the total energy radiated in the form of α rays by the permanent radioactive bodies is about 1000 times greater than the energy radiated in the form of β rays. This result was obtained on the assumption that the total number of ions produced by the two types of rays when completely absorbed in air, is a measure of the energy radiated. The α rays are thus the most important factor in the radiation of energy from active bodies, and, in consequence, any estimate of the energy radiated based on the β rays alone leads to much too small a value.

Experiments are in progress to determine the charge carried by the α rays, and from these it is hoped to deduce the rate of emission of energy in the form of α rays from the active substances.

The projection character of the α rays very readily explains some of their characteristic properties. On this view the ionization of the gas by the α rays is due to collisions of the projected masses with the gas molecules. The variation of the rate of production of the ions with the pressure of the gas and the variation of absorption of the rays in solids and gases with the density at once follows. It also offers a simple explanation of the remarkable fact that the absorption of the α rays in a given thickness of matter, when determined by the electrical method, *increases* with the thickness of matter previously traversed. It is only necessary to suppose that as the velocity of the projected particles decreases in consequence of collision with the molecules of the absorbing medium, the ionizing power of the rays decreases rapidly. This is most probably the case, for there seems to be no doubt that the positive carrier cannot ionize

* Rutherford and Grier, Phil. Mag. Sept. 1902.

the gas below a certain velocity, which is very great compared with the velocity of translation of the molecules.

It is of interest to consider the probable part that the α rays play in the radioactive bodies on the general view of radioactivity that has been put forward by Mr. Soddy and myself in the Phil. Mag. Sept. and Nov. 1902. It is there shown that radioactivity is due to a succession of chemical changes in which new types of radioactive matter are being continuously formed, and that the constant radioactivity of the well known active bodies is an equilibrium process, where the rate of production of fresh active matter is balanced by the decay of activity of that already produced. Some very interesting points arose in the course of these investigations. It was found that the residual activity of uranium and thorium when freed from UrX and ThX by chemical processes consisted entirely of α rays. On the other hand, the radiation of UrX * consisted almost entirely of β rays, while that of ThX † consisted of both α and β rays. Similar results probably hold also for radium, for the Curies have shown that radium dissolved in water and then evaporated to dryness temporarily loses to a large extent its power of emitting β rays.

It thus appears probable that the emission of α rays goes on quite independently of the emission of β rays. There seems to be no doubt that the emission of β rays by active substances is a secondary phenomenon, and that the α rays play the most prominent part in the changes occurring in radioactive matter. The results obtained so far point to the conclusion that the beginning of the succession of chemical changes taking place in radioactive bodies is due to the emission of the α rays, *i. e.* the projection of a heavy charged mass from the atom. The portion left behind is unstable, undergoing further chemical changes which are again accompanied by the emission of α rays, and in some cases also of β rays.

The power possessed by the radioactive bodies of apparently spontaneously projecting large masses with enormous velocities supports the view that the atoms of these substances are made up, in part at least, of rapidly rotating or oscillating systems of heavy charged bodies large compared with the electron. The sudden escape of these masses from their orbit may be due either to the action of internal forces or external forces of which we have at present no knowledge.

It also follows from the projection nature of the α rays that the radioactive bodies, when inclosed in sealed vessels

* Soddy, Proc. Chem. Soc. 1902.
† Rutherford and Grier, Phil. Mag. Sept. 1902.

sufficiently thin to allow the α rays to escape, must *decrease in weight*. Such a decrease has been recently observed by Heydweiler* for radium, but apparently under such conditions that the α rays would be largely absorbed in the glass tube containing the active matter.

In this connexion it is very important to decide whether the loss of weight observed by Heydweiler is due to a decrease of weight of the radium itself or to a decrease of weight of the glass envelope; for it is well known that radium rays produce rapid colourations throughout a glass tube, and it is possible that there may be a chemical change reaching to the surface of the glass which may account for the effects observed.

McGill University,
Montreal, Nov. 10, 1902.

XLI. *The Mass and Velocity of the α particles expelled from Radium and Actinium. By* E. Rutherford, *F.R.S., Macdonald Professor of Physics, McGill University, Montreal**.

[Plate V.]

THE present paper contains an account of investigations that have been made to determine, as accurately as possible, the mass and velocity of the α particles expelled from some of the products of radium and actinium. At the present stage of our knowledge of radioactivity, such measurements have an important theoretical value in throwing light on the following questions :—

1. Has the α particle expelled from all radioactive products the same mass?

2. Does the value of e/m of the α particle vary in its passage through matter?

3. What is the connexion between the velocity of the α particle and its range of ionization in air?

4. What is the connexion, if any, between the α particle and the helium atom?

5. Is the heating effect of radium or other radioactive substance due to the bombardment of the radioactive matter by the α particles expelled throughout its own mass?

In the course of these investigations, sufficient data have been accumulated, if not to answer completely all of the above questions, at least to indicate with some certainty the relations that exist between the various quantities.

The experiments outlined in this paper have been in progress for more than a year†, but publication has been delayed in order to determine the mass of the α particle from thorium and actinium as well as from radium.

The investigations on the mass of the α particle from thorium have been made in conjunction with Dr. Hahn, and are described in a following paper.

Determinations of the mass and velocity of the α particles from radium have been made by several observers. In 1902, using the electroscopic method and radium of activity 19000, I showed that the α particles from radium consisted of positively charged particles which were appreciably deflected in

---

* Communicated by the Author.

† A preliminary account of the measurements of the value of e/m for the particle from radium C was given before the American Physical Society, December 1905. An abstract of the results appeared in the Physical Review, Feb. 1906.

intense magnetic and electric fields*. I deduced that the value of e/m—the ratio of the charge on the α particle to its mass—was about 6×10^3, and that the swiftest α particles emitted from radium had a velocity of about $2 \cdot 5 \times 10^9$ cms. per second. Shortly afterwards, these experiments were repeated by Des Coudres†, using the photographic method and with pure radium bromide as a source of rays. He found the value of e/m to be $6 \cdot 3 \times 10^3$, and the average velocity to be $1 \cdot 65 \times 10^9$ cms. per second.

On account of the difficulty of obtaining a sufficiently large deflexion of the α rays in passing through an electric field, the values of e/m and of the velocity of the α particles obtained by Rutherford and Des Coudres could only be considered as a first approximation to the true values.

Recently the question has again been attacked by Mackenzie‡, using the photographic method and pure radium bromide as a source of rays. Fairly large deflexions of the pencil of rays were obtained by using strong magnetic and electric fields. He showed that the α particles emitted by a thick layer of radium bromide were unequally deflected in a magnetic and electric field, and presumably consisted of α particles moving with different velocities. By assuming that the value of e/m was the same for all the α particles, he deduced that the value of e/m for the average ray was $4 \cdot 6 \times 10^3$, and that the average velocity was $1 \cdot 37 \times 10^9$ cms. per second.

It will be seen that all of these investigators have used a thick layer of radium in radioactive equilibrium as a source of rays. We know that the α particles from radium in equilibrium come from four distinct α ray products. The α particles from each of these products have different ranges of ionization in air and different velocities of projection. In addition, the α particles from each single product reach the surface from different depths of radioactive matter, and consequently have different velocities. It is thus seen that the α radiation from radium is very complex, and consists of four groups of α particles, each of which is made up of α particles which escape at widely different velocities.

On account of the dispersion of the pencil of rays in passing through an electric and magnetic field, it is difficult to interpret with certainty the deflexions observed. The difficulties which arise are clearly pointed out by Mackenzie in his paper (*loc. cit.*)

In a previous paper (Phil. Mag. July 1905) I pointed out

---

* Rutherford, *Phys. Zeit.* iv. p. 235 (1902); Phil. Mag. Feb. 1903.
† Des Coudres, *Phys. Zeit.* iv. p. 483 (1903).
‡ Mackenzie, Phil. Mag. Nov. 1905.

that these difficulties would disappear if a homogeneous pencil of α rays was employed. I showed that such a homogeneous pencil could be obtained by using as a source of rays a small wire which had been made very active by exposure to the radium emanation. Fifteen minutes after removal from the emanation, radium A has been transformed, and the α particles are then emitted only from radium C.

An examination of the deflexion of the rays in a magnetic field showed that such an active wire fulfilled the conditions necessary for a homogeneous source of rays. The α particles all escaped from the thin film of radioactive matter at the same speed, and all suffered the same reduction of velocity in passing through an absorbing screen. On account of the rapid decay of the activity of the active deposit, it is necessary to employ an intensely active wire to obtain a strong photographic effect. In most of the experiments described later, the active deposit was concentrated on the wire by making it the only negatively charged surface in a vessel containing a large quantity of the radium emanation. In this way, very active wires were obtained which served as suitable sources of homogeneous α rays.

Electric Deflexion of the α Rays.

The determination of e/m and of the velocity of the α particle was made in the usual way by measuring the deflexion of a pencil of rays in passing through both a magnetic and electric field of known strength. The method employed for measuring the magnetic deflexion has already been described in a previous paper. After some preliminary experiments, the following arrangement was adopted to determine the deflexion of the α rays in passing through an electric field. The rays from the active wire W (fig. 1), after traversing a thin mica plate in the base of the brass vessel M, passed between two parallel insulated plates A and B about 4 cms. high and 0·21 mm. apart. The distance between the plates was fixed by thin strips of mica placed at the four corners, and the plates were rigidly held together by rubber bands. The terminals of a storage-battery were connected with A and B so that a strong electric field could be produced between the two plates. The pencil of rays, after emerging from the plates, fell on a photographic plate P. The latter was rigidly fixed to a ground-brass plate which fitted accurately on the top surface of the vessel. The ground surfaces were air-tight, and the photographic plate could thus easily be placed in position or removed without disturbing the rest of the apparatus. The vessel was connected to a mercury pump and exhausted to a low vacuum. If necessary, the exhaustion was completed by means of a side tube filled with cocoanut charcoal and immersed in liquid air.

Fig. 1.

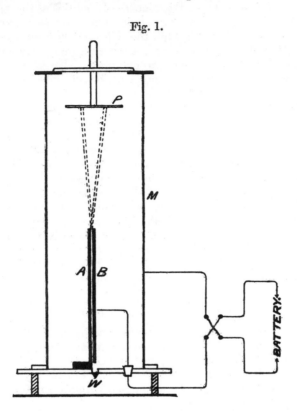

The plates A and B were placed close together for several reasons. In the first place, a strong electric field could be produced between the plates for a comparatively small voltage. The greatest P.D. necessary in the experiments was about 500 volts. Since the plates were about one-fifth of a millimetre apart, this voltage produced an electric field between the plates corresponding to 25000 volts per cm. One advantage of the arrangement lies in the fact that, provided the P.D. is below about 350 volts, there is no danger of a discharge between the plates, even if there is not a good vacuum. This is particularly convenient where it is found necessary to expose the photographic plate to a weak source of radiation for several days, for there is no necessity to continually watch the state of the vacuum.

On account of the small distance between the plates, there is no necessity to correct for the disturbance of the electric field near the ends of the plates. In addition, the parallel plates acted as a slit in order to obtain a narrow pencil of rays. In its passage through the electric field each α particle describes a parabolic path, and after emergence travels in a straight line to the photographic plate. By reversing the electric field at intervals, the direction of deflexion of the pencil of rays is reversed.

The general effect of the electric field in altering the appearance of the trace of the pencil of rays impinging on the photographic plate is shown in fig. 2 (Pl. V.) A shows the natural width of the line without an electric field, B for a P.D. of 255 volts, C for 340 volts, and D for 497 volts. These are reproduced from the actual photographs (magnification about 1·4 times). When a small P.D. is applied, the natural width of the photographic trace is broadened. Above a certain voltage, the single band breaks into two. As the voltage is further increased, the distance apart of these bands increases while the width of each band steadily narrows. The outside edge of each band is sharply defined, but it is difficult to fix with certainty the inner boundary of the bands.

Theory of the Experiment.

The theory of the experimental arrangement where the parallel plates act both as a slit and a means of applying the electric field, is more complicated than the ordinary case where a narrow pencil of α rays is made to pass between the two parallel plates of the condenser without impinging on the sides.

A diagram of the experimental arrangement is shown in fig. 3. AB and CD are the two charged parallel plates, and CE the radiant source which was of greater width than the distance between the plates. It is required to find the width of the trace on the photographic plate when a P.D. V is applied between the plates.

Let $m =$ mass of α particle,
$e =$ charge on α particle,
$u =$ velocity of α particle in passing between plates,
AB $= l_1$, CD $= l_2$, B $b = l_3$,
$d =$ distance between plates,
D $=$ distance between extreme edges of the photographic trace for reversal of the electric field.

There are two cases of the theory which must be separately considered :—

Case 1, when the deflexion of the α particle in passing through the electric field is less than *d*, the distance between the plates,

Case 2, when the deflexion is greater than *d*.

Fig. 3 A.   Fig. 3 B.

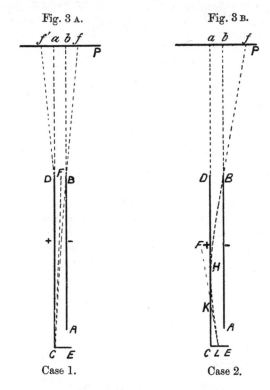

Case 1.   Case 2.

Case 1.—We shall now consider the theory for the first case. On entering the electric field at A, each α particle describes a parabolic path, and on emergence from the field moves in a straight line, the direction of which is a tangent to the parabolic path at the moment of emergence. The distance between the plates (0·21 mm.) is so small compared with the length AB (3·77 cms.), that we may assume without sensible error that the electric field is everywhere normal to the path of the rays. Suppose that the electric field is applied in such a direction that the α particle is urged in the direction of the plate AB. Some of the α particles, which before the field was applied fell on the photographic plate, are now

Phil. Mag. S. 6. Vol. 12. No. 70. Oct. 1906.   2 A

stopped by the plate AB, but other α particles previously stopped by the plate CD are able to emerge.

Suppose that the α particle in passing through the electric field is deflected normally through a distance S represented by FB. All the α particles which before the application of the electric field passed through the point F now just emerge at B at grazing incidence. The α particle which forms the extreme edge of the photographic trace at f must obviously be projected initially in the direction CF, and after emergence will travel along the line Bf.

Since the normal acceleration of the α particle in passing through the electric field is $\dfrac{Ve}{dm}$, and the time occupied in passing between the charged plates is $\dfrac{l_1}{u}$, the distance

$$FB = s = \frac{Ve}{2dm} \cdot \frac{l_1^2}{u^2},$$

or

$$s = \lambda l_1^2, \quad \text{where } \lambda = \frac{e}{2m} \cdot \frac{V}{du^2}.$$

At the moment of leaving the electric field, the tangent of the angle θ, which the direction of motion makes with the initial direction of projection CF, is given by $\tan \theta = 2\lambda l_1$.

If the angle $DCF = \theta_1$, the emerging ray makes an angle $\vartheta + \theta_1$ with the direction of the plates B b. The distance $bf = l_3 \tan(\theta + \theta_1)$. Since the angles θ and θ_1 are small,

$$bf = l_3(\theta + \theta_1)$$

$$= l_3\left(2\lambda l_1 + \frac{d-s}{l_2}\right).$$

In a similar way when the electric field is reversed, the corresponding distance

$$af' = l_3\left(2\lambda l_1 + \frac{d-s}{l_1}\right).$$

In this case, the α particle which is most deflected enters the electric field at grazing incidence at the point A.

The distance D between the extreme edges ff' of the photographic impression is consequently given by

$$D = bf + ab + af'$$

$$= 4\lambda l_1 l_3 + l_3(d-s)\left(\frac{1}{l_1} + \frac{1}{l_2}\right) + d.$$

Substituting the value $s = \lambda l_1^2$,

$$D = \lambda l_1 l_3\left(3 - \frac{l_1}{l_2}\right) + \left(\frac{l_3}{l_2} + \frac{l_3}{l_2} + 1\right)d.$$

But it is easily seen that the natural width of the photographic band without the electric field is given by

$$\left(\frac{l_3}{l_2} + \frac{l_3}{l_1} + 1\right)d.$$

Therefore the *increase* D_1 of the breadth of the band by the reversal of the electric field is given by

$$D_1 = \lambda\, l_1\, l_3\left(3 - \frac{l_1}{l_2}\right).$$

Substituting the value of λ,

$$\frac{mu^2}{e} = \frac{V\, l_1\, l_3}{2d D_1}\left(3 - \frac{l_1}{l_2}\right). \quad \cdots \quad (1)$$

This gives the formula required for determining the value of $\frac{mu^2}{e}$ for case 1.

Case 2.—In this case the electric field is supposed to be sufficiently strong to deflect the α particle in passing between the charged plates through a distance greater than d.

Suppose the electric field urges the α particle towards the plate AB (fig. 3 B). A little consideration shows that the α particle which forms the extreme edge of the photographic impression at f must touch at grazing incidence the plate CD. Let LKF be the direction of projection of such an α particle, intersecting the plate CD at K. The path of the α particle under the action of the electric field is shown by the dotted line in the figure. The path touches the plate CD at H and emerges at B at grazing incidence.

Let $DH = y$.

Then with the same notation as before, $d = \lambda y^2$.

The angle θ which the tangent to the parabola at B makes with the direction of the plate AB is given by

$$\tan \theta = 2\lambda y.$$

The distance $bf = l_3 \tan \theta = 2\lambda y l_3$.

The total distance D between the extreme edges of the photographic impression on the plate P by reversal of the field is consequently given by

$$D = 4\lambda y l_3 + d.$$

Then

$$(D - d)^2 = 16\lambda d l_3^2.$$

Substituting the value of λ as before,

$$\frac{mu^2}{e} = \frac{8V l_3^2}{(D - d)^2}. \quad \cdots \quad (2)$$

2 A 2

49

It is interesting to note that this formula for the determination of $\dfrac{mu^2}{e}$ does not involve l_1 or l_2, and only involves the distance d to a subordinate extent. For example, in one experiment where $l_3 = 10$ cms., the value of d was only 1/15 D. This is a great advantage, as the distance d is difficult to measure with accuracy.

While the distance l_1 is not involved in the final formula, it must be remembered that the formula (2) only applies when the α particle is deflected through a distance greater than d in passing between the plates. If l_1 is made smaller, the value of V must be made correspondingly greater before the formula can be applied.

It has been mentioned that the width of two deflected traces obtained by reversal of the electric field decreases in width with increase in strength of the electric field. The reason of this can readily be shown from theoretical considerations. For example, it is seen that the inside edge of the deflected pencil (fig. 3 B) is produced by the α particles whose paths touch at grazing incidence the plate AB at A and also touch the plate CD. These conditions determine the direction of the α particle in entering the electric field at A. All α particles passing through A which make a greater angle with the plate AB than the above α particle are stopped by the plate CD. As the width of the trace is not required in the experiment, it has not been thought necessary to include here the connexion between the width of the deflected pencil and the strength of the electric field. The calculations, though a little long, are not difficult.

It is now necessary to consider how we are able to know from the photographs obtained whether the formula (1) or (2) is to be applied. The formula (1) holds provided the distance of deflexion of the α particle is not greater than d. Suppose that the α particle is deflected through a distance d in passing between the charged plates. The outside edge of the photographic impression, for example, on the right of the plate P (fig. 3) is due to the α particles which start from the point C parallel to the plate CD. With the same notation as before,

$$d = \lambda l_1^2.$$

Following the same method of calculation as for case (2), it is seen that the value of D is given by

$$D = 4\lambda\, l_1\, l_3 + d.$$

Substituting the value $\lambda = \dfrac{d}{l_1{}^2}$,

$$D = d\left(\frac{4l_3}{l_1} + 1\right).$$

In most of the experiments to be described later,

$$l_3 = 3\cdot94 \text{ cms.}, \quad l_1 = 3\cdot77 \text{ cms.}, \quad d = \cdot21 \text{ mm.}$$

Consequently, $\qquad D = 1\cdot09 \text{ mm.}$

From the data given below it will be seen that the formula (2) applies for all voltages greater than about 300, while the formula (1) applies for all values smaller than this.

Results of Experiments.

The electrostatic deflexion of the α rays from radium C was first determined for different voltages between the plates. The rays from the active wire passed through a mica plate in the base of the vessel, equivalent in stopping power to about 3·5 cms. of air. The extreme distance D between the outside edges of the photographic impressions obtained on the plate by reversal of the electric field was measured by the lantern method described in a previous paper[*].

In most of the experiments, the value l_3 of the distance of the photographic plate above the parallel plates was 3·94 cms. In one experiment this distance was 10·00 cms.

$$l_1 = 3\cdot77 \text{ cms.}, \quad l_2 = 4\cdot165 \text{ cms.}, \quad d = 0\cdot210 \text{ mm.}$$

The values of $\dfrac{mu^2}{e}$ obtained for different voltages and distances of the photographic plate are tabulated below.

Volts between plates.	l_3.	D.	$\dfrac{mu^2}{e}$.
171	3·94 cms.	0·857 mms.	$5\cdot1 \times 10^{14}$
255	,, ,,	0·995 ,,	$4\cdot9 \times 10^{14}$
340	,, ,,	1·136 ,,	$4\cdot93 \times 10^{14}$
497	,, ,,	1·346 ,,	$4\cdot79 \times 10^{14}$
508·6	10·00 ,,	3·10 ,,	$4\cdot87 \times 10^{14}$

Each of the values of D given above is the mean of a large number of separate measurements which agreed closely among

[*] Rutherford, Phil. Mag. August 1906.

themselves. The values for 171 and 255 volts are calculated from formula (1), the natural width of the photographic trace being 0·61 mm., and for the higher voltages from formula (2). Some of the photographs from which the measurements were made are reproduced in fig. 2, magnification about 1·4.

Two good photographs were obtained with a P.D. of 340 volts. In each case two active wires were used successively to give a strong photographic impression. On account of the greater distance, the photographic impression was not so strongly marked for the distance 10 cms.

Giving a weight 1 to the measurement of $\dfrac{mu^2}{e}$ for 497 volts, and a weight 2 for both 340 and 508·6 volts, the mean value is given by

$$\frac{mu^2}{e} = 4·87 \times 10^{14} \text{ electromagnetic units.} \quad . \quad . \quad . \quad (3)$$

By measurement of the magnetic deflexion, the maximum value of $\dfrac{mu}{e}$ for the α rays from radium C was found to be $4·06 \times 10^5$. The mica screen cut down the velocity of the rays to ·763 of the initial velocity, so that the value of $\dfrac{mu}{e}$ for the rays which passed through the electric field is given by

$$\frac{mu}{e} = 3·10 \times 10^5. \quad . \quad . \quad . \quad . \quad (4)$$

By combining equations (3) and (4)

$$u = 1·57 \times 10^9 \text{ cms. per second,}$$
$$e/m = 5·07 \times 10^3 \text{ electromagnetic units.}$$

I think that the values of u and e/m are certainly correct within two per cent.

The initial velocity of the α particles expelled from radium C is consequently $2·06 \times 10^9$ cms. per second.

Does the value of e/m for the α particle vary in its passage through matter?

In order to test this point, the value of e/m for the α particle was determined under the following conditions :—

(1) The active wire was placed on top instead of under

the mica screen, so that the electrostatic deflexion was determined for the α particle from the unscreened wire.

(2) The α particles passed through a mica screen equivalent in stopping power to 3·5 cms. of air. The value of e/m under these conditions has been determined in the previous section.

(3) The α particles passed through a screen of mica and aluminium equivalent to about 6·5 cms. of air.

The magnetic and electrostatic deflexion were separately determined. The former gives the value of $\frac{mu}{e}$ and the latter $\frac{mu^2}{e}$. The results of the measurements are collected in the following table, where D has the same meaning as before. The value of l_3 in all cases was 3·94 cms.

Interposed absorbing screen in terms of air.	Volts.	D.	$\frac{mu}{e}$.	$\frac{mu^2}{e}$.	$\frac{e}{m}$.
0	340	0·88 mm.	$4·06 \times 10^5$	$9·4 \times 10^{14}$	$5·7 \times 10^3$
3·5 cms.	...	...	$3·10 \times 10^5$	$4·87 \times 10^{14}$	$5·07 \times 10^3$
6·5 cms.	340	1·62 mm.	$2·11 \times 10^5$	$2·11 \times 10^{14}$	$4·8 \times 10^3$

The deflexion for the rays from the bare wire was small, but could be measured with fair certainty. I think the value of e/m obtained in this case, viz. $5·7 \times 10^3$, is undoubtedly too high. On removing the active wire after completion of the experiment, it was noticed that its position was displaced somewhat to the side of the opening of the parallel plates. This would tend to make the observed width of the photographic trace too small, and consequently to give too great a value of e/m, when calculated from formula (1), which is based on the assumption that the active source completely covers the opening between the parallel plates.

The impression on the photographic plate due to the α particles which have passed through an absorbing screen equivalent to 6·5 cms. of air was weak but clearly defined, and admitted of fairly accurate measurement. Allowing for an error in the estimation of e/m for the α particles from the bare wire, I think the agreement of the values of e/m obtained under the different conditions is sufficiently close to prove definitely that the value of e/m for the α particle is unaltered in its passage through matter.

Value of e/m *for the α particles from Radium* A.

In a previous paper (*loc. cit.*) I gave the results of the measurements by the photographic method of $\frac{mu}{e}$ for the α particle emitted from radium A. For the unscreened wire the value of $\frac{mu}{e} = 3\cdot67 \times 10^{5}$, and for the wire covered with a mica plate of the same thickness as that over the opening in the base of the electrostatic apparatus, I found the value of $\frac{mu}{e} = 2\cdot19 \times 10^{5}$.

I pointed out in that paper the difficulty of accurately measuring the magnetic deflexion of the α particles from such a rapidly changing product as radium A, which is half transformed in three minutes. The difficulty of obtaining a sufficiently marked photographic impression, in order to measure the electric deflexions of the rays, was still greater. It was found necessary to place twenty active wires successively in position under the base of the apparatus, in order to obtain a measurable darkening of the photographic plate. Each wire was exposed for two minutes as negative electrode in a vessel containing a large quantity of the radium emanation. For such a short exposure, the initial radiation from the wire mainly comes from radium A. The wire was rapidly removed from the emanation vessel and placed in position and left for six minutes. In that time, the α ray activity of radium A is reduced to one quarter of its initial value. The α rays from the active wire passed through the standard mica plate before entering the electric field. The electric deflexion of the α rays from radium A is considerably greater than that for the swifter α particles from radium C; so that there is no danger of confusion between the two types of rays, even though the photographic impression of the rays from radium C present on the active wire is comparable with that due to the rays from radium A.

In the experiment the voltage was 255; $l_3 = 3\cdot94$ cms.; and D $= 1\cdot30$ mm. This gave

$$\frac{mu^2}{e} = 2\cdot67 \times 10^{14}.$$

The value $\frac{mu}{e}$ for the α rays from radium A after traversing the standard mica was $2\cdot19 \times 10^5$. This gives the values

$$u = 1\cdot22 \times 10^9 \text{ cms. per sec.}$$
$$e/m = 5\cdot6 \ \times 10^3.$$

It was found by experiment that the measured value of D —the distance between the extreme edges of the trace—was always underestimated for a very feeble photographic trace. An underestimate of the value of D gives too large a value for e/m. Taking this factor into consideration, the values of e/m obtained for the α particles from radium A and from radium C agree within the limit of experimental error. This shows that the α particles expelled from radium A and C have the same mass and differ only in their initial velocities of projection.

Mass of the α particle from Radium F.

A bismuth rod coated with radiotellurium was used as a source of α rays. It is now definitely established that the active constituent in both radiotellurium and polonium is the same and consists of the transformation product of radium, radium F. The active matter is deposited in the form of a thin film on the bismuth rod, and the α particles all escape from the surface at practically the same velocity. A piece of the rod was placed in position inside the electrostatic apparatus, and the photographic plate exposed for four days to the action of the α rays from the bare rod. The value $l_3 = 10\cdot00$ cms, the voltage $= 443$, and the observed value $D = 2\cdot72$ mm.

This gives a value $\dfrac{mu^2}{e} = 5\cdot63 \times 10^{14}$ for the α rays from the unscreened source. The value of $\dfrac{mu}{e} = 3\cdot2 \times 10^5$ was deduced by me in a previous paper from measurement of the range of the α particles from radium F in air. The experimental value found directly by Mackenzie (*loc. cit.*) was $3\cdot3 \times 10^5$. Taking the mean value $\dfrac{mu}{e} = 3\cdot25 \times 10^5$, we find that $e/m = 5\cdot3 \times 10^3$, and $u = 1\cdot73 \times 10^9$ cms. per second.

The actual photograph obtained was very weak in intensity, and, for the reasons previously mentioned, there is no doubt that the value e/m obtained is too large. We may consequently conclude that the α particle from radium F has the same mass as that expelled from radium C. Using a more active rod or a longer time of exposure, the value of e/m should be obtained with much greater precision; but there can be no doubt that it would be found identical with that observed for the α particle from radium C.

Mass of the α particles from Actinium.

In order to obtain a homogeneous source of α rays, the active deposit of actinium was used. The active deposit was concentrated on a small copper plate by making it the negative electrode in a small vessel containing the emanating actinium compound. This active deposit consists of two products, actinium A and B, the former of which is rayless. The activity imparted to a plate, ten minutes after removal from the emanation, decays exponentially with a period of 36 minutes. The rays emitted are all of one kind and have a range in air, found by Dr. Hahn in this laboratory, of 5·5 cms.

The preparation of actinium * employed was not very active, and the activity imparted to the copper plate was too weak to produce appreciable photographic action at the distances required. With the experience gained in the previous experiments with weak radioactive sources, it was recognized that at least twenty active wires, placed successively in position, would have been required to produce a measurable photographic effect in the magnetic deflexion apparatus. Three or four times this number would have been necessary in the electrostatic experiment. In order to avoid the necessity of such a procedure, the apparatus was constructed so that the copper plate could be kept active in the position required for any length of time. The actinium compound, wrapped in thin paper, was placed round the sides of a small brass vessel, which was attached to the base of the magnetic or electric deflexion apparatus. A small insulated copper plate, with its plane slightly inclined to the vertical, was placed below a narrow slit covered with mica in the base of the apparatus and was kept negatively charged. The activity on the plate reached a maximum after three hours and then remained constant. The radiation passing through the slit into the magnetic deflexion apparatus was mainly due to the α rays from actinium B. The photographic effect of the radiations from the emanation close to the active plate was too weak to be observed. The magnetic deflexion of the pencil of the α rays was determined under identically the same conditions as in the experiments using radium C as a source of rays. The photographic plate was exposed for ten hours in a constant magnetic field which was reversed at intervals. Two fine well-defined lines were obtained on the plate. The amount of the magnetic deflexion

* I am indebted to Mr. H. Lieber of New York for his kindness in lending me the sample of actinium used in this experiment.

was then directly compared with that due to the rays from radium C under the same conditions. For this purpose, the copper plate was removed and made active by exposure to the radium emanation. It was then placed back in its original position, and another photograph taken. The mica plate, covering the opening in the base of the magnetic apparatus, was of the same thickness as that used in the base of the electrostatic apparatus. The following numbers illustrate the results obtained :—

Distance between centres of deflected bands due to rays from actinium B = 1·85 mm.

Distance between centres of deflected bands due to rays from radium C = 1·53 mm.

We have previously shown that the value of $\frac{mu}{e}$ for the α particles of radium C after passing through the standard mica screen, absorbing-power equal to 3·5 cms. of air, is $3·10 \times 10^5$. Consequently the value of $\frac{mu}{e}$ for the α particles from actinium B is given by

$$\frac{mu}{e} = \frac{1·53}{1·85} \times 3·10 \times 10^5 = 2·56 \times 10^5.$$

It is interesting to note that the comparative magnetic deflexions observed for the rays of actinium B and of radium C agree with those to be expected from their known ranges in air, assuming the value of e/m for the α particle to be the same in both cases.

I have shown in a previous paper that the velocity V of an α particle of range r cms. in air is given by

$$\frac{V}{V_0} = ·348\sqrt{r+1·25},$$

where V_0 is the maximum velocity of the rays from radium C which have a range of 7·06 cms. Now, after passing through the mica screen, the rays from actinium B have a range $5·5 - 3·5 = 2·0$ cms., while those from radium C have a range $7·06 - 3·5 = 3·56$ cms.

Consequently,

$$\frac{\text{velocity of rays from radium C after passage through mica}}{\text{velocity of rays from actinium B after passage through mica}} =$$

$$= \sqrt{\frac{3·56 + 1·25}{2·0 + 1·25}} = 1·22.$$

The experimental ratio is 1·21. From the agreement between the experimental and the theoretical ratios, it could be concluded with confidence that the mass of the α particle from actinium is the same as that from radium C. This, however has been experimentally verified by measuring the electric deflexion of the α rays from actinium B.

The apparatus for determining the electric deflexion of the α rays was the same as that used in the radium experiments. The copper plate which served as a source of α rays was kept active by an arrangement similar to that used for the magnetic deflexion. The photographic plate was exposed for six days. Through an accident in the connexions, the electric field was not acting between the plates for the first three days. The photographic plate consequently showed the undeflected trace of the rays and the deflected trace on one side of it. The distance between the centre of the undeflected trace and the outside edge of the deflected trace gives the value of $\dfrac{D}{2}$. The value of l_3 was 10·00 cms. ; the voltage 340, and D was 3·174 cms. Consequently the value of $\dfrac{mu^2}{e}$ for the rays after passing through the standard mica was

$$\frac{mu^2}{e} = 3{\cdot}10 \times 10^{14}.$$

We have previously shown that

$$\frac{mu}{e} = 2{\cdot}56 \times 10^5,$$

Therefore

$$\frac{e}{m} = 4{\cdot}7 \times 10^3,$$

and

$$u = 1{\cdot}21 \times 10^9 \text{ cms. per second.}$$

We may thus conclude that the α particle from actinium has the same mass as that from radium.

Connexion of the α particle with the helium atom.

We have seen that, within the limit of experimental error, the mass of the α particle expelled from radium A, radium C, radium F, or actinium B is the same. In a later paper, in conjunction with Dr. Hahn, it will be shown that the mass of the α particle expelled from thorium C is also identical with that expelled from the radium products. We have also shown in a previous paper that the amount of the magnetic deflexion of the α particle from radium itself is in agreement with that to be deduced from its range in air—a result which is only to be expected if the α particle from radium has the same mass as that from radium C.

There then remains only one α ray product of radium, viz. the emanation, whose radiation has not been closely examined. There is, however, no reason to suppose that the α particles from the emanation differ in mass from those of the other products. An examination of the complex pencil of rays from a layer of radium in equilibrium shows no evidence of the presence of α rays which suffer an abnormal amount of deflexion. I think there can be no doubt that the α particles emitted from the various products of radium have an identical mass, but differ only in the initial velocities of projection. Although the mass of the α particles has been determined for only a single product of thorium and of actinium, the analogy with radium would lead us to expect that the α particle has the same mass for all the products of these substances.

We may thus reasonably conclude that the α particles expelled from the different radio-elements have the same mass in all cases. This is an important conclusion; for it shows that uranium, thorium, radium, and actinium, which behave chemically as distinct elements, have a common product of transformation. The α particle constitutes one of the fundamental units of matter of which the atoms of these elements are built up. When it is remembered that in the process of their transformation radium and thorium each expel five α particles, actinium four, and uranium one, and that radium is in all probability a transformation product of uranium, it is seen that the α particle is an important fundamental constituent of the atoms of the radio-elements proper. I have often pointed out what an important part the α particles play in radioactive transformations. In comparison, the β and γ rays play quite a secondary rôle.

It is now necessary to consider what deductions can be drawn from the observed value of e/m found for the α particle. The value of e/m for the hydrogen ion in the electrolysis of water is known to be very nearly 10^4. The hydrogen ion is supposed to be the hydrogen atom with a positive charge, so that the value of e/m for the hydrogen atom is 10^4. The observed value of e/m for the α particle is $5\cdot1 \times 10^3$, or, in round numbers, one half of that of the hydrogen atom. The density of helium has been found to be $1\cdot98$ times that of hydrogen, and from observations of the velocity of sound in helium, it has been deduced that helium is a monatomic gas. From this it is concluded that the helium atom has an atomic weight 3·96. If a helium atom carries the same charge as the hydrogen ion, the value of *e/m* for the helium atom should consequently be about $2·5 \times 10^3$. If we assume that the α particle carries the same charge as the hydrogen ion, the mass of the α particle is twice that of the hydrogen atom. We are here unfortunately confronted with several possibilities between which it is difficult to make a definite decision.

The value of *e/m* for the α particle may be explained on the assumptions that the α particle is (1) a *molecule* of hydrogen carrying the ionic charge of hydrogen, (2) a helium atom carrying *twice* the ionic charge of hydrogen, or (3) *one half* of the helium atom carrying a single ionic charge.

The hypothesis that the α particle is a molecule of hydrogen seems for many reasons improbable. If hydrogen is a constituent of radioactive matter, it is to be expected that it would be expelled in the atomic, and not in the molecular state. In addition, it seems improbable that, even if the hydrogen were initially projected in the molecular state, it would escape decomposition into its component atoms in passing through matter, for the α particle is projected at an enormous velocity, and the shock of the collisions of the α particle with the molecules of matter must be very intense, and tend to disrupt the bonds that hold the hydrogen atoms together. If the α particle is hydrogen, we should expect to find a large quantity of hydrogen present in the old radioactive minerals, which are sufficiently compact to prevent its escape. This does not appear to be the case, but, on the other hand, the comparatively large amount of helium present supports the view that the α particle is a helium atom. A strong argument in support of the view of a connexion between helium and the α particle rests on the observed facts* that helium is produced by actinium as well as by radium. The only point of identity between these two substances lies in the expulsion of α particles of the same mass. The production of helium by both substances is at once obvious if the helium is derived from the accumulated α particles, but is difficult to explain on any other hypothesis. We are thus reduced to the view that either the α particle is a helium atom carrying twice the ionic charge of hydrogen, or is half of a helium atom carrying a single ionic charge.

The latter assumption involves the conception that helium, while consisting of a monovalent atom under ordinary chemical and physical conditions, may exist in a still more elementary state as a component of the atoms of radioactive matter,

---

* Debierne, *C. R.* cxli. p. 383 (1905).

and that, after expulsion, the parts of the atom lose their charge and recombine to form atoms of helium; while such a view cannot be dismissed as inherently improbable, there is as yet no direct evidence in its favour. On the other hand, the second hypothesis has the merit of greater simplicity and probability.

On this view, the α particle is in reality a helium atom which is either expelled with a double ionic charge or acquires this charge in its passage through matter. Even if the α particle were initially projected without charge, it would certainly acquire one after the first few collisions with the molecules in its path. We know that the α particle is a very efficient ionizer, and there is every reason to suppose that it would itself be ionized by its collisions with the molecules in its path, *i. e.* it would lose one or more electrons and retain a positive charge. If the α particle can remain stable with the loss of two electrons, these electrons would almost certainly be removed as a result of the intense disturbance set up by the collision of the α particle with the molecules of matter. The α particle would then have twice the normal ionic charge, and the value of e/m, as found by measurement, would be quite consistent with the view that the α particle is an atom of helium.

In a previous paper * I showed, from measurement of the charge carried by the α rays, that $6 \cdot 2 \times 10^{10}$ α particles were expelled per second from one gram of radium at its minimum activity. This was based on the assumption that each α particle carried a positive charge equal to the ionic charge of hydrogen, viz. $3 \cdot 4 \times 10^{-10}$ electrostatic units. Assuming that the α particle carries two ionic charges, the corresponding number is reduced to one half of the above, viz. $3 \cdot 1 \times 10^{10}$. This would make the calculated period of radium 2600 years instead of 1300 years (see 'Radioactivity,' second edition, 1905, p. 457). In a similar way, the calculated volume of the emanation released from one gram of radium would be $0 \cdot 4$ cubic mm. instead of $0 \cdot 8$ cubic mm. The calculated volume of helium produced per year per gram of radium would be $0 \cdot 11$ cubic cms. ('Radioactivity,' p. 481).

On the hypothesis that the α particle is a helium atom, the atomic weight of each product is diminished by four units, in consequence of the expulsion of an α particle. On the hypothesis that the α particle is half a helium atom carrying a single ionic charge, the atomic weight is diminished by two units instead of four. Taking the latter hypothesis, the number of α particles expelled per second from one gram of

* Phil. Mag, August 1905.

radium at its minimum activity is 6.2×10^{10}. The calculated volume of the emanation is 0.8 cubic mms., while the production of helium per year is 0.11 cubic cms. per gram. The two hypotheses thus lead to the same rate of production of helium by radium.

Age of Radioactive Minerals.

I have previously pointed out that the age of the radio-active minerals can be calculated from the amount of helium contained in them. The method is based on the assumption that, in a compact mineral, the greater part of the helium is mechanically imprisoned in the mineral and is unable to escape. Let us consider, for example, the mineral fergu-sonite, which was found by Ramsay and Travers to contain 1.81 c.c. of helium per gram of the mineral. The fergusonite contains about 7 per cent. of uranium. The amount of helium per gram of uranium is consequently 26 c.c. Now we have seen that one gram of radium produces 0.11 c.c. of helium per year. The content of radium per gram of uranium is 3.8×10^{-7} gram *. Supposing that uranium emits only one α particle corresponding to the five emitted by radium in equilibrium where the product radium F is present, the production of helium per year per gram of uranium is $\frac{6}{4} \times .11 \times 3.8 \times 10^{-7}$ or 6.3×10^{-8} c.c. per year. Assuming as a first approximation that the rate of production of helium has been constant since the formation of the mineral, the time required for a production of 26 c.c. of helium is about 400 million years. This is a minimum estimate, for some of the helium has probably escaped from the mineral.

As another example, consider the mineral thorianite, which contains about 72 per cent. of thorium and 10 per cent. of uranium. The evolution of helium per gram of the mineral was found by Ramsay to be 9.5 c.c. Bragg (Phil. Mag. June 1906) has shown that thorium breaks up at $.26$ of the rate of uranium. This was based on measurements made with ordinary commercial thorium. Boltwood (Amer. Journ. Sci. June 1906) has, however, drawn attention to the fact that ordinary commercial thorium has in many cases only about one half of the activity obtained by direct preparation of the thorium from the radioactive minerals. This would double the rate of breaking up of thorium observed by Bragg. Remembering that a thorium atom during its transformations emits five α particles, and assuming that thorium breaks up at half the rate of uranium, it is seen that 72 per cent. of thorium in a mineral corresponds as a producer of helium to

---

* Rutherford and Boltwood, Amer. Journ. Sci. July 1906.

about $\dfrac{5}{6} \times \dfrac{72}{2} = 30$ per cent. of uranium. The amount of helium corresponding to one gram of uranium or its equivalent in the mineral is consequently 24 c.c. As before, the age of the mineral works out to be about 400 million years.

Numerous other examples may be given, but these serve to illustrate the method of calculation from radioactive data of the age of some radioactive minerals, and indirectly, in some cases, of the geological strata in which they are found.

Velocity and Energy of the α particles expelled from Radium products.

If the value of e/m is the same for the α particle expelled from the various radium products, the maximum velocity of each set of α particles can be deduced from their range in air, knowing the velocity of the α particles expelled from radium C. The velocities so determined are probably more accurate than those obtained by direct measurement under difficult conditions. In the following table, the second column gives the range in air of the α particles from the radium products, found by Bragg and Kleeman; in the fourth column is given the value of $\dfrac{mu^2}{e}$, where u is the initial velocity of projection of the α particles.

Product.	Range of α particle in cms.	Velocity in cms. per sec.	$\dfrac{mu^2}{e}$.
Radium	3·50 cms.	$1·56 \times 10^9$	$4·78 \times 10^{14}$
Emanation.........	4·36 ,,	$1·70 \times 10^9$	$5·65 \times 10^{14}$
Radium A	4·83 ,,	$1·77 \times 10^9$	$6·12 \times 10^{14}$
Radium C	7·06 ,,	$2·06 \times 10^9$	$8·37 \times 10^{14}$
Radium F *	3·86 ,,	$1·61 \times 10^9$	$5·15 \times 10^{14}$

* The range of the rays for polonium (radium F) has been recently measured by Levin (Amer. Journ. Sci. July 1906).

Disregarding radium F, the average energy of the α particle expelled from radium in equilibrium is $3·11 \times 10^{14} e$, where e is the charge carried by the α particle. Assuming that the heating effect of radium is a measure of the kinetic energy of the expelled α particles, we can at once deduce the total number of α particles expelled per second per gram of radium in equilibrium. One gram of radium in equilibrium emits 100 gram-calories of heat per hour. This rate of emission of energy is mechanically equivalent to $1 \cdot 16 \times 10^6$ ergs per second. Since the average energy of the expelled α particle is $3 \cdot 11 \times 10^{14} e$, the number of α particles expelled per second from one gram of radium in equilibrium is $\dfrac{3 \cdot 65}{10^9 e}$. The number previously found by the writer by measuring the total charge carried by the α particles was $\dfrac{2 \cdot 82}{10^9 e}$, *i. e.* 77 per cent. of the theoretical number. The agreement between theory and experiment is thus fairly good. In the above estimate, it is assumed that the heating effect is due entirely to the kinetic energy of the expelled α particles. It is known experimentally that the heating effect of the β and γ rays is only a small percentage of that due to the α rays. The expulsion of an α particle from an atom should lead to the recoil of the residue of the atom. Assuming that the momentum of the atom is equal and opposite to that of the α particle, the velocity of recoil of the atom can be simply calculated. Taking the mass of the α particle as 4 and of the radium atom as 225, the velocity of recoil of the disintegrated radium atom, for example, is $1/55 \times 1 \cdot 56 \times 10^9$ or $2 \cdot 8 \times 10^7$ cms. per second. The heating effect resulting from this recoil is thus only about 2 per cent. of that due to the α particle.

Assuming that each α particle carries a single ionic charge of $1 \cdot 13 \times 10^{-20}$ electromagnetic units, the number of α particles which must be expelled per second from one gram of radium in order to account entirely for the heating effect is $3 \cdot 2 \times 10^{11}$. The experimental number is $2 \cdot 5 \times 10^{11}$. If it is assumed that the α particle carries twice the usual ionic charge, each of these numbers is reduced by one half.

It is of interest to calculate the distribution of the heating effect of radium in equilibrium amongst the various α ray products. The theoretical percentages of the total heating effect are given in column 1. These are calculated from the known energy of the α particles expelled from each product. The observed percentages are deduced from the experimental numbers and curves given by Rutherford and Barnes (Phil. Mag. Feb. 1904).

Product.	Calculated heating effect.	Observed heating effect.
Radium	19·2	23
Emanation	22·7 ⎫ 47·2	45
Radium A	24·5 ⎭	
Radium C	33·6	32

The observed heating effects of the emanation and radium A are given together, as it is very difficult experimentally to determine their separate effects. It will be seen that there is a substantial agreement between the calculated and observed values.

Connexion between the Velocity and Amount of Ionization produced by the α particle.

Bragg (Phil. Mag. Nov. 1905) has shown that the ionization produced by a single α particle increases with the distance from the source to nearly the end of its range, when the ionization falls off very abruptly. He has shown that the ionization produced by the α particle at a distance r cms. from the end of the path is inversely proportional to $\sqrt{r+c}$, where c is a constant equal to 1·33. In a previous paper (Phil. Mag. Aug. 1906) I have shown that the velocity of an α particle at a distance r cms. from the end of its range is proportional to $\sqrt{r+d}$, where d is a constant equal to 1·25. The close agreement between these two expressions shows that the ionization produced per unit path by the α particle is inversely proportional to its velocity. This is in agreement with the theoretical views of Bragg, who supposed that the rate of expenditure of energy of the α particle in ionization at any point is inversely proportional to the energy of motion which it possesses.

A comparison of the velocities of the α particles expelled from the various products of the radio-elements, and a discussion of the connexion that exists between the velocity of expulsion of the α particle and the character of the transformation will be given in a later paper.

I desire to express my thanks to Dr. Hahn and Dr. Levin for their assistance in the measurement of the numerous photographs obtained in this investigation.

Berkeley, California, July 20, 1906.

RUTHERFORD.]

FIG. 2.

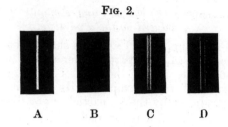

A   B   C   D

XXI. *The Nature of the α Particle from Radioactive Substances. By* Professor E. RUTHERFORD, *F.R.S., and* T. ROYDS, *M.Sc., 1851 Exhibition Science Scholar* *.

THE experimental evidence collected during the last few years has strongly supported the view that the α particle is a charged helium atom, but it has been found exceedingly difficult to give a decisive proof of the relation. In recent papers, Rutherford and Geiger † have supplied still further evidence of the correctness of this point of view. The number of α particles from one gram of radium have been counted, and the charge carried by each determined. The values of several radioactive quantities, calculated on the assumption that the α particle is a helium atom carrying two unit charges, have been shown to be in good agreement with the experimental numbers. In particular, the good agreement between the calculated rate of production of helium by radium and the rate experimentally determined by Sir James Dewar ‡, is strong evidence in favour of the identity of the α particle with the helium atom.

The methods of attack on this problem have been largely indirect, involving considerations of the charge carried by the helium atom and the value of *e/m* of the α particle. The proof of the identity of the α particle with the helium atom is incomplete until it can be shown that the α particles, accumulated quite independently of the matter from which they are expelled, consist of helium. For example, it might be argued that the appearance of helium in the radium emanation was a result of the expulsion of the α particle, in the same way that the appearance of radium A is a consequence of the expulsion of an α particle from the emanation. If one atom of helium appeared for each α particle expelled, calculation and experiment might still agree, and yet the α particle itself might be an atom of hydrogen or of some other substance.

We have recently made experiments to test whether helium appears in a vessel into which the α particles have been fired, the active matter itself being enclosed in a vessel sufficiently thin to allow the α particles to escape, but impervious to the passage of helium or other radioactive products.

* Communicated by the Authors.
† Proc. Roy. Soc. A. lxxxi. pp. 141–173 (1908).
‡ Proc. Roy. Soc. A. lxxxi. p. 280 (1908).

The experimental arrangement is clearly seen in the figure
The equilibrium quantity of emanation from about 140 milligrams of radium was purified and compressed by means of a

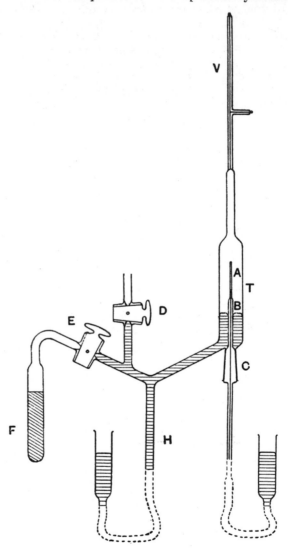

mercury-column into a fine glass tube A about 1·5 cms. long.
This fine tube, which was sealed on a larger capillary tube B,
was sufficiently thin to allow the α particles from the emanation and its products to escape, but sufficiently strong to

withstand atmospheric pressure. After some trials, Mr. Baumbach succeeded in blowing such fine tubes very uniform in thickness. The thickness of the wall of the tube employed in most of the experiments was less than $\frac{1}{100}$ mm., and was equivalent in stopping power of the α particle to about 2 cms. of air. Since the ranges of the α particles from the emanation and its products radium A and radium C are 4·3, 4·8, and 7 cms. respectively, it is seen that the great majority* of the α particles expelled by the active matter escape through the walls of the tube. The ranges of the α particles after passing through the glass were determined with the aid of a zinc-sulphide screen. Immediately after the introduction of the emanation the phosphorescence showed brilliantly when the screen was close to the tube, but practically disappeared at a distance of 3 cms. After an hour, bright phosphorescence was observable at a distance of 5 cms. Such a result is to be expected. The phosphorescence initially observed was due mainly to the α particles of the emanation and its product radium A (period 3 mins.). In the course of time the amount of radium C, initially zero, gradually increased, and the α radiations from it of range 7 cms. were able to cause phosphorescence at a greater distance.

The glass tube A was surrounded by a cylindrical glass tube T, 7·5 cms. long and 1·5 cms. diameter, by means of a ground-glass joint C. A small vacuum-tube V was attached to the upper end of T. The outer glass tube T was exhausted by a pump through the stopcock D, and the exhaustion completed with the aid of the charcoal tube F cooled by liquid air. By means of a mercury column H attached to a reservoir, mercury was forced into the tube T until it reached the bottom of the tube A.

Part of the α particles which escaped through the walls of the fine tube were stopped by the outer glass tube and part by the mercury surface. If the α particle is a helium atom, helium should gradually diffuse from the glass and mercury into the exhausted space, and its presence could then be detected spectroscopically by raising the mercury and compressing the gases into the vacuum-tube.

In order to avoid any possible contamination of the apparatus with helium, freshly distilled mercury and entirely new glass apparatus were used. Before introducing the emanation into A, the absence of helium was confirmed

---

* The α particles fired at a very oblique angle to the tube would be stopped in the glass. The fraction stopped in this way would be small under the experimental conditions.

experimentally. At intervals after the introduction of the emanation the mercury was raised, and the gases in the outer tube spectroscopically examined. After 24 hours no trace of the helium yellow line was seen ; after 2 days the helium yellow was faintly visible; after 4 days the helium yellow and green lines were bright; and after 6 days all the stronger lines of the helium spectrum were observed. The absence of the neon spectrum shows that the helium present was not due to a leakage of air into the apparatus.

There is, however, one possible source of error in this experiment. The helium may not be due to the α particles themselves, but may have *diffused* from the emanation through the thin walls of the glass tube. In order to test this point the emanation was completely pumped out of A, and after some hours a quantity of helium, about 10 times the previous volume of the emanation, was compressed into the same tube A.

The outer tube T and the vacuum-tube were removed and a fresh apparatus substituted. Observations to detect helium in the tube T were made at intervals, in the same way as before, but no trace of the helium spectrum was observed over a period of eight days.

The helium in the tube A was then pumped out and a fresh supply of emanation substituted. Results similar to the first experiment were observed. The helium yellow and green lines showed brightly after four days.

These experiments thus show conclusively that the helium could not have diffused through the glass walls, but must have been derived from the α particles which were fired through them. In other words, the experiments give a decisive proof that the α particle after losing its charge is an atom of helium.

Other Experiments.

We have seen that in the experiments above described helium was not observed in the outer tube in sufficient quantity to show the characteristic yellow line until two days had elapsed. Now the equilibrium amount of emanation from 100 milligrams of radium should produce helium at the rate of about ·03 c.mm. per day. The amount produced in one day, if present in the outer tube, should produce a bright spectrum of helium under the experimental conditions. It thus appeared probable that the helium fired into the glass must escape very slowly into the exhausted space, for if the helium escaped at once, the presence of helium should have been detected a few hours after the introduction of the emanation.

In order to examine this point more closely the experiments were repeated, with the addition that a cylinder of thin sheet lead of sufficient thickness to stop the α particles was placed over the fine emanation tube. Preliminary experiments, in the manner described later, showed that the lead-foil did not initially contain a detectable amount of helium. Twenty-four hours after the introduction into the tube A of about the same amount of emanation as before, the yellow and green lines of helium showed brightly in the vacuum-tube, and after two days the whole helium spectrum was observed. The spectrum of helium in this case after one day was of about the same intensity as that after the fourth day in the experiments without the lead screen. It was thus clear that the lead-foil gave up the helium fired into it far more readily than the glass.

In order to form an idea of the rapidity of escape of the helium from the lead some further experiments were made. The outer cylinder T was removed and a small cylinder of lead-foil placed round the thin emanation-tube surrounded the air at atmospheric pressure. After exposure for a definite time to the emanation, the lead screen was removed and gested for helium as follows. The lead-foil was placed in a glass tube between two stopcocks. In order to avoid a possible release of the helium present in the lead by pumping out the air, the air was displaced by a current of pure electrolytic oxygen*. The stopcocks were closed and the tube attached to a subsidiary apparatus similar to that employed for testing for the presence of neon and helium in the gases produced by the action of the radium emanation on water (Phil. Mag. Nov. 1908). The oxygen was absorbed by charcoal and the tube then heated beyond the melting-point of lead to allow the helium to escape. The presence of helium was then spectroscopically looked for in the usual way. Using this method, it was found possible to detect the presence of helium in the lead which had been exposed for only four hours to the α rays from the emanation. After an exposure of 24 hours the helium yellow and green lines came out brightly. These experiments were repeated several times with similar results.

A number of blank experiments were made, using samples of the lead-foil which had not been exposed to the α rays, but in no case was any helium detected. In a similar way,

* That the air was completely displaced was shown by the absence of neon in the final spectrum.

the presence of helium was detected in a cylinder of tinfoil exposed for a few hours over the emanation-tube.

These experiments show that the helium does not escape at once from the lead, but there is on the average a period of retardation of several hours and possibly longer.

The detection of helium in the lead and tin foil, as well as in the glass, removes a possible objection that the helium might have been in some way present in the glass initially, and was liberated as a consequence of its bombardment by the α particles.

The use of such thin glass tubes containing emanation affords a simple and convenient method of examining the effect on substances of an intense α radiation quite independently of the radioactive material contained in the tube.

We can conclude with certainty from these experiments that the α particle after losing its charge is a helium atom. Other evidence indicates that the charge is twice the unit charge carried by the hydrogen atom set free in the electrolysis of water.

University of Manchester,
   Nov. 13, 1908.

Group 2

THE ATOM

It is clearly not possible to comment upon every fascinating question raised by this group of papers, but the following points are perhaps worth making.

1. The belief in the indestructibility of the atom has already been noted. The proof by J. J. Thomson that the electron was a sub-atomic particle common to all the gases he tested was vigorously questioned by the German School, particularly Hertz. It was argued that the cathode rays were electromagnetic in nature and that the application of a magnetic field distorted the medium in which the rays travelled and, therefore, caused them to depart from a rectilinear path—a phenomenon somewhat similar to the Faraday effect. This view was based on a failure to obtain a deflection of the beam when an electrostatic field was applied, and the discovery by Hertz and Lenard that the rays could pass through gold and aluminium foil, apparently without affecting the vacuum, the foil or the rays. Furthermore, Hertz was unable to show that the cathode rays themselves carried negative charge. A deflection of the particles in an electrostatic field was obtained once a sufficiently good vacuum had been produced. Previously some of the residual atoms of the gas had been ionised by the bombardment of the electrons and the ions had adhered to the plates, thereby nullifying the field.

Sir J. J. Thomson's qualities as an experimental physicist were unusual. As he freely admitted, his manual skill was very limited but he made up for this deficiency with an extraordinary ability to understand the working of a complex piece of apparatus, merely by looking at it. He relied, too, on his laboratory staff. 'A very important person in a physical laboratory is the man in charge of the workshop. The smooth running of the laboratory depends upon him almost more than upon anyone else, and to be successful he must have many qualifications.'[1]

2. Once the electron was established it was necessary to construct a model of an atom to fit the available evidence. This J. J. Thomson did in 1904.[2] He conceived it to be a sphere of uniform positive electrification in which rings of electrons may rotate, the number in each ring increasing with the radius. The mass of the atom is very nearly the sum of the masses of the electrons. He showed that instability

occurs as electrons are added, in such a way that the regularity of the Periodic Table is explained. The spectrum of an element arises from two sources: the rotation of the electrons in their rings and the vibrations which will occur after the shape of a ring of electrons has been momentarily distorted.

Thomson proved that if the angular velocity for a group of, say, four electrons drops below a certain value, the group becomes unstable. Large atoms might consist of a number of sub-atoms, each with a ring of electrons rotating very quickly. If, as a consequence of slowly radiating energy, the angular velocity drops to its critical value, an explosion will take place during which a sub-atom is expelled and this could be the mechanism of radioactive decay.

This model, with which there were always difficulties, e.g. a hydrogen atom must have about eighteen hundred electrons, was abandoned when Geiger and Marsden succeeded in detecting α particles which had been scattered through an angle greater than 90°. The experiment is too well known to need any comment, but the theoretical structure erected by Bohr, to account for the properties of the Rutherford atom, to which the experiment led, was strikingly original. Bohr applied Planck's theory of radiation to the electrons rotating round the central massive nucleus.

Now the essential point in Planck's theory of radiation, is that energy radiation from an atomic system does not take place in the continuous way assumed in the ordinary electrodynamics, but that it, on the contrary, takes place in distinctly separated emissions, the amount of energy radiated out from an atomic vibrator of frequency ν in a single emission being equal to $\tau h\nu$, where τ is an entire number and h is a universal constant.[3]

He made two assumptions in his calculations. One was that a state of dynamical equilibrium was susceptible to treatment by ordinary mechanics and the second that the transition of an electron from one energy level to another was accompanied by the emission of homogeneous radiation. His theory was brilliantly successful in clearing up difficulties and predicting new properties, but there was an uncomfortable feeling that it was a mathematical device, rather imperfectly grounded in reality. J. J. Thomson expressed his doubts thus: 'It is, I think, however, not unfair to say that to many minds the arithmetical basis of the theory seems much more satisfactory than the physical'.[4]

3. Rutherford's 1920 Bakerian lecture is remarkable because in it he discussed the existence of three new particles; a proton in conjunction with an electron (a neutron); two protons and an electron (a deuteron); and three protons and an electron (the nucleus of an isotope of helium). He mentioned a fourth due to Harkins, made up of three protons and two electrons (a tritium nucleus). The third on the list represents one of Rutherford's rare mistakes, and it occurred in his effort to identify a strange particle which he thought came from oxygen when these atoms

were bombarded with α particles. It was later shown to be due to an α particle hitherto unnoticed, from radium C, which had an extra long range. Also, it was recognised subsequently that electrons could not be part of the nucleus because they are too large and, for a second and more important reason, that the calculated values of nuclear spin did not agree with experimental ones. Once the neutron had been discovered by Chadwick, Heisenberg (1932) proposed a nucleus comprising neutrons and protons. The difficulties then disappeared.

4. Moseley's extraordinary promise is amply demonstrated in his work on high-frequency spectra of the elements. No one had given a precise idea of the physical reality underlying the Periodic Table; it was little more than a mnemonic. Clearly the elements could be arranged in stepwise fashion but non-integral atomic weights and occasional misplacements were very perplexing. Moseley succeeded in showing that there is a characteristic of the atom which changes in integral steps and this is to be identified with the number of protons in the nucleus, that is, the atomic number. Since the atom is neutral the atomic number equals the number of electrons it possesses, upon which the physical and chemical properties of the elements largely depend. The various isotopes of a given element behaved identically in this work and could not affect the result.

[1] J. J. Thomson, *Recollections and Reflections*, p. 115.
[2] J. J. Thomson, *Phil. Mag.*, 1904, A, **7**.
[3] N. D. Bohr, *Phil. Mag.*, 1913, A, **26**.
[4] J. J. Thomson, *Phil. Mag.*, 1919, A, **36**.

THE

LONDON, EDINBURGH, AND DUBLIN

PHILOSOPHICAL MAGAZINE

AND

JOURNAL OF SCIENCE.

◆

[FIFTH SERIES.]

OCTOBER 1897.

XL. *Cathode Rays.* By J. J. THOMSON, *M.A., F.R.S.,*
Cavendish Professor of Experimental Physics, Cambridge*.

THE experiments† discussed in this paper were undertaken
in the hope of gaining some information as to the
nature of the Cathode Rays. The most diverse opinions are
held as to these rays ; according to the almost unanimous
opinion of German physicists they are due to some process
in the æther to which—inasmuch as in a uniform magnetic
field their course is circular and not rectilinear—no phenomenon hitherto observed is analogous : another view of these
rays is that, so far from being wholly ætherial, they are in fact
wholly material, and that they mark the paths of particles of
matter charged with negative electricity. It would seem at
first sight that it ought not to be difficult to discriminate
between views so different, yet experience shows that this is
not the case, as amongst the physicists who have most deeply
studied the subject can be found supporters of either theory.

The electrified-particle theory has for purposes of research
a great advantage over the ætherial theory, since it is definite
and its consequences can be predicted; with the ætherial theory
it is impossible to predict what will happen under any given
circumstances, as on this theory we are dealing with hitherto

---

* Communicated by the Author.
† Some of these experiments have already been described in a paper read
before the Cambridge Philosophical Society (Proceedings, vol. ix. 1897),
and in a Friday Evening Discourse at the Royal Institution ('Electrician,'
May 21, 1897).

Phil. Mag. S. 5. Vol. 44. No. 269. *Oct.* 1897.   Y unobserved phenomena in the æther, of whose laws we are ignorant.

The following experiments were made to test some of the consequences of the electrified-particle theory.

Charge carried by the Cathode Rays.

If these rays are negatively electrified particles, then when they enter an enclosure they ought to carry into it a charge of negative electricity. This has been proved to be the case by Perrin, who placed in front of a plane cathode two coaxial metallic cylinders which were insulated from each other : the outer of these cylinders was connected with the earth, the inner with a gold-leaf electroscope. These cylinders were closed except for two small holes, one in each cylinder, placed so that the cathode rays could pass through them into the inside of the inner cylinder. Perrin found that when the rays passed into the inner cylinder the electroscope received a charge of negative electricity, while no charge went to the electroscope when the rays were deflected by a magnet so as no longer to pass through the hole.

This experiment proves that something charged with negative electricity is shot off from the cathode, travelling at right angles to it, and that this something is deflected by a magnet; it is open, however, to the objection that it does not prove that the cause of the electrification in the electroscope has anything to do with the cathode rays. Now the supporters of the ætherial theory do not deny that electrified particles are shot off from the cathode; they deny, however, that these charged particles have any more to do with the cathode rays than a rifle-ball has with the flash when a rifle is fired. I have therefore repeated Perrin's experiment in a form which is not open to this objection. The arrangement used was as follows:— Two coaxial cylinders (fig. 1) with slits in them are placed in a bulb connected with the discharge-tube; the cathode rays from the cathode A pass into the bulb through a slit in a metal plug fitted into the neck of the tube ; this plug is connected with the anode and is put to earth. The cathode rays thus do not fall upon the cylinders unless they are deflected by a magnet. The outer cylinder is connected with the earth, the inner with the electrometer. When the cathode rays (whose path was traced by the phosphorescence on the glass) did not fall on the slit, the electrical charge sent to the electrometer when the induction-coil producing the rays was set in action was small and irregular; when, however, the rays were bent by a magnet so as to fall on the slit there was a large charge of negative electricity sent to the electrometer. I was surprised at the magnitude of the charge ; on some occasions enough negative electricity went through the narrow slit into the inner cylinder in one second to alter the potential of a capacity of 1·5 microfarads by 20 volts. If the rays were so

Fig. 1.

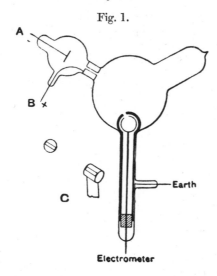

much bent by the magnet that they overshot the slits in the cylinder, the charge passing into the cylinder fell again to a very small fraction of its value when the aim was true. Thus this experiment shows that however we twist and deflect the cathode rays by magnetic forces, the negative electrification follows the same path as the rays, and that this negative electrification is indissolubly connected with the cathode rays.

When the rays are turned by the magnet so as to pass through the slit into the inner cylinder, the deflexion of the electrometer connected with this cylinder increases up to a certain value, and then remains stationary although the rays continue to pour into the cylinder. This is due to the fact that the gas in the bulb becomes a conductor of electricity when the cathode rays pass through it, and thus, though the inner cylinder is perfectly insulated when the rays are not passing, yet as soon as the rays pass through the bulb the air between the inner cylinder and the outer one becomes a conductor, and the electricity escapes from the inner cylinder to the earth. Thus the charge within the inner cylinder does not go on continually increasing ; the cylinder settles down into a state of equilibrium in which the rate at which it gains negative electricity from the rays is equal to the rate at which it loses it by conduction through the air. If the inner cylinder has initially a positive charge it rapidly loses that

Y 2

charge and acquires a negative one; while if the initial charge is a negative one, the cylinder will leak if the initial negative potential is numerically greater than the equilibrium value.

Deflexion of the Cathode Rays by an Electrostatic Field.

An objection very generally urged against the view that the cathode rays are negatively electrified particles, is that hitherto no deflexion of the rays has been observed under a small electrostatic force, and though the rays are deflected when they pass near electrodes connected with sources of large differences of potential, such as induction-coils or electrical machines, the deflexion in this case is regarded by the supporters of the ætherial theory as due to the discharge passing between the electrodes, and not primarily to the electrostatic field.   Hertz made the rays travel between two parallel plates of metal placed inside the discharge-tube, but found that they were not deflected when the plates were connected with a battery of storage-cells; on repeating this experiment I at first got the same result, but subsequent experiments showed that the absence of deflexion is due to the conductivity conferred on the rarefied gas by the cathode rays.   On measuring this conductivity it was found that it diminished very rapidly as the exhaustion increased; it seemed then that on trying Hertz's experiment at very high exhaustions there might be a chance of detecting the deflexion of the cathode rays by an electrostatic force.

The apparatus used is represented in fig. 2.

Fig. 2.

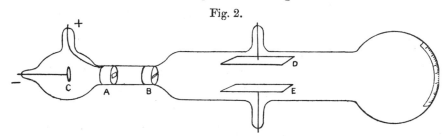

The rays from the cathode C pass through a slit in the anode A, which is a metal plug fitting tightly into the tube and connected with the earth; after passing through a second slit in another earth-connected metal plug B, they travel between two parallel aluminium plates about 5 cm. long by 2 broad and at a distance of 1·5 cm. apart; they then fall on the end of the tube and produce a narrow well-defined phosphorescent patch.   A scale pasted on the outside of the tube serves to measure the deflexion of this patch.

At high exhaustions the rays were deflected when the two aluminium plates were connected with the terminals of a battery of small storage-cells; the rays were depressed when the upper plate was connected with the negative pole of the battery, the lower with the positive, and raised when the upper plate was connected with the positive, the lower with the negative pole. The deflexion was proportional to the difference of potential between the plates, and I could detect the deflexion when the potential-difference was as small as two volts. It was only when the vacuum was a good one that the deflexion took place, but that the absence of deflexion is due to the conductivity of the medium is shown by what takes place when the vacuum has just arrived at the stage at which the deflexion begins. At this stage there is a deflexion of the rays when the plates are first connected with the terminals of the battery, but if this connexion is maintained the patch of phosphorescence gradually creeps back to its undeflected position. This is just what would happen if the space between the plates were a conductor, though a very bad one, for then the positive and negative ions between the plates would slowly diffuse, until the positive plate became coated with negative ions, the negative plate with positive ones; thus the electric intensity between the plates would vanish and the cathode rays be free from electrostatic force. Another illustration of this is afforded by what happens when the pressure is low enough to show the deflexion and a large difference of potential, say 200 volts, is established between the plates; under these circumstances there is a large deflexion of the cathode rays, but the medium under the large electromotive force breaks down every now and then and a bright discharge passes between the plates; when this occurs the phosphorescent patch produced by the cathode rays jumps back to its undeflected position. When the cathode rays are deflected by the electrostatic field, the phosphorescent band breaks up into several bright bands separated by comparatively dark spaces; the phenomena are exactly analogous to those observed by Birkeland when the cathode rays are deflected by a magnet, and called by him the magnetic spectrum.

A series of measurements of the deflexion of the rays by the electrostatic force under various circumstances will be found later on in the part of the paper which deals with the velocity of the rays and the ratio of the mass of the electrified particles to the charge carried by them. It may, however, be mentioned here that the deflexion gets smaller as the pressure diminishes, and when in consequence the potential-difference in the tube in the neighbourhood of the cathode increases.

Conductivity of a Gas through which Cathode Rays are passing.

The conductivity of the gas was investigated by means of the apparatus shown in fig. 2. The upper plate D was connected with one terminal of a battery of small storage-cells, the other terminal of which was connected with the earth; the other plate E was connected with one of the coatings of a condenser of one microfarad capacity, the other coating of which was to earth; one pair of quadrants of an electrometer was also connected with E, the other pair of quadrants being to earth. When the cathode rays are passing between the plates the two pairs of quadrants of the electrometer are first connected with each other, and then the connexion between them was broken. If the space between the plates were a non-conductor, the potential of the pair of quadrants not connected with the earth would remain zero and the needle of the electrometer would not move; if, however, the space between the plates were a conductor, then the potential of the lower plate would approach that of the upper, and the needle of the electrometer would be deflected. There is always a deflexion of the electrometer, showing that a current passes between the plates. The magnitude of the current depends very greatly upon the pressure of the gas; so much so, indeed, that it is difficult to obtain consistent readings in consequence of the changes which always occur in the pressure when the discharge passes through the tube.

We shall first take the case when the pressure is only just low enough to allow the phosphorescent patch to appear at the end of the tube; in this case the relation between the current between the plates and the initial difference of potential is represented by the curve shown in fig. 3. In this

Fig. 3.

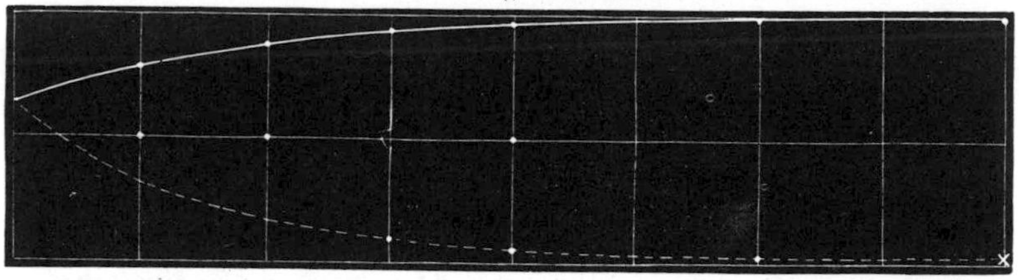

figure the abscissæ represent the initial difference of potential between the plates, each division representing two volts, and the ordinates the rise in potential of the lower plate in one minute each division again representing two volts. The quantity of electricity which has passed between the plates in one minute is the quantity required to raise 1 microfarad to the potential-difference shown by the curve. The upper and lower curve relates to the case when the upper plate is connected with the negative and positive pole respectively of the battery.

Even when there is no initial difference of potential between the plates the lower plate acquires a negative charge from the impact on it of some of the cathode rays.

We see from the curve that the current between the plates soon reaches a value where it is only slightly affected by an increase in the potential-difference between the plates; this is a feature common to conduction through gases traversed by Röntgen rays, by uranium rays, by ultra-violet light, and, as we now see, by cathode rays. The rate of leak is not greatly different whether the upper plate be initially positively or negatively electrified.

The current between the plates only lasts for a short time ; it ceases long before the potential of the lower plate approaches that of the upper. Thus, for example, when the potential of the upper plate was about 400 volts above that of the earth, the potential of the lower plate never rose above 6 volts: similarly, if the upper plate were connected with the negative pole of the battery, the fall in potential of the lower plate was very small in comparison with the potential-difference between the upper plate and the earth.

These results are what we should expect if the gas between the plates and the plug B (fig. 2) were a very much better conductor than the gas between the plates, for the lower plate will be in a steady state when the current coming to it from the upper plate is equal to the current going from it to the plug: now if the conductivity of the gas between the plate and the plug is much greater than that between the plates, a small difference of potential between the lower plate and the plug will be consistent with a large potential-difference between the plates.

So far we have been considering the case when the pressure is as high as is consistent with the cathode rays reaching the end of the tube ; we shall now go to the other extreme and consider the case when the pressure is as low as is consistent with the passage of a discharge through the bulb. In this case, when the plates are not connected with the battery we get a negative charge communicated to the lower plate, but only very slowly in comparison with the effect in the previous case. When the upper plate is connected with the negative pole of a battery, this current to the lower plate is only slightly increased even when the difference of potential is as much as 400 volts: a small potential-difference of about

20 volts seems slightly to decrease the rate of leak. Potential-differences much exceeding 400 volts cannot be used, as though the dielectric between the plates is able to sustain them for some little time, yet after a time an intensely bright arc flashes across between the plates and liberates so much gas as to spoil the vacuum. The lines in the spectrum of this glare are chiefly mercury lines; its passage leaves very peculiar markings on the aluminium plates.

If the upper plate was charged positively, then the negative charge communicated to the lower plate was diminished, and stopped when the potential-difference between the plates was about 20 volts; but at the lowest pressure, however great (up to 400 volts) the potential-difference, there was no leak of positive electricity to the lower plate at all comparable with the leak of negative electricity to this plate when the two plates were disconnected from the battery. In fact at this very low pressure all the facts are consistent with the view that the effects are due to the negatively electrified particles travelling along the cathode rays, the rest of the gas possessing little conductivity. Some experiments were made with a tube similar to that shown in fig. 2, with the exception that the second plug B was absent, so that a much greater number of cathode rays passed between the plates. When the upper plate was connected with the positive pole of the battery a luminous discharge with well-marked striations passed between the upper plate and the earth-connected plug through which the cathode rays were streaming; this occurred even though the potential-difference between the plate and the plug did not exceed 20 volts. Thus it seems that if we supply cathode rays from an external source to the cathode a small potential-difference is sufficient to produce the characteristic discharge through a gas.

Magnetic Deflexion of the Cathode Rays in Different Gases.

The deflexion of the cathode rays by the magnetic field was studied with the aid of the apparatus shown in fig. 4. The cathode was placed in a side-tube fastened on to a bell-jar; the opening between this tube and the bell-jar was closed by a metallic plug with a slit in it; this plug was connected with the earth and was used as the anode. The cathode rays passed through the slit in this plug into the bell-jar, passing in front of a vertical plate of glass ruled into small squares. The bell-jar was placed between two large parallel coils arranged as a Helmholtz galvanometer. The course of the rays was determined by taking photographs of the bell-jar when the cathode rays were passing through it ; the divisions on the plate enabled the path of the rays to be determined. Under the action of the magnetic field the narrow beam of cathode rays spreads out into a broad fan-shaped luminosity in the gas. The luminosity in this fan is not uniformly

Fig. 4.

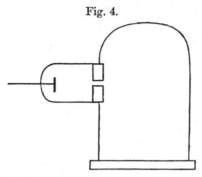

distributed, but is condensed along certain lines. The phosphorescence on the glass is also not uniformly distributed ; it is much spread out, showing that the beam consists of rays which are not all deflected to the same extent by the magnet. The luminosity on the glass is crossed by bands along which the luminosity is very much greater than in the adjacent parts. These bright and dark bands are called by Birkeland, who first observed them, the magnetic spectrum. The brightest spots on the glass are by no means always the terminations of the brightest streaks of luminosity in the gas ; in fact, in some cases a very bright spot on the glass is not connected with the cathode by any appreciable luminosity, though there may be plenty of luminosity in other parts of the gas. One very interesting point brought out by the photographs is that in a given magnetic field, and with a given mean potential-difference between the terminals, the path of the rays is independent of the nature of the gas. Photographs were taken of the discharge in hydrogen, air, carbonic acid, methyl iodide, *i. e.*, in gases whose densities range from 1 to 70, and yet, not only were the paths of the most deflected rays the same in all cases, but even the details, such as the distribution of the bright and dark spaces, were the same ; in fact, the photographs could hardly be distinguished from each other. It is to be noted that the pressures were not the same ; the pressures in the different gases were adjusted so that the mean potential-differences between the cathode and the anode were the same in all the gases. When the pressure of a gas is lowered, the potential-difference between the terminals increases, and the deflexion of the rays produced by a magnet diminishes, or at any rate the deflexion of the rays when the phosphorescence is a maximum diminishes. If an air-break is inserted an effect of the same kind is produced.

In the experiments with different gases, the pressures were as high as was consistent with the appearance of the phosphorescence on the glass, so as to ensure having as much as possible of the gas under consideration in the tube.

As the cathode rays carry a charge of negative electricity, are deflected by an electrostatic force as if they were negatively electrified, and are acted on by a magnetic force in just the way in which this force would act on a negatively electrified body moving along the path of these rays, I can see no escape from the conclusion that they are charges of negative electricity carried by particles of matter. The question next arises, What are these particles? are they atoms, or molecules, or matter in a still finer state of subdivision? To throw some light on this point, I have made a series of measurements of the ratio of the mass of these particles to the charge carried by it. To determine this quantity, I have used two independent methods. The first of these is as follows :— Suppose we consider a bundle of homogeneous cathode rays. Let m be the mass of each of the particles, e the charge carried by it. Let N be the number of particles passing across any section of the beam in a given time; then Q the quantity of electricity carried by these particles is given by the equation

$$N e = Q.$$

We can measure Q if we receive the cathode rays in the inside of a vessel connected with an electrometer. When these rays strike against a solid body, the temperature of the body is raised; the kinetic energy of the moving particles being converted into heat; if we suppose that all this energy is converted into heat, then if we measure the increase in the temperature of a body of known thermal capacity caused by the impact of these rays, we can determine W, the kinetic energy of the particles, and if v is the velocity of the particles,

$$\tfrac{1}{2} N m v^2 = W.$$

If ρ is the radius of curvature of the path of these rays in a uniform magnetic field H, then

$$\frac{m v}{e} = H \rho = I,$$

where I is written for Hρ for the sake of brevity. From these equations we get

$$\frac{1}{2}\frac{m}{e}v^2 = \frac{W}{Q}.$$

$$v = \frac{2W}{QI},$$

$$\frac{m}{e} = \frac{I^2 Q}{2W}.$$

Thus, if we know the values of Q, W, and I, we can deduce the values of v and m/e.

To measure these quantities, I have used tubes of three different types. The first I tried is like that represented in fig. 2, except that the plates E and D are absent, and two coaxial cylinders are fastened to the end of the tube. The rays from the cathode C fall on the metal plug B, which is connected with the earth, and serves for the anode ; a horizontal slit is cut in this plug. The cathode rays pass through this slit, and then strike against the two coaxial cylinders at the end of the tube ; slits are cut in these cylinders, so that the cathode rays pass into the inside of the inner cylinder. The outer cylinder is connected with the earth, the inner cylinder, which is insulated from the outer one, is connected with an electrometer, the deflexion of which measures Q, the quantity of electricity brought into the inner cylinder by the rays. A thermo-electric couple is placed behind the slit in the inner cylinder ; this couple is made of very thin strips of iron and copper fastened to very fine iron and copper wires. These wires passed through the cylinders, being insulated from them, and through the glass to the outside of the tube, where they were connected with a low-resistance galvanometer, the deflexion of which gave data for calculating the rise of temperature of the junction produced by the impact against it of the cathode rays. The strips of iron and copper were large enough to ensure that every cathode ray which entered the inner cylinder struck against the junction. In some of the tubes the strips of iron and copper were placed end to end, so that some of the rays struck against the iron, and others against the copper ; in others, the strip of one metal was placed in front of the other ; no difference, however, could be detected between the results got with these two arrangements. The strips of iron and copper were weighed, and the thermal capacity of the junction calculated. In one set of junctions this capacity was 5×10^{-3}, in another 3×10^{-3}. If we assume that the cathode rays which strike against the junction give their energy up to it, the deflexion of the galvanometer gives us W or $\frac{1}{2}Nmv^2$.

The value of I, *i. e.*, Hρ, where ρ is the curvature of the path of the rays in a magnetic field of strength H was found as follows :—The tube was fixed between two large circular coils placed parallel to each other, and separated by a distance equal to the radius of either; these coils produce a uniform magnetic field, the strength of which is got by measuring with an ammeter the strength of the current passing through them. The cathode rays are thus in a uniform field, so that their path is circular. Suppose that the rays, when deflected by a magnet, strike against the glass of the tube at E

Fig. 5.

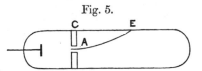

(fig. 5), then, if ρ is the radius of the circular path of the rays,

$$2\rho = \frac{CE^2}{AC} + AC ;$$

thus, if we measure CE and AC we have the means of determining the radius of curvature of the path of the rays.

The determination of ρ is rendered to some extent uncertain, in consequence of the pencil of rays spreading out under the action of the magnetic field, so that the phosphorescent patch at E is several millimetres long; thus values of ρ differing appreciably from each other will be got by taking E at different points of this phosphorescent patch. Part of this patch was, however, generally considerably brighter than the rest; when this was the case, E was taken as the brightest point; when such a point of maximum brightness did not exist, the middle of the patch was taken for E. The uncertainty in the value of ρ thus introduced amounted sometimes to about 20 per cent.; by this I mean that if we took E first at one extremity of the patch and then at the other, we should get values of ρ differing by this amount.

The measurement of Q, the quantity of electricity which enters the inner cylinder, is complicated by the cathode rays making the gas through which they pass a conductor, so that though the insulation of the inner cylinder was perfect when the rays were off, it was not so when they were passing through the space between the cylinders; this caused some of the charge communicated to the inner cylinder to leak away so that the actual charge given to the cylinder by the cathode rays was larger than that indicated by the electrometer.

To make the error from this cause as small as possible, the inner cylinder was connected to the largest capacity available, 1·5 microfarad, and the rays were only kept on for a short time, about 1 or 2 seconds, so that the alteration in potential of the inner cylinder was not large, ranging in the various experiments from about ·5 to 5 volts. Another reason why it is necessary to limit the duration of the rays to as short a time as possible, is to avoid the correction for the loss of heat from the thermo-electric junction by conduction along the wires; the rise in temperature of the junction was of the order 2° C.; a series of experiments showed that with the same tube and the same gaseous pressure Q and W were proportional to each other when the rays were not kept on too long.

Tubes of this kind gave satisfactory results, the chief drawback being that sometimes in consequence of the charging up of the glass of the tube, a secondary discharge started from the cylinder to the walls of the tube, and the cylinders were surrounded by glow; when this glow appeared, the readings were very irregular; the glow could, however, be got rid of by pumping and letting the tube rest for some time. The results got with this tube are given in the Table under the heading Tube 1.

The second type of tube was like that used for photographing the path of the rays (fig. 4); double cylinders with a thermo-electric junction like those used in the previous tube were placed in the line of fire of the rays, the inside of the bell-jar was lined with copper gauze connected with the earth. This tube gave very satisfactory results; we were never troubled with any glow round the cylinders, and the readings were most concordant; the only drawback was that as some of the connexions had to be made with sealing-wax, it was not possible to get the highest exhaustions with this tube, so that the range of pressure for this tube is less than that for tube 1. The results got with this tube are given in the Table under the heading Tube 2.

The third type of tube was similar to the first, except that the openings in the two cylinders were made very much smaller; in this tube the slits in the cylinders were replaced by small holes, about 1·5 millim. in diameter. In consequence of the smallness of the openings, the magnitude of the effects was very much reduced; in order to get measurable results it was necessary to reduce the capacity of the condenser in connexion with the inner cylinder to ·15 microfarad, and to make the galvanometer exceedingly sensitive, as the rise in temperature of the thermo-electric junction was in these experiments only about ·5° C. on the average. The results obtained in this tube are given in the Table under the heading Tube 3.

The results of a series of measurements with these tubes are given in the following Table :—

Gas.	Value of W/Q.	I.	m/e	v.
Tube 1.				
Air	$4·6 \times 10^{11}$	230	$·57 \times 10^{-7}$	4×10^{9}
Air	$1·8 \times 10^{12}$	350	$·34 \times 10^{-7}$	1×10^{10}
Air	$6·1 \times 10^{11}$	230	$·43 \times 10^{-7}$	$5·4 \times 10^{9}$
Air	$2·5 \times 10^{12}$	400	$·32 \times 10^{-7}$	$1·2 \times 10^{10}$
Air	$5·5 \times 10^{11}$	230	$·48 \times 10^{-7}$	$4·8 \times 10^{9}$
Air	1×10^{12}	285	$·4 \times 10^{-7}$	7×10^{9}
Air	1×10^{12}	285	$·4 \times 10^{-7}$	7×10^{9}
Hydrogen	6×10^{12}	205	$·35 \times 10^{-7}$	6×10^{9}
Hydrogen	$2·1 \times 10^{12}$	460	$·5 \times 10^{-7}$	$9·2 \times 10^{9}$
Carbonic acid	$8·4 \times 10^{11}$	260	$·4 \times 10^{-7}$	$7·5 \times 10^{9}$
Carbonic acid	$1·47 \times 10^{12}$	340	$·4 \times 10^{-7}$	$8·5 \times 10^{9}$
Carbonic acid	$3·0 \times 10^{12}$	480	$·39 \times 10^{-7}$	$1·3 \times 10^{10}$
Tube 2.				
Air	$2·8 \times 10^{11}$	175	$·53 \times 10^{-7}$	$3·3 \times 10^{9}$
Air	$4·4 \times 10^{11}$	195	$·47 \times 10^{-7}$	$4·1 \times 10^{9}$
Air	$3·5 \times 10^{11}$	181	$·47 \times 10^{-7}$	$3·8 \times 10^{9}$
Hydrogen	$2·8 \times 10^{11}$	175	$·53 \times 10^{-7}$	$3·3 \times 10^{9}$
Air	$2·5 \times 10^{11}$	160	$·51 \times 10^{-7}$	$3·1 \times 10^{9}$
Carbonic acid	2×10^{11}	148	$·54 \times 10^{-7}$	$2·5 \times 10^{9}$
Air	$1·8 \times 10^{11}$	151	$·63 \times 10^{-7}$	$2·3 \times 10^{9}$
Hydrogen	$2·8 \times 10^{11}$	175	$·53 \times 10^{-7}$	$3·3 \times 10^{9}$
Hydrogen	$4·4 \times 10^{11}$	201	$·46 \times 10^{-7}$	$4·4 \times 10^{9}$
Air	$2·5 \times 10^{11}$	176	$·61 \times 10^{-7}$	$2·8 \times 10^{9}$
Air	$4·2 \times 10^{11}$	200	$·48 \times 10^{-7}$	$4·1 \times 10^{9}$
Tube 3.				
Air	$2·5 \times 10^{11}$	220	$·9 \times 10^{-7}$	$2·4 \times 10^{9}$
Air	$3·5 \times 10^{11}$	225	$·7 \times 10^{-7}$	$3·2 \times 10^{9}$
Hydrogen	3×10^{11}	250	$1·0 \times 10^{-7}$	$2·5 \times 10^{9}$

It will be noticed that the value of m/e is considerably greater for Tube 3, where the opening is a small hole, than for Tubes 1 and 2, where the opening is a slit of much greater area. I am of opinion that the values of m/e got from Tubes 1 and 2 are too small, in consequence of the leakage from the inner cylinder to the outer by the gas being rendered a conductor by the passage of the cathode rays.

It will be seen from these tables that the value of m/e is independent of the nature of the gas. Thus, for the first tube the mean for air is $\cdot40 \times 10^{-7}$, for hydrogen $\cdot42 \times 10^{-7}$, and for carbonic acid gas $\cdot4 \times 10^{-7}$; for the second tube the mean for air is $\cdot52 \times 10^{-7}$, for hydrogen $\cdot50 \times 10^{-7}$, and for carbonic acid gas $\cdot54 \times 10^{-7}$.

Experiments were tried with electrodes made of iron instead of aluminium; this altered the appearance of the discharge and the value of v at the same pressure, the values of m/e were, however, the same in the two tubes ; the effect produced by different metals on the appearance of the discharge will be described later on.

In all the preceding experiments, the cathode rays were first deflected from the cylinder by a magnet, and it was then found that there was no deflexion either of the electrometer or the galvanometer, so that the deflexions observed were entirely due to the cathode rays ; when the glow mentioned previously surrounded the cylinders there was a deflexion of the electrometer even when the cathode rays were deflected from the cylinder.

Before proceeding to discuss the results of these measurements I shall describe another method of measuring the quantities m/e and v of an entirely different kind from the preceding; this method is based upon the deflexion of the cathode rays in an electrostatic field. If we measure the deflexion experienced by the rays when traversing a given length under a uniform electric intensity, and the deflexion of the rays when they traverse a given distance under a uniform magnetic field, we can find the values of m/e and v in the following way :—

Let the space passed over by the rays under a uniform electric intensity F be l, the time taken for the rays to traverse this space is l/v, the velocity in the direction of F is therefore

$$\frac{Fe}{m} \frac{l}{v},$$

so that θ, the angle through which the rays are deflected when they leave the electric field and enter a region free from electric force, is given by the equation

$$\theta = \frac{\mathrm{F}e}{m}\frac{l}{v^2}.$$

If, instead of the electric intensity, the rays are acted on by a magnetic force H at right angles to the rays, and extending across the distance l, the velocity at right angles to the original path of the rays is

$$\frac{\mathrm{H}ev}{m}\frac{l}{v},$$

so that ϕ, the angle through which the rays are deflected when they leave the magnetic field, is given by the equation

$$\phi = \frac{\mathrm{H}e}{m}\frac{l}{v}.$$

From these equations we get

$$v = \frac{\phi}{\theta}\frac{\mathrm{F}}{\mathrm{H}}$$

and

$$\frac{m}{e} = \frac{\mathrm{H}^2\theta \cdot l}{\mathrm{F}\phi^2}.$$

In the actual experiments H was adjusted so that $\phi = \theta$; in this case the equations become

$$v = \frac{\mathrm{F}}{\mathrm{H}},$$

$$\frac{m}{e} = \frac{\mathrm{H}^2 l}{\mathrm{F}\theta}.$$

The apparatus used to measure v and m/e by this means is that represented in fig. 2. The electric field was produced by connecting the two aluminium plates to the terminals of a battery of storage-cells. The phosphorescent patch at the end of the tube was deflected, and the deflexion measured by a scale pasted to the end of the tube. As it was necessary to darken the room to see the phosphorescent patch, a needle coated with luminous paint was placed so that by a screw it could be moved up and down the scale ; this needle could be seen when the room was darkened, and it was moved until it coincided with the phosphorescent patch. Thus, when light was admitted, the deflexion of the phosphorescent patch could be measured.

The magnetic field was produced by placing outside the tube two coils whose diameter was equal to the length of the plates; the coils were placed so that they covered the space occupied by the plates, the distance between the coils was equal to the radius of either. The mean value of the magnetic force over the length l was determined in the following way : a narrow coil C whose length was l, connected with a ballistic galvanometer, was placed between the coils ; the plane of the windings of C was parallel to the planes of the coils; the cross section of the coil was a rectangle 5 cm. by 1 cm. A given current was sent through the outer coils and the kick a of the galvanometer observed when this current was reversed. The coil C was then placed at the centre of two very large coils, so as to be in a field of uniform magnetic force : the current through the large coils was reversed and the kick β of the galvanometer again observed ; by comparing a and β we can get the mean value of the magnetic force over a length l ; this was found to be

$$60 \times \iota,$$

where ι is the current flowing through the coils.

A series of experiments was made to see if the electrostatic deflexion was proportional to the electric intensity between the plates ; this was found to be the case. In the following experiments the current through the coils was adjusted so that the electrostatic deflexion was the same as the magnetic :—

Gas.	θ.	H.	F.	l.	m/e.	v.
Air	8/110	5·5	$1\cdot5 \times 10^{10}$	5	$1\cdot3 \times 10^{-7}$	$2\cdot8 \times 10^{9}$
Air	9·5/110	5·4	$1\cdot5 \times 10^{10}$	5	$1\cdot1 \times 10^{-7}$	$2\cdot8 \times 10^{9}$
Air	13/110	6·6	$1\cdot5 \times 10^{10}$	5	$1\cdot2 \times 10^{-7}$	$2\cdot3 \times 10^{9}$
Hydrogen	9/110	6·3	$1\cdot5 \times 10^{10}$	5	$1\cdot5 \times 10^{-7}$	$2\cdot5 \times 10^{9}$
Carbonic acid...	11/110	6·9	$1\cdot5 \times 10^{10}$	5	$1\cdot5 \times 10^{-7}$	$2\cdot2 \times 10^{9}$
Air	6/110	5	$1\cdot8 \times 10^{10}$	5	$1\cdot3 \times 10^{-7}$	$3\cdot6 \times 10^{9}$
Air	7/110	3·6	1×10^{10}	5	$1\cdot1 \times 10^{-7}$	$2\cdot8 \times 10^{9}$

The cathode in the first five experiments was aluminium, in the last two experiments it was made of platinum ; in the last experiment Sir William Crookes's method of getting rid of the mercury vapour by inserting tubes of pounded sulphur, sulphur iodide, and copper filings between the bulb and the pump was adopted. In the calculation of m/e and v no allowance has been made for the magnetic force due to the coil in

Phil. Mag. S. 5. Vol. 44. No. 269. *Oct.* 1897.   Z

the region outside the plates; in this region the magnetic force will be in the opposite direction to that between the plates, and will tend to bend the cathode rays in the opposite direction : thus the effective value of H will be smaller than the value used in the equations, so that the values of m/e are larger, and those of v less than they would be if this correction were applied. This method of determining the values of m/e and v is much less laborious and probably more accurate than the former method ; it cannot, however, be used over so wide a range of pressures.

From these determinations we see that the value of m/e is independent of the nature of the gas, and that its value 10^{-7} is very small compared with the value 10^{-4}, which is the smallest value of this quantity previously known, and which is the value for the hydrogen ion in electrolysis.

Thus for the carriers of the electricity in the cathode rays m/e is very small compared with its value in electrolysis. The smallness of m/e may be due to the smallness of m or the largeness of e, or to a combination of these two. That the carriers of the charges in the cathode rays are small compared with ordinary molecules is shown, I think, by Lenard's results as to the rate at which the brightness of the phosphorescence produced by these rays diminishes with the length of path travelled by the ray. If we regard this phosphorescence as due to the impact of the charged particles, the distance through which the rays must travel before the phosphorescence fades to a given fraction (say $1/e$, where $e = 2.71$) of its original intensity, will be some moderate multiple of the mean free path. Now Lenard found that this distance depends solely upon the density of the medium, and not upon its chemical nature or physical state. In air at atmospheric pressure the distance was about half a centimetre, and this must be comparable with the mean free path of the carriers through air at atmospheric pressure. But the mean free path of the molecules of air is a quantity of quite a different order. The carrier, then, must be small compared with ordinary molecules.

The two fundamental points about these carriers seem to me to be (1) that these carriers are the same whatever the gas through which the discharge passes, (2) that the mean free paths depend upon nothing but the density of the medium traversed by these rays.

It might be supposed that the independence of the mass of the carriers of the gas through which the discharge passes was due to the mass concerned being the quasi mass which a charged body possesses in virtue of the electric field set up in its neighbourhood ; moving the body involves the production of a varying electric field, and, therefore, of a certain amount of energy which is proportional to the square of the velocity. This causes the charged body to behave as if its mass were increased by a quantity, which for a charged sphere is $\frac{1}{5} e^2/\mu a$ ('Recent Researches in Electricity and Magnetism '), where e is the charge and a the radius of the sphere. If we assume that it is this mass which we are concerned with in the cathode rays, since m/e would vary as e/a, it affords no clue to the explanation of either of the properties (1 and 2) of these rays. This is not by any means the only objection to this hypothesis, which I only mention to show that it has not been overlooked.

The explanation which seems to me to account in the most simple and straightforward manner for the facts is founded on a view of the constitution of the chemical elements which has been favourably entertained by many chemists : this view is that the atoms of the different chemical elements are different aggregations of atoms of the same kind. In the form in which this hypothesis was enunciated by Prout, the atoms of the different elements were hydrogen atoms ; in this precise form the hypothesis is not tenable, but if we substitute for hydrogen some unknown primordial substance X, there is nothing known which is inconsistent with this hypothesis, which is one that has been recently supported by Sir Norman Lockyer for reasons derived from the study of the stellar spectra.

If, in the very intense electric field in the neighbourhood of the cathode, the molecules of the gas are dissociated and are split up, not into the ordinary chemical atoms, but into these primordial atoms, which we shall for brevity call corpuscles ; and if these corpuscles are charged with electricity and projected from the cathode by the electric field, they would behave exactly like the cathode rays. They would evidently give a value of m/e which is independent of the nature of the gas and its pressure, for the carriers are the same whatever the gas may be ; again, the mean free paths of these corpuscles would depend solely upon the density of the medium through which they pass. For the molecules of the medium are composed of a number of such corpuscles separated by considerable spaces; now the collision between a single corpuscle and the molecule will not be between the corpuscles and the molecule as a whole, but between this corpuscle and the individual corpuscles which form the molecule ; thus the number of collisions the particle makes as it moves through a crowd of these molecules will be proportional, not to the number of the

Z 2

molecules in the crowd, but to the number of the individual corpuscles. The mean free path is inversely proportional to the number of collisions in unit time, and so is inversely proportional to the number of corpuscles in unit volume; now as these corpuscles are all of the same mass, the number of corpuscles in unit volume will be proportional to the mass of unit volume, that is the mean free path will be inversely proportional to the density of the gas. We see, too, that so long as the distance between neighbouring corpuscles is large compared with the linear dimensions of a corpuscle the mean free path will be independent of the way they are arranged, provided the number in unit volume remains constant, that is the mean free path will depend only on the density of the medium traversed by the corpuscles, and will be independent of its chemical nature and physical state : this from Lenard's very remarkable measurements of the absorption of the cathode rays by various media, must be a property possessed by the carriers of the charges in the cathode rays.

Thus on this view we have in the cathode rays matter in a new state, a state in which the subdivision of matter is carried very much further than in the ordinary gaseous state : a state in which all matter—that is, matter derived from different sources such as hydrogen, oxygen, &c.—is of one and the same kind ; this matter being the substance from which all the chemical elements are built up.

With appliances of ordinary magnitude, the quantity of matter produced by means of the dissociation at the cathode is so small as to almost to preclude the possibility of any direct chemical investigation of its properties. Thus the coil I used would, I calculate, if kept going uninterruptedly night and day for a year, produce only about one three-millionth part of a gramme of this substance.

The smallness of the value of m/e is, I think, due to the largeness of e as well as the smallness of m. There seems to me to be some evidence that the charges carried by the corpuscles in the atom are large compared with those carried by the ions of an electrolyte. In the molecule of HCl, for example, I picture the components of the hydrogen atoms as held together by a great number of tubes of electrostatic force; the components of the chlorine atom are similarly held together, while only one stray tube binds the hydrogen atom to the chlorine atom. The reason for attributing this high charge to the constituents of the atom is derived from the values of the specific inductive capacity of gases : we may imagine that the specific inductive capacity of a gas is due to the setting in the electric field of the electric doublet formed by the two oppositely electrified atoms which form the molecule of the gas. The measurements of the specific inductive capacity show, however, that this is very approximately an additive quantity : that is, that we can assign a certain value to each element, and find the specific inductive capacity of HCl by adding the value for hydrogen to the value for chlorine ; the value of H_2O by adding twice the value for hydrogen to the value for oxygen, and so on. Now the electrical moment of the doublet formed by a positive charge on one atom of the molecule and a negative charge on the other atom would not be an additive property ; if, however, each atom had a definite electrical moment, and this were large compared with the electrical moment of the two atoms in the molecule, then the electrical moment of any compound, and hence its specific inductive capacity, would be an additive property. For the electrical moment of the atom, however, to be large compared with that of the molecule, the charge on the corpuscles would have to be very large compared with those on the ion.

If we regard the chemical atom as an aggregation of a number of primordial atoms, the problem of finding the configurations of stable equilibrium for a number of equal particles acting on each other according to some law of force —whether that of Boscovich, where the force between them is a repulsion when they are separated by less than a certain critical distance, and an attraction when they are separated by a greater distance, or even the simpler case of a number of mutually repellent particles held together by a central force —is of great interest in connexion with the relation between the properties of an element and its atomic weight. Unfortunately the equations which determine the stability of such a collection of particles increase so rapidly in complexity with the number of particles that a general mathematical investigation is scarcely possible. We can, however, obtain a good deal of insight into the general laws which govern such configurations by the use of models, the simplest of which is the floating magnets of Professor Mayer. In this model the magnets arrange themselves in equilibrium under their mutual repulsions and a central attraction caused by the pole of a large magnet placed above the floating magnets.

A study of the forms taken by these magnets seems to me to be suggestive in relation to the periodic law. Mayer showed that when the number of floating magnets did not exceed 5 they arranged themselves at the corners of a regular polygon— 5 at the corners of a pentagon, 4 at the corners of a square, and so on. When the number exceeds 5, however, this law no longer holds : thus 6 magnets do not arrange themselves at the corners of a hexagon, but divide into two systems, consisting of 1 in the middle surrounded by 5 at the corners of a pentagon. For 8 we have two in the inside and 6 outside ; this arrangement in two systems, an inner and an outer, lasts up to 18 magnets. After this we have three systems : an inner, a middle, and an outer ; for a still larger number of magnets we have four systems, and so on.

Mayer found the arrangement of magnets was as follows:—

1.	2.	3.	4.	5.
$\begin{cases} 1.5 \\ 1.6 \\ 1.7 \end{cases}$	$\begin{cases} 2.6 \\ 2.7 \end{cases}$	$\begin{cases} 3.7 \\ 3.8 \end{cases}$	$\begin{cases} 4.8 \\ 4.9 \end{cases}$	5.9
$\begin{cases} 1.5.9 \\ 1.6.9 \\ 1.6.10 \\ 1.6.11 \end{cases}$	$\begin{cases} 2.7.10 \\ 2.8.10 \\ 2.7.11 \end{cases}$	$\begin{cases} 3.7.10 \\ 3.7.11 \\ 3.8.10 \\ 3.8.11 \\ 3.8.12 \\ 3.8.13 \end{cases}$	$\begin{cases} 4.8.12 \\ 4.8.13 \\ 4.9.12 \\ 4.9.13 \end{cases}$	$\begin{cases} 5.9.12 \\ 5.9.13 \end{cases}$
$\begin{cases} 1.5.\ 9.12 \\ 1.5.\ 9.13 \\ 1.6.\ 9.12 \\ 1.6.10.12 \\ 1.6.10.13 \\ 1.6.11.12 \\ 1.6.11.13 \\ 1.6.11.14 \\ 1.6.11.15 \\ 1.7.12.14 \end{cases}$	$\begin{cases} 2.7.10.15 \\ 2.7.12.14 \end{cases}$	$\begin{cases} 3.7.12.13 \\ 3.7.12.14 \\ 3.7.13.14 \\ 3.7.13.15 \end{cases}$	$\begin{cases} 4.9.13.14 \\ 4.9.13.15 \\ 4.9.14.15 \end{cases}$	

where, for example, 1.6.10.12 means an arrangement with one magnet in the middle, then a ring of six, then a ring of ten, and a ring of twelve outside.

Now suppose that a certain property is associated with two magnets forming a group by themselves; we should have this property with 2 magnets, again with 8 and 9, again with 19 and 20, and again with 34, 35, and so on. If we regard the system of magnets as a model of an atom, the number of magnets being proportional to the atomic weight, we should have this property occurring in elements of atomic weight 2, (8, 9), 19, 20, (34, 35). Again, any property conferred by three magnets forming a system by themselves would occur with atomic weights 3, 10, and 11 ; 20, 21, 22, 23, and 24 ; 35, 36, 37 and 39 ; in fact, we should have something quite analogous to the periodic law, the first series corresponding to the arrangement of the magnets in a single group, the second series to the arrangement in two groups, the third series in three groups, and so on.

Velocity of the Cathode Rays.

The velocity of the cathode rays is variable, depending upon the potential-difference between the cathode and anode, which is a function of the pressure of the gas—the velocity increases as the exhaustion improves ; the measurements given above show, however, that at all the pressures at which experiments were made the velocity exceeded 10^9 cm./sec. This velocity is much greater than the value 2×10^7 which I previously obtained (Phil. Mag. Oct. 1894) by measuring directly the interval which separated the appearance of luminosity at two places on the walls of the tube situated at different distances from the cathode.

In my earlier experiments the pressure was higher than in the experiments described in this paper, so that the velocity of the cathode rays would on this account be less. The difference between the two results is, however, too great to be wholly explained in this way, and I attribute the difference to the glass requiring to be bombarded by the rays for a finite time before becoming phosphorescent, this time depending upon the intensity of the bombardment. As this time diminishes with the intensity of bombardment, the appearance of phosphorescence at the piece of glass most removed from the cathode would be delayed beyond the time taken for the rays to pass from one place to the other by the difference in time taken by the glass to become luminous ; the apparent velocity measured in this way would thus be less than the true velocity. In the former experiments endeavours were made to diminish this effect by making the rays strike the glass at the greater distance from the cathode less obliquely than they struck the glass nearer to the cathode; the obliquity was adjusted until the brightness of the phosphorescence was approximately equal in the two cases. In view, however, of the discrepancy between the results obtained in this way and those obtained by the later method, I think that it was not successful in eliminating the lag caused by the finite time required by the gas to light up.

Experiments with Electrodes of Different Materials.

In the experiments described in this paper the electrodes were generally made of aluminium. Some experiments, however, were made with iron and platinum electrodes.

Though the value of m/e came out the same whatever the material of the electrode, the appearance of the discharge varied greatly; and as the measurements showed, the potential-difference between the cathode and anode depended greatly upon the metal used for the electrode ; the pressure being the same in all cases.

To test this point further I used a tube like that shown in fig. 6, where *a, b, c* are cathodes made of different metals, the anodes being in all cases platinum wires. The cathodes were disks of aluminium, iron, lead, tin, copper, mercury, sodium amalgam, and silver chloride ; the potential-difference

Fig. 6.

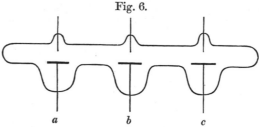

between the cathode and anode was measured by Lord Kelvin's vertical voltmeter, and also by measuring the length of spark in air which, when placed in parallel with the anode and cathode, seemed to allow the discharge to go as often through the spark-gap as through the tube. With this arrangement the pressures were the same for all the cathodes. The potential-difference between the anode and cathode and the equivalent spark-length depended greatly upon the nature of the cathode. The extent of the variation in potential may be estimated from the following table :—

Cathode.	Mean Potential-Difference between Cathode and Anode.
Aluminium	1800 volts.
Lead	2100 ,,
Tin	2400 ,,
Copper	2600 ,,
Iron....................	2900 ,,

The potential-difference when the cathode was made of sodium amalgam or silver chloride was less even than that of aluminium.

The order of many of the metals changed about very capriciously, experiments made at intervals of a few minutes frequently giving quite different results. From the abrupt way in which these changes take place I am inclined to think that gas absorbed by the electrode has considerable influence on the passage of the discharge.

I have much pleasure in thanking Mr. Everitt for the assistance he has given me in the preceding investigation.

Cambridge, Aug. 7, 1897.

LVII. *On the Charge of Electricity carried by the Ions produced by Röntgen Rays.* By J. J. Thomson, *M.A., F.R.S., Cavendish Professor of Experimental Physics, Cambridge* *.

THE following experiments were made in order to determine the magnitude of the charge of electricity carried by the ions which are produced when Röntgen rays pass through a gas.

The theory of the method used is as follows :—By measuring the current passing through a gas exposed to Röntgen rays and acted upon by a known electromotive force, we determine the value of the product nev, where n is the number of ions in unit volume of the gas, e the charge on an ion, and v the mean velocity of the positive and negative ions under the electromotive force to which they are exposed.

Mr. Rutherford (Phil. Mag. vol. xliv. p. 422, 1897) has determined the value of v for a considerable number of gases ; using these values, the measurement of the current through a gas gives us the product ne ; hence if we can determine n, we can deduce the value of e.

The method I have employed to determine n is founded on the discovery made by Mr. C. T. R. Wilson (Phil. Trans. A, 1897, p. 265) that when Röntgen rays pass through dust-free air a cloud is produced by an expansion which is incapable of producing cloudy condensation when the gas is not exposed to these rays. When a determinate expansion is suddenly produced in dust-free air a definite and calculable amount of water is deposited in consequence of the lowering of the temperature of the air by adiabatic expansion. When the gas is exposed to the rays the ions caused by the rays seem to act as nuclei around which the water condenses. I have shown ('Applications of Dynamics to Physics and Chemistry,' p. 164) that on a charged sphere of less than a certain

* Communicated by the Author.

radius the effect of the charge in promoting condensation will more than counterbalance the effect of surface-tension in preventing it. So that a charged ion will produce a very small drop of water which may act as a nucleus. If each ion acts as the nucleus for a drop, then if we know the size of the drop and the mass of water deposited per unit volume, we shall be able to determine the number of drops, and hence the number of ions in unit volume of the gas. One part of the investigation is thus the determination of the size of the drops: this gives us n; and as we know from the electrical investigation ne, we have the means of determining e.

The measurement of the size of the drops in the cloud gave a great deal of trouble. Two methods were tried ; at first I attempted to measure the size of the drops by an optical method ; when a narrow beam of light from an arc lamp is sent through the cloud, and the light after passing through the cloud received on a screen, several coloured rings are visible. If we assume that these rings arise entirely from diffraction the size of the rings would enable us to deduce the size of the drops. The method, however, failed in practice from two causes. In the first place, in order to get the rays bright enough to allow their diameter to be accurately measured the fog must be dense, in order, however, to get a dense cloud the number of ions produced by the rays must be large ; when, however, the number of ions is large experience shows that they are not all brought down by the first cloud formed by a sudden expansion. This is proved by the fact that if after the first cloud has subsided, the rays having been cut off immediately after the first expansion, another expansion be made, a second cloud will be formed, and though this is less dense than the first cloud it may require two or three expansions to remove the effects of previous exposure to the Röntgen rays. It is only when the ions are so few that no cloud is produced by the second expansion that we can feel any confidence that the number of drops in the first cloud is equal to the number of ions formed by the rays, and in this case the cloud is so thin that the coloured rays are not bright enough to allow their diameters to be accurately measured. Though this objection is fatal there is yet another reason against using this method of measuring the size of the drops, as observations made on the dimensions of the various coloured rings seemed to indicate that the rings are not produced entirely by diffraction, but that they are influenced by the interference of rays which have passed through the transparent drops with those which have not done so, and that therefore we could not employ the usual formula connecting the size of the rings with the size of the drops.

The method finally employed to measure the size of the drops was to observe the rate at which the cloud sank and then to determine the radius of the drops from the formula

$$v = \frac{2}{9}\frac{ga^2}{\mu}$$

where v is the velocity with which the drops fall, a the radius of the drop, μ the coefficient of viscosity of the gas through which the drops fall, and g the value of gravity.

The velocity was determined by observing the time the top layer of the cloud, which was illuminated by an arc light, took to fall a given distance; observations made on the times taken to fall different distances showed that the rate of fall was uniform, so that the drops had reached their limiting velocity.

I began by making experiments to test whether the drops in the cloud formed by expansion were deposited round the ions which gave to the gas its electrical conductivity; this point is fundamental, as the method used in this paper to determine the charge carried by an ion depends on the assumption that it is the ionization of the gas which causes the fog produced by expansion, and that each ion can act as the nucleus for a water drop.

In the first place we have direct evidence of the power of an electrified particle to act as a nucleus for a drop of water, inasmuch as condensation takes place in a steam-jet when placed near an electrode from which electricity is escaping, and, further, Mr. Wilson has shown that a cloud is produced by expansion in dust-free air when an electrode discharging electricity is placed in the air. A more direct proof of the point under consideration is afforded by the following experiment:—If the ions produced by the Röntgen rays act as nuclei for the drops, then, since these ions can be withdrawn from the gas by applying to it a strong electric field, it follows that a cloud ought not to be formed when the air which is expanded is exposed to a strong electric field while the rays are passing through it. This was found to be the case, and the experiment is a striking one. Two parallel plates were placed in the vessel containing the dust-free air; these plates were about 5 centim. apart, and were large enough to include the greater part of the air between them. The plates could be connected with the terminals of a battery of small storage-cells giving a potential-difference of about 400 volts. Röntgen rays passed through the gas between the plates: this gas had previously been freed from dust. When the plates were disconnected from the battery expansion produced a dense cloud; when, however, the plates were connected with the battery only a very light cloud was produced by the expansion, and this cloud was almost as dense when the Röntgen rays did not pass through the air as when they did.

Another point which had to be investigated was whether the cloud produced by the expansion caught all the ions. In this connexion it is necessary to point out that it is only possible to use expansions comprised within somewhat narrow limits. The ratio of the final to the initial volume of the gas has to be between 1·25 and 1·40. For, as Mr. Wilson (*loc. cit.*) has shown, when the expansion exceeds the larger of these values a dense cloud is produced even when the gas is not exposed to Röntgen rays, with these large expansions the cloud is so dense that the increase produced by the Röntgen rays is barely perceptible ; while when the expansion is less than the smaller of these values no cloud at all is produced. With expansions comprised between these limits it was found that when the Röntgen rays were strong an increase in the strength of the rays did not increase the number of drops in the cloud, as determined by the rate of fall of the drops, nearly so fast as it increased the number of ions as measured by the electrical conductivity of the gas. But with these strong rays it was found that the effect of the Röntgen rays in producing a cloud was not exhausted by the first expansion, even when the rays were cut off immediately after that expansion took place ; for a cloud was produced when a second expansion was made, and with strong rays it sometimes required six or seven expansions, occupying perhaps five or six minutes, before the effect of the rays had disappeared. In the face of this it is evident that when the rays are strong we are not entitled to assume that all the ions are brought down by the cloud produced by the first expansion. The first expansion, however, though it does not bring all the ions down, seems to increase the size of those left and makes them more permanent, for the ions which are left after the first expansion exert an appreciable cloud-producing effect for several minutes ; whereas if no expansion had occurred the effect of the rays in producing a cloud would only have lasted for a few seconds after the rays had been cut off. Again, these modified ions are able to cause a cloud to settle with an expansion less than 1·25, the minimum expansion which gives a cloud with the original ions. When once a cloud has been produced the secondary clouds produced by subsequent expansions are but little affected by an electric field, this again indicating that the modified ions are larger and more sluggish than the original ones; the presence of these modified ions does not seem to give any appreciable conductivity to the gas. Mr. Wilson found that when in gas not exposed to Röntgen rays a dense cloud was produced in dust-free air by a large expansion and then allowed to settle, a subsequent small expansion (which under ordinary circumstances would not produce a cloud at all unless dust were present) would produce a cloud, and that it was necessary to produce several clouds and allow them to settle before the gas returned to its normal state. In this case Mr. Wilson's experiments seem to show that the original nuclei were excessively minute drops of water, and the formation of the subsequent cloud would seem to indicate that on those drops which did not grow large enough to be carried down by the first cloud some moisture was deposited, and that this was prevented from evaporating by some kind of chemical change at its surface such as the formation of hydrogen peroxide.

Whatever the explanation of these secondary clouds may be it is evident that when the rays are strong enough to produce them we cannot deduce the number of ions from observations on the primary cloud. In the experiments described below the intensity of the rays was weakened by interposing screens of aluminium between the bulb and the gas exposed to the rays until there was no more cloud produced by the second expansion than would have been produced if the gas had never been exposed to the rays.

Another point which had to be investigated was whether the expansion used was sufficient to bring down all the ions, or whether the number brought down increased with the amount of the expansion. To test this measurements were made of the rate of fall of the clouds formed under exposure to the rays by different expansions. The results of these experiments are shown in the following table:—

Pressure of air 768·08 millim.   Temperature 18° C.

Expansion.	Time of fall through 25 millim.	
	with rays.	without rays.
$\dfrac{752\cdot72}{535\cdot72}=1\cdot4$	19	10
$\dfrac{752\cdot72}{545\cdot72}=1\cdot38$	18	6
$\dfrac{752\ 72}{555\cdot72}=1\cdot35$	14	4

The amount of water deposited per cub. centim. by an expansion of 1·4 is $4\cdot94\times10^{-6}$ gram., while the amount deposited by an expansion of 1·35 is $4·74 \times 10^{-6}$ gram. If N is the number of ions per cub. centim. in the first case when the rays are on, M the number when the rays are off, a the radius of the drops when the rays are on, b the radius when the rays are off, Q the quantity of water deposited :

$$N \tfrac{4}{3}\pi a^3 = M \tfrac{4}{3}\pi b^3 = Q.$$

The rate of fall varies as the square of the radius of the drops, so that

$$\frac{a}{b} = \frac{\sqrt{10}}{\sqrt{19}}.$$

If dashed letters refer to the second expansion,

$$N' \tfrac{4}{3}\pi a'^3 = M' \tfrac{4}{3}\pi b'^3 = Q',$$

so that

$$\frac{N-M}{N'-M'} = \frac{Q\left\{\dfrac{1}{a^3} - \dfrac{1}{b^3}\right\}}{Q'\left\{\dfrac{1}{a'^3} - \dfrac{1}{b'^3}\right\}}$$

$$= \frac{4·94}{4·74}\frac{\left\{19\sqrt{19} - 10\sqrt{10}\right\}}{\left\{14\sqrt{14} - 4\sqrt{4}\right\}}$$

$$= 1·2 \text{ approximately.}$$

Thus the number of the ions produced by the rays which are caught by the larger expansion is slightly greater than that caught by the former. I think that the greater rapidity with which the larger expansions are made, in consequence of the greater time the driving force acts on the piston whose motion produces the expansion, is sufficient to account for this; for when the expansion is slow the drops first formed can grow before the expansion is completed, and thus rob the others of the water-vapour, so that we should expect to get slightly more drops as we increased the rapidity of the expansion.

Some experiments made with smaller expansions seemed rather to indicate a considerable increase in the number of ions deposited when the expansion was taken from below 1·3 to above it. An increase which seemed rather too large to be attributed wholly to the increased velocity of expansion, and to suggest that the ions had not all the same power of acting as nuclei. I hope to make an independent investigation of this point, as it is evidently one which might have considerable bearing on the problems of atmospheric electricity; for if the negative ions, say, were to differ in their power of condensing water around them from the positive, then we might get a cloud formed round one set of ions and not round the other. The ions in the cloud would fall under gravity, and thus we might have separation of positive and negative ions and the production of an electric field, the work required for the production of the field being done by gravity.

To return, however, to the experiments under consideration. The method employed for making the cloud and for measuring the expansion is the same as that used by Mr. Wilson and described by him in the 'Proceedings of the Cambridge Philosophical Society,' vol. ix. p. 333. The gas which is exposed to the rays is contained in the vessel A; this vessel communicates by the tube B with the vertical tube C, the lower end

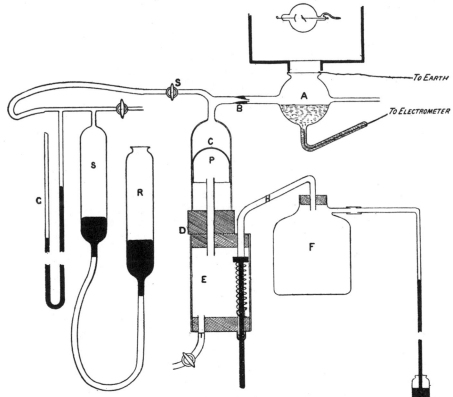

of this tube is carefully ground so as to be in a plane perpendicular to its axis, and is fastened down to the indiarubber stopper D. Inside this tube there is an inverted thin-walled test-tube, P, with the lip removed and the open end ground so as to be in a plane perpendicular to the axis of the tube.

The test-tube slides freely up and down the larger tube and serves as a piston. Its lower end is always below the surface of the water which fills the lower part of the outer tube. A glass tube passing through the indiarubber stopper puts the inside of the test-tube in connexion with the space E. This space is in connexion with an exhausted vessel, F, through the tube H. The end of this tube is ground flat and is closed by an indiarubber stopper which presses against it; the stopper is fixed to a rod, by pulling the rod down smartly the pressure inside the test-tube is lowered and it falls rapidly until the test-tube P strikes against the indiarubber stopper. The tube T, which can be closed by a stop-cock, puts the vessel E in connexion with the outside air. The tubes R and S are for the purpose of regulating the amount of the expansion. To do this, the mercury-vessel R is raised or lowered when the test-tube is in the lowest position until the gauge G indicates that the pressure in A is the desired amount below the atmospheric pressure. The clip S is then closed, and air is admitted into the interior of the piston by opening the clip T. The piston then rises until the pressure in A differs from the atmospheric pressure only by the amount required to support the piston, this is only a fraction of a millimetre.

If Π is the barometric pressure, then the pressure of the air before expansion is

$$P_1 = \Pi - \pi,$$

where π is the maximum vapour-pressure of water at the temperature of the experiment. The pressure of the air after the expansion when the temperature has risen to its former value is

$$P_2 = P_1 - p,$$

where p is the pressure due to the difference of level of the mercury in the two arms of the gauge.

Thus if v_2 is the final and v_1 the initial volume,

$$\frac{v_2}{v_1} = \frac{P_1}{P_2} = \frac{\Pi - \pi}{\Pi - \pi - p}.$$

A is the vessel in which the rate of fall of the fog was measured and the electrical conductivity of the gas tested. It is a glass tube about 36 millim. in diameter covered with an aluminium plate ; a piece of wet blotting-paper is placed on the lower side of the plate and the current of electricity passed from the blotting-paper to the horizontal surface of the water in this vessel. The blotting-paper was placed over the aluminium plate to avoid the abnormal ionization which occurs near the surface of a metal against which Röntgen rays strike normally. M. Langevin has shown that this abnormal ionization is practically absent when the surfaces are wet.

The coil and focus-bulb producing the rays were placed in a large iron tank elevated on supports; in the bottom of the tank a hole was cut and closed by an aluminium window. The vessel A was placed underneath this window and the bulb giving out the rays some distance behind it, so that the beam of rays escaping from the tank were not very divergent. The rays were reduced in intensity to any required degree by inserting different numbers of layers of tinfoil or sheets of aluminium between the bulb and the vessel. The tank and the aluminium plate at the top of A were connected with earth and with one pair of quadrants of an electrometer. The other pair of quadrants were connected with the water-surface B; this surface was charged up by connecting it with one of the poles of a battery consisting generally of two Leclanché cells, the other pole of which was connected with earth. After the surface was charged it was disconnected from the battery and the insulation of the apparatus tested by observing whether there was any leak when the Röntgen rays were not on : the insulation having been proved to be good, the rays were turned on, when the charge began to leak; by measuring the rate of leak, the quantity of electricity crossing in one second the gas exposed to the rays can be determined if the capacity of the system is known. The effective capacity of the system consisting of the discharging vessel, the connecting wires, and the quadrants of the electrometer depends to a large extent on the charge in the electrometer, and increases so quickly with the charge that the rate of movement of the spot of light reflected from the mirror of the electrometer increases but slowly when the charge in the electrometer is increased beyond a certain value. The reason for this is shown by the following investigation.

Let Q_1 be the charge on the system consisting of the pair of quadrants and the apparatus connected with it, V_1 the potential of this pair of quadrants, V_2 the potential of the other pair, and V_3 the potential of the needle ; then we have

$$Q_1 = q_{11}V_1 + q_{12}V_2 + q_{13}V_3,$$

where q_{11}, q_{12}, q_{13} are coefficients of capacity. Let θ be the azimuth of the needle, then if the two pairs of quadrants and the needle are at the same potential, Q_1 will not depend upon θ if the quadrants are symmetrical with respect to the axis of the needle. Hence

$$\frac{dq_{11}}{d\theta} + \frac{dq_{12}}{d\theta} + \frac{dq_{13}}{d\theta} = 0.$$

If the needle is initially placed symmetrically with respect to the quadrants, then

$$\frac{dq_{12}}{d\theta} = 0$$

approximately when θ is small.

Thus if $\mathbf{q}_{11}$, $\mathbf{q}_{13}$ denote the values of q_{11}, q_{13} when θ is zero we have approximately, if $\beta = \dfrac{dq_{13}}{d\theta}$,

$$q_{11} = \mathbf{q}_{11} - \beta\theta\ ; \qquad\qquad q_{13} = \mathbf{q}_{13} + \beta\theta,$$

and

$$Q_1 = \mathbf{q}_{11}V_1 + \mathbf{q}_{12}V_2 + \mathbf{q}_{13}V_3 + \beta\theta(V_3 - V_1)\ ;$$

if $V_2 = 0$ we have, since the deflexion of the needle is approximately proportional to the product of the potential-difference between the quadrants and the potential of the needle,

$$\theta = kV_1V_3.$$

Hence $Q_1 = \mathbf{q}_{11}V_1 + \mathbf{q}_{13}V_3 + k\beta V_1V_3{}^2 - K\beta V_1{}^2V_3\ ;$

the fourth term on the right-hand side is small compared with the third ; hence we have

$$\frac{dQ_1}{dV_1} = \mathbf{q}_{11} + k\beta V_3{}^2.$$

Thus the effective capacity is $\mathbf{q}_{11} + k\beta V_3{}^2$.

The effective capacity was measured by connecting **a** parallel-plate condenser with the quadrants and then observing, when the system was insulated, the change in the deflexion when the distance between the plates was increased by a known amount.   Supposing the capacity of the parallel-plate condenser was C in the first position and C' in the second, then we have, if V_1 and V_1' are the corresponding potentials,

$$Q_1 = (\mathbf{q}_{11} + C)V_1 + \mathbf{q}_{13}V_3 + \beta kV_1V_3{}^2$$
$$= (\mathbf{q}_{11} + C')V_1' + \mathbf{q}_{13}V_3 + \beta kV_1'V_3{}^2\ ;$$

thus

$$\frac{V_1}{V_1'} = \frac{\mathbf{q}_{11} + \beta kV_3{}^2 + C'}{\mathbf{q}_{11} + \beta kV_3{}^2 + C}.$$

Since V_1, V_1' are proportional to the deflexion in the two cases and C' and C are known, this equation enables us to calculate $\mathbf{q}_{11} + \beta kV_3{}^2$, the effective capacity of the system.

If, when the rays are on, the movement of the spot of light indicates a change in the potential equal to V per second, then the quantity of electricity flowing in that time across the cross-section of the vessel exposed to the rays is CV.   But if n is the number of ions, both positive and negative, per cubic centimetre of the gas, u_0 the mean velocity of the positive and negative ions under unit potential gradient, A the area of the plates, E the potential-gradient, this quantity of electricity is also equal to neu_0EA, hence we have

$$CV = neu_0EA ;$$

so that if we know n and u_0 we can from this equation deduce the value of e.

The method of making the experiments was as follows :—
The aluminium plate and the water-surface were connected with the poles of two Leclanché cells, and the rate of fall, r_1, of the drops produced by an expansion when the rays were not on measured ; the rays were now turned on, and the rate of fall, r_2, of the cloud now produced by the expansion determined ; the rays were now turned off, and a third expansion taken, and the rate of fall of the cloud, r_3, found ; if r_3 was appreciably less than r_1, it was taken as indicating that the ions produced by the rays were too numerous to be caught by one expansion, and the intensity of the rays was therefore cut down by inserting aluminium foil between the bulb and the vessel ; this process was repeated until r_3 was equal to r_1, and then it was assumed that all the ions were caught by the cloud produced by the expansion.   From the rate of fall the size of the drops was calculated from the formula

$$v = \frac{2}{9}\frac{ga^2}{\mu},$$

where v is the velocity, a the radius of the drop, and μ the coefficient of viscosity of the gas through which the drop falls.   If q is the mass of water deposited from a cubic centimetre of the gas, we have

$$q = n\tfrac{4}{3}\pi a^3.$$

The method used to determine q is that given by Wilson in his paper on the formation of clouds in dust-free air (Phil. Trans. 1897, A, p. 299).   We have the equation

$$Lq = CM(t - t_2),$$

where L is the latent heat of evaporation of water, C the specific heat of the gas at constant volume, M the mass of unit volume of the gas, t_2 the lowest temperature reached by the expansion, t the temperature when the drops are fully grown.

Since

$$q = \rho_1 - \rho,$$

where ρ_1 is the density of the water-vapour before condensation begins, and ρ the density at the temperature t; hence we have

$$\rho = \rho_1 - \frac{CM}{L}(t - t_2).$$

Since ρ is a function of t, this equation enables us to determine t. If x is the ratio of the final to the initial volume and t_0 the temperature before expansion, then, since the mass of unit volume of air is $\cdot00129$ grm. at $0°$ C. and under a pressure of 760 mm. of mercury, we have

$$M = \frac{\cdot00129}{x} \times \frac{273}{273 + t_0},$$

if we take the initial pressure to be 760.

Again,

$$\rho_1 = \frac{\rho_0}{x},$$

where ρ_0 is the density of water-vapour at the temperature t_0. The cooling caused by the expansion is determined by the equation

$$\log \frac{273 + t_0}{273 + t_2} = \cdot41 \log x;$$

$$C = \cdot167; \qquad L = 606.$$

Thus

$$\rho = \frac{\rho_0}{x} - \frac{\cdot167}{606} \times \frac{\cdot00129}{x} \frac{273}{273 + t_0}(t - t_2).$$

Let us apply these equations to a special case. In one of the experiments $t_0 = 16°$ C. and

$$x = \frac{760 - 13\cdot5}{760 - 13\cdot5 - 197} = 1\cdot36,$$

$$\log \frac{273 + 16}{273 + t_2} = \cdot41 \log 1\cdot36$$

$$= \log 1\cdot134;$$

hence

$$273 + t_2 = 254\cdot8,$$

$$t_2 = -18\cdot2,$$

$$\rho_0 = \cdot0000134,$$

$$\frac{\rho_0}{1\cdot36} = 98\cdot4 \times 10^{-7},$$

and

$$\frac{\cdot167 \times \cdot00129 \times 273}{606 \times 1\cdot36 \times 289} = 2\cdot46 \times 10^{-7};$$

hence

$$\rho = 98\cdot4 \times 10^{-7} - 2\cdot46 \times 10^{-7}(t + 18\cdot2).$$

If we put $t = 1 \cdot 2$, we get from this equation

$$\rho = 50 \cdot 7 \times 10^{-7},$$

which is very nearly the value of ρ at $1 \cdot 2°$ C.; hence we conclude $t = 1 \cdot 2$ and q, the amount of water deposited per unit volume of the expanded gas, is $47 \cdot 7 \times 10^{-7}$ grms.

It was found that, when the rays were on, the velocity of the drops was $\cdot 14$ cm./sec., while without the rays the velocity was $\cdot 41$ cm./sec.

Connexion between the Velocity and Size of the Drop.

If v is the velocity with which a drop of water of radius a falls through a gas whose coefficient of viscosity is μ, then if we neglect the density of the gas in comparison with that of the drop

$$\tfrac{4}{3}\pi g a^3 = 6\pi\mu a \mathrm{V} \, \frac{1 + 4\dfrac{\mu}{\beta a} + 6\left(\dfrac{\mu}{\beta a}\right)^2}{\left(1 + \dfrac{3\mu}{\beta a}\right)^2}$$

(see Lamb's 'Hydrodynamics,' ed. i. p. 230), where β is the slipping coefficient. If there is no slip between the sphere and the gas, β is infinite, and we have

$$\mathrm{V} = \frac{2}{9}\frac{g a^2}{\mu} ; \quad \cdots \cdots \cdots \quad (1)$$

while if $\mu/\beta a$ is large we have

$$\mathrm{V} = \frac{1}{3}\frac{g a^2}{\mu}.$$

Since a occurs in the denominator in the terms involving $1/\beta$, the influence of slipping on the motion of very small spheres such as those we are considering will be much more important than its influence on the motion of spheres of the size used for the bobs of pendulums, for which the influence of slipping has been shown to be too small to be detected. We cannot, therefore, without further consideration neglect in our case the terms involving $1/\beta a$. Some light is thrown on the question by the Kinetic Theory of Gases, for according to that theory (see Maxwell, "Stresses in Rarefied Gases;" Collected Works, vol. ii. p. 709) μ/β is of the order of the mean free path of a molecule, $i.\,e.$, for air at atmospheric pressure of the order 10^{-5} centim.; hence, if a is large compared with the mean free path, we should expect the relation between the velocity and size to be that given by equation (1).

Taking the equation

$$v = \frac{2}{9}\frac{g a^2}{\mu},$$

and putting
$$v = \cdot 14, \qquad g = 981, \qquad \mu = 1 \cdot 8 \times 10^{-4},$$
we find
$$a^2 = 11 \cdot 5 \times 10^{-8},$$
$$a = 3 \cdot 39 \times 10^{-4},$$
$$\tfrac{4}{3}\pi a^3 = 1 \cdot 63 \times 10^{-10}.$$

As the radius of the drop is considerable compared with the mean free path in air at atmospheric pressure we may feel some confidence that equation (1) will be true for drops of this size.

Hence
$$n = \frac{q}{\tfrac{4}{3}\pi a^3} = 2 \cdot 94 \times 10^4.$$

This is the number of ions in 1 cub. centim. of the expanded gas; the number in 1 cub. centim. of the gas before expansion
$$= 2 \cdot 94 \times 1 \cdot 36 \times 10^4 = 4 \times 10^4.$$

We now consider the electrical part of the experiment. The electrometer gave a deflexion of 90 scale-divisions for two Leclanché cells, the capacity of the system consisting of the cell containing the gas exposed to the rays, the connecting wires, and the quadrants was 38, on the electrostatic system of units. The diameter of the circular electrodes between which the leak took place was 3·6 centim., and the distance between them 2 centim. When the rays were on, and the potential-difference between the electrodes that due to two Leclanchés, the leak was at the rate of 9 scale-divisions per minute; hence if E is the electromotive force of a Leclanché cell, the quantity of electricity passing in one second through a cross-section of the discharge-tube is equal to
$$\frac{38}{300}\,\text{E}.$$
But this is equal to
$$A n e u_0 \text{E}',$$
where A is the area of the electrodes and equals $\pi(1\cdot8)^2$, n the number of ions per cub. centim. $= 4 \times 10^4$, e the charge on an ion, u_0 the mean velocity of the positive and negative ion under unit potential gradient, Mr. Rutherford found this to be $1\cdot6 \times 3 \times 10^2$. E' is the potential gradient, assumed to be uniform, in our case it was E. Substituting these values, we get
$$\frac{38}{300}\text{E} = \pi(1\cdot8)^2 \times 4 \times 10^4 \times e \times 4\cdot8 \times 10^2 \times \text{E};$$
hence
$$e = 6\cdot3 \times 10^{-10}.$$

Phil. Mag. S. 5. Vol. 46. No. 283. *Dec.* 1898.   2 P

In the preceding investigation we have assumed that the nuclei producing the cloud are those which cause the conductivity, and are produced by the rays; there is, however, a small cloud produced even when no rays are on; if we assume that the nuclei which produce this cloud are still active when the rays are on, it follows that in the preceding investigation we have over-estimated the number of ions engaged in carrying the current by the number of nuclei present when the rays are not passing through the gas. As the cloud fell three times faster when the rays were not on than it did when the rays were on, the number of nuclei when the rays are not on is to the number when the rays are on as 1 is to $3^{\frac{3}{2}}$, or as $1 : 5\cdot2$; hence $1/5\cdot2$ of the nuclei are not engaged in carrying the current, so that to get the charge on the ions we must increase the value just given in the ratio of $1 + 1/5\cdot2$ to 1; this makes

$$e = 7\cdot4 \times 10^{-10}.$$

The results of other experiments on air are given in the following table :—

Expansion.	Temp.	Current through gas.	Rate of fall of cloud.	e uncorrected for nuclei present without rays.	e corrected.
1·36	16	·243 E	·09	$6\cdot7 \times 10^{-10}$	7·6
1·36	16	·133 E	·147	6·4	7·2
1·38	16	·143 E	·156	7·3	8·4
1·36	16	·196 E	·104	6·3	7·4
1·36	16	·115 E	·125	5·0	6·0

The mean of these values and the one previously obtained is

$$e = 7\cdot3 \times 10^{-10} \text{ electrostatic units.}$$

Another correction has to be made to allow for the conductivity of the walls of the vessel A due to the film of moisture with which it is coated. Though the walls are insulated from the aluminium plate at the top of the vessel, and there is no leak between them when the rays are not passing through the glass, the conductivity of the glass when the rays are on causes the current to travel partly from the aluminium plate and along the walls of the vessel instead of wholly through the air as has been assumed in the calculations. To estimate the correction two vessels were made of the same shape and size, the one precisely similar to that used in these experiments with water at the bottom, while the other had the walls covered with shellac varnish, and the water at the bottom was replaced by an aluminium plate of the same area, and at the same distance from the top plate as the upper surface of the water in the other vessel. The aluminium covers for the two vessels were cut from the same sheet of metal. When these vessels were exposed to the Röntgen rays the current through the vessel containing water was to that through the other vessel as 9 to 8. Thus the current passing directly between the plates was 8/9 of the current observed. Applying this correction the mean value of e is equal to

$$\tfrac{8}{9} \times 7 \cdot 3 \times 10^{-10} = 6 \cdot 5 \times 10^{-10}.$$

A series of experiments of a similar kind were made, using hydrogen instead of air. The number of ions in this gas was smaller than in the case of air, and the smaller viscosity of hydrogen made the drops fall much faster; the drops formed without the rays fell so fast, only taking a second or two, that the rate could not be determined with accuracy, nor was it certain that they had reached a steady state. The velocity of the hydrogen ion through hydrogen under unit potential gradient is taken as three times that of air and the coefficient of viscosity as $9 \cdot 3 \times 10^{-5}$.

The results of the experiments are given in the following table :—

Expansion.	Temp.	Current through gas.	Rate of fall of cloud.	e uncorrected for nuclei present without rays.
1·36	16	·21	·415 cm./sec.	$6 \cdot 3 \times 10^{-10}$
1·38	16	·127	·5	5·5
1·37	17	·083	·83	6·9
1·35	17	·19	·5	8·0
			Mean	$6 \cdot 7 \times 10^{-10}$

The value of e for hydrogen has not been corrected in the way that the value of e for air has been by allowing for the part of the cloud formed independently of the rays. Allowing for this the experiments seem to show that the charge on the ion in hydrogen is the same as in air. This result has very

2 P 2

evident bearings on the theory of the ionization of gases produced by the Röntgen rays.

In obtaining the above values certain assumptions have been made to simplify the calculation which would have the effect of making the value of *e* differ from the true value. Thus, for example, we have assumed that the potential gradient is constant between the plates.   Prof. Zeleny has shown (Phil. Mag. July 1898) that this is not strictly true ; the potential fall near the plates is greater than the average, while that in the body of the gas is less.   Thus the potential gradient in the gas is less than the difference of potential between the plates divided by the distance between them, which is the value we took in the preceding calculations.   For the very much enfeebled rays we used in these experiments the difference between the true and the assumed value is so small that it did not seem worth while making the elaborate experiments necessary to calculate the correction, especially as the variations in the coil &c. produced disturbing effects far greater than would result from this cause.   We have assumed, too, that all the ions produced by the rays are brought down by the cloud ; if there were any left behind then the value we have deduced for the charge would be greater than the true value.   The value we have found for the charge on the ion produced by Röntgen rays is greater than that usually given for the charge on the hydrogen atom in electrolysis.   There seems, however, to be no valid reason against the latter charge having as high a value as that we have found.   We get from the laws of electrolysis, if *e* is the charge on the hydrogen ion in electrostatic units, N the number of molecules in 1 cub. centim. at standard temperature and pressure,

$$Ne = 129 \times 10^8$$

(see Richarz, *Bonn Sitzungsberichten*, 1891, p. 23) ; if we take $e = 6 \cdot 5 \times 10^{-10}$ we get

$$N = 20 \times 10^{18},$$

where N, deduced from experiments on the viscosity of air, is 21×10^{18}.   Though the measurements of the coefficients of viscosity of other gases give in general higher values of N, yet the agreement between the value of N deduced from these experiments and the value of N got by the Kinetic Theory of Gases by viscosity experiments is sufficient to show that that theory is consistent with the value we have found for *e* being equal to, or at any rate of the same order as, the charge carried by the hydrogen ion in electrolysis.

In connexion with this result it is interesting to find

that Professor H. A. Lorentz (*Koninkligke Akademie van Wetenschappen te Amsterdam*, April 6, 1898) has shown that the charge on the ions whose motion causes those lines in the spectrum which are affected by the Zeeman effect is of the same order as the charge on a hydrogen ion in electrolysis.

I wish to thank my assistant Mr. E. Everett for the help he has given in these investigations.

LVIII. *On the Masses of the Ions in Gases at Low Pressures. By* J. J. Thomson, *M.A., F.R.S., Cavendish Professor of Experimental Physics, Cambridge* *.

IN a former paper (Phil. Mag. Oct. 1897) I gave a determination of the value of the ratio of the mass, m, of the ion to its charge, e, in the case of the stream of negative electrification which constitutes the cathode rays. The results of this determination, which are in substantial agreement with those subsequently obtained by Lenard and Kaufmann, show that the value of this ratio is very much less than that of the corresponding ratio in the electrolysis of solutions of acids and salts, and that it is independent of the gas through which the discharge passes and of the nature of the electrodes. In these experiments it was only the value of m/e which was determined, and not the values of m and e separately. It was thus possible that the smallness of the ratio might be due to e being greater than the value of the charge carried by the ion in electrolysis rather than to the mass m being very much smaller. Though there were reasons for thinking that the charge e was not greatly different from the electrolytic one, and that we had here to deal with masses smaller than the atom, yet, as these reasons were somewhat indirect, I desired if possible to get a direct measurement of either m or e as well as of m/e. In the case of cathode rays I did not

* Communicated by the Author: read at the Meeting of the British Association at Dover.

see my way to do this; but another case, where negative electricity is carried by charged particles (*i. e.* when a negatively electrified metal plate in a gas at low pressure is illuminated by ultra-violet light), seemed more hopeful, as in this case we can determine the value of *e* by the method I previously employed to determine the value of the charge carried by the ions produced by Röntgen-ray radiation (Phil. Mag. Dec. 1898). The following paper contains an account of measurements of *m/e* and *e* for the negative electrification discharged by ultra-violet light, and also of *m/e* for the negative electrification produced by an incandescent carbon filament in an atmosphere of hydrogen. I may be allowed to anticipate the description of these experiments by saying that they lead to the result that the value of *m/e* in the case of the ultra-violet light, and also in that of the carbon filament, is the same as for the cathode rays; and that in the case of the ultra-violet light, *e* is the same in magnitude as the charge carried by the hydrogen atom in the electrolysis of solutions. In this case, therefore, we have clear proof that the ions have a very much smaller mass than ordinary atoms; so that in the convection of negative electricity at low pressures we have something smaller even than the atom, something which involves the splitting up of the atom, inasmuch as we have taken from it a part, though only a small one, of its mass.

The method of determining the value of *m/e* for the ions carrying the negative electrification produced by ultra-violet light is as follows :—Elster and Geitel (Wied. *Ann.* xli. p. 166) have shown that the rate of escape of the negative electrification at low pressures is much diminished by magnetic force if the lines of magnetic force are at right angles to the lines of electric force. Let us consider what effect a magnetic force would have on the motion of a negatively electrified particle. Let the electric force be uniform and parallel to the axis of *x*, while the magnetic force is also uniform and parallel to the axis of *z*. Let the pressure be so low that the mean free path of the particles is long compared with the distance they move while under observation, so that we may leave out of account the effect of collisions on the movements of the particles.

If *m* is the mass of a particle, *e* its charge, X the electric force, H the magnetic force, the equations of motion are :—

$$m\frac{d^2x}{dt^2} = \mathrm{X}e - \mathrm{H}e\frac{dy}{dt},$$

$$m\frac{d^2y}{dt^2} = \mathrm{H}e\frac{dx}{dt}.$$

Eliminating x we have :—

$$m\frac{d^3y}{dt^3} = \frac{\mathrm{H}e}{m}\left(\mathrm{X}e - \mathrm{H}e\frac{dy}{dt}\right).$$

The solutions of these equations, if x, y, dx/dt, dy/dt all vanish when $t=0$, is expressed by

$$y = \frac{\mathrm{X}m}{e\mathrm{H}^2}\left\{\frac{e}{m}\mathrm{H}t - \sin\left(\frac{e}{m}\mathrm{H}t\right)\right\},$$

$$x = \frac{\mathrm{X}m}{e\mathrm{H}^2}\left\{1 - \cos\left(\frac{e}{m}\mathrm{H}t\right)\right\}.$$

The equations show that the path of the particle is a cycloid, the generating circle of which has a diameter equal to $2\mathrm{X}m/e\mathrm{H}^2$, and rolls on the line $x=0$.

Suppose now that we have a metal plate AB exposed to ultra-violet light, placed parallel to a larger metal plate CD perforated so as to allow the light to pass through it and fall upon the plate AB. Then, if CD is at a higher electric potential than AB, all the negatively electrified particles which start from AB will reach CD if this plate is large compared with AB, the particles travelling along the lines of electric force. Let us now suppose that a uniform magnetic force equal to H, and at right angles to the electric force, acts on the particles; these particles will now describe cycloids and will reach a distance $2\mathrm{X}m/e\mathrm{H}^2$ from the place from which they start, and after reaching this distance they will again approach the plate. Thus if the plate CD is distant from AB by less than $2\mathrm{X}m/e\mathrm{H}^2$, every particle which leaves AB will reach CD provided CD stretches forward enough to prevent the particles passing by on one side. Now the distance parallel to y through which the particle has travelled when it is at the greatest distance from AB is $\pi\mathrm{X}m/e\mathrm{H}^2$: hence if CD stretches beyond AB by this distance at least, all the particles will be caught by CD and the magnetic field will produce no diminution in the rate of leak between AB and CD. If, on the other hand, the distance between the plates is greater than $2\mathrm{X}m/e\mathrm{H}^2$, then a particle starting from AB will turn back before it reaches CD: it will thus never reach it, and the rate at which CD acquires negative electrification will be diminished by the magnetic force. Hence, if this view of the action of the magnetic field is correct, if we begin with the plates very near together and gradually increase the distance between them, we should expect that, at first with the plates quite close together, the rate at which CD received a negative charge would not be affected by the magnetic force, but as soon as the distance between the plates was equal to $2X\ me\mathrm{H}^2$ the magnetic force would greatly diminish the rate at which CD received a negative charge, and would in fact reduce the rate almost to zero if all the negatively electrified particles came from the surface of AB. Hence, if we measure the distance between the plates when the magnetic force first diminishes the rate at which CD receives a negative charge, we shall determine the value of $2Xm/e\mathrm{H}^2$; and as we can easily determine X and H, we can deduce the value of m/e.

The way in which this method was carried into practice was as follows, the apparatus being shown in fig. 1.

AB is a carefully polished zinc plate about 1 centim. in diameter, while CD is a grating composed of very fine wires crossing each other at right angles, the ends being soldered into a ring of metal; the wires formed a network with a mesh about 1 millim. square. This was placed parallel to AB on the quartz plate EF, which was about 4 millim. thick. The grating was very carefully insulated. The system was enclosed in a glass tube which was kept connected with a mercury-pump provided with a McLeod gauge. The ultra-violet light was supplied from an arc about 3 millim. long between zinc terminals. The induction-coil giving the arc was placed in a metal box, and the light passed through a window cut in the top of the box; over this window the quartz base of the vessel was

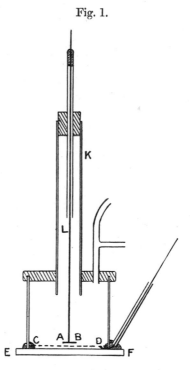

Fig. 1.

placed, a piece of wire gauze connected with the earth being placed between the quartz and the window. The plate AB was carried by the handle L which passed through a sealing-wax stopper in the tube K. The magnet used was an electromagnet of the horseshoe type. The magnetic force due to the magnet was determined by observing the deflexion of a ballistic galvanometer when an exploring coil, of approximately the same vertical dimen-

sion as the distance between the plates AB and CD, was
withdrawn from between its poles. The coil was carefully placed so as to occupy the same part of the magnetic
field as that occupied by the space between AB and CD
when the magnet was used to affect the rate of leak of
electricity between AB and CD. In this way the intensity
of the magnetic field between the poles of the magnet was
determined for a series of values of the current through the
magnetizing-coils of the electromagnet ranging between 1
and 4·5 amperes, and a curve was drawn which gave the
magnetic force when the magnetizing-current (observed by
an amperemeter) was known.

The pressure of the gas in the tube containing the plate was
reduced by the mercury-pump to 1/100 of a millim. of mercury.
As the mean free path of hydrogen molecules at atmospheric
pressure and 0° C. is $1·85 \times 10^{-5}$ centim. (Emil Meyer,
Kinetische Theorie der Gase, p. 142), and of air 10^{-5} centim.,
the mean free paths of these gases at the pressure of 1/100
of a millim. of mercury are respectively 14 and 7·6 millim.,
and are consequently considerably greater than the greatest
distance, 4 millim., through which the electrified particles have
to travel in any of the experiments. These are the free
paths for molecules of the gas ; if, as we shall see reason to
believe, the actual carriers of the negative electrification are
much smaller than the molecules, the free paths of these
carriers will be larger than the numbers we have quoted.

The rate of leak of negative electricity to CD when AB
was exposed to ultra-violet light was measured by a quadrant-
electrometer. The zinc plate was connected with the negative
pole of a battery of small storage-cells, the positive pole of
which was put to earth. One pair of the quadrants of the
electrometer was kept permanently connected with the earth,
the other pair of quadrants was connected with the wire
gauze CD. Initially the two pairs of quadrants were connected together, the connexion was then broken, and the
ultra-violet light allowed to fall on the zinc plate ; the negative charge received by the wire gauze in a given time is
proportional to the deflexion of the electrometer in that time.
By this method the following results were obtained : when
the difference of potential between the illuminated plate and
the wire gauze was greater than a certain value, depending
upon the intensity of the magnetic force and the distance
between AB and CD, no diminution in the deflexion of the
electrometer was produced by the magnetic field, in fact in
some cases the deflexion was just a little greater in the magnetic field. . The theory just given indicates that the deflexion

2 Q 2

ought to be the same : the small increase (amounting to not more than 3 or 4 per cent.) may be due to the obliquity of the path of the particles in the magnetic field, causing more of them to be caught by the wires of the grating than would be the case if the paths of the particles were at right angles to the plane of the gauze. When the difference of potential is reduced below a certain value, the deflexion of the electrometer is very much reduced by the magnetic field ; it is not, however, at once entirely destroyed when the potential-difference passes through the critical value. The simple theory just given would indicate a very abrupt transition from the case when the magnetic force produces no effect, to that in which it entirely stops the flow of negative electricity to CD. In practice, however, I find that the transition is not abrupt: after passing a certain difference of potential the diminution in the electric charge received by CD increases gradually as the potential-difference is reduced, and there is not an abrupt transition from zero effect to a complete stoppage of the leak between AB and CD. I think this is due to the ionization not being confined to the gas in contact with the illuminated plate, but extending through a layer of gas whose thickness at very low pressures is quite appreciable. The existence of a layer of this kind is indicated by an experiment of Stoletow's. Stoletow found that the maximum current between two plates depended at low pressures to a considerable extent upon the distance between the plates, increasing as the distance between the plates was increased. Now the maximum current is the one that in one second uses up as many ions as are produced in that time by the ultra-violet light. If all the ions are produced close to the illuminated plate, increasing the distance between the plates will not increase the number of ions available for carrying the current ; if, however, the ions are produced in a layer of sensible thickness, then, until the distance between the plates exceeds the thickness of this layer, an increase in the distance between the plates will increase the number of ions, and so increase the maximum current. If this layer has a sensible thickness, then the distance d which has to be traversed by the ions before reaching the gauze connected with the electrometer ranges from the distance between the plates to the difference between this distance and the thickness of the layer. The first ions to be stopped by the magnetic field will be those coming from the surface of the illuminated plate, as for these d has the greatest value : hence we may use the equation

$$d = \frac{2Xm}{eH^2}, \qquad \cdots \cdots \cdots \quad (1)$$

if d represents the distance between the plates, X the value of the electric field when the rate of leak first begins to be affected by the magnetic force H. Assuming that the field is uniform,

$$X = V/d,$$

where V is the potential-difference between the plates ; and equation (1) becomes

$$d^2 = \frac{2Vm}{eH^2}.$$

The negative ions travelling between the plates will disturb to some extent the uniformity of the field between the plates ; but if the intensity of the ultra-violet light is not too great, so that the rate of leak and the number of ions between the plates is not large, this want of uniformity will not be important. A calculation of the amount of variation due to this cause showed that its effect was not large enough to make it worth while correcting the observations for this effect, as the variation in the intensity of the ultra-violet light was sufficient to make the errors of experiments much larger than the correction.

The following is a specimen of the observations :—

Distance between the plates ·29 centim.

Strength of magnetic field 164. Pressure 1/100 millim.

Potential-difference between Plates, in volts.	Deflexion of Electrometer in 30 secs.	
	Magnet off.	Magnet on.
240	180	190
120	160	165
80	160	140
40	130	75

These observations showed that the critical value of the potential-difference was about 80 volts. A series of observations were then made with potential-differences increasing from 80 volts by 2 volts at a time, and it was found that 90 volts was the largest potential-difference at which any effect due to the magnet could be detected. The results of a number of experiments are given in the following table :—

d (in cm.).	H.	V in absolute measure.	e/m.
·18	170	40×10^8	$8·5 \times 10^6$
·19	170	30×10^8	$5·8 \times 10^6$
·20	181	46×10^8	$7·0 \times 10^6$
·29	167	84×10^8	$7·1 \times 10^6$
·29	164	90×10^8	$7·6 \times 10^6$
·30	160	86×10^8	$7·4 \times 10^6$
·45	100	80×10^8	$7·9 \times 10^6$

giving a mean value for e/m equal to $7·3 \times 10^6$. The value I found for e/m for the cathode rays was 5×10^6; the value found by Lenard was $6·4 \times 10^6$. Thus the value of e/m in the case of the convection of electricity under the influence of ultra-violet light is of the same order as in the case of the cathode rays, and is very different from the value of e/m in the case of the hydrogen ions in ordinary electrolysis when it is equal to 10^4. As the measurements of e, the charge carried by the ions produced by ultra-violet light to be described below, show that it is the same as e for the hydrogen ion in electrolyis, it follows that the mass of the carrier in the case of the convection of negative electricity under the influence of ultra-violet light is only of the order of 1/1000 of that of the hydrogen atom. Thus with ultra-violet light, as with cathode rays, the negative electrification at low pressures is found associated with masses which are exceedingly small fractions of the smallest mass hitherto known—that of the hydrogen atom.

I have examined another case in which we have convection of electricity at low pressures by means of negatively electrified particles—that of the discharge of electricity produced by an incandescent carbon filament in an atmosphere of hydrogen. In this case, as Elster and Geitel (Wied. *Ann.* xxxviii. p. 27) have shown, we have negative ions produced in the neighbourhood of the filament, and the charge on a positively electrified body in the neighbourhood of the filament is discharged by these ions, while if the body is negatively electrified it is not discharged. If the filament is negatively, and a neighbouring body positively electrified, there will be a current of electricity between the filament and the body, while there will be no leak if the filament is positively and the body negatively electrified. Elster and Geitel (Wied.

Ann. xxxviii. p. 27) showed that the rate of leak from a negatively electrified filament was at low pressures diminished by the action of the magnetic field. On the theory of charged ions, the effect of the magnet in diminishing the rate of leak could be explained in the same way as the effect on the convection due to ultra-violet light. A series of experiments were made which showed that the effects due to the magnetic field were consistent with this explanation, and led to a determination of e/m for the carriers of the negative electricity.

The apparatus was of the same type as that used in the preceding experiments. The wire gauze and the zinc plate were replaced by two parallel aluminium disks about 1·75 centim. in diameter; between these disks, and quite close to the upper disk, there was a small semicircular carbon filament which was raised to a red heat by the current from four storage-cells. The carbon filament was placed close to the axis of the disks; the object of the upper disk was to make the electric field between the disks more uniform. The lower plate was connected with the electrometer. The plates and filaments were enclosed in a glass tube which was connected with a mercury-pump, by means of which the pressure, after the vessel had been repeatedly filled with hydrogen, was reduced to ·01 millim. of mercury. Great difficulty was found at first in getting any consistent results with the incandescent carbon filament: sometimes the filament would discharge positive as well as negative electricity; indeed sometimes it would discharge positive and not negative. Most of these irregularities were traced to gas given out by the incandescent filament; and it was found that by keeping the filament almost white-hot for several hours, and continually pumping and refilling with hydrogen, and then using the filament at a much lower temperature than that to which it had been raised in this preliminary heating, the irregularities were nearly eliminated, and nothing but negative electrification was discharged from the filament. When this state was attained, the effect of magnetic force showed the same characteristics as in the case of ultra-violet light. When the difference of potential between the filament and the lower plate was small, the effect of the magnetic force was very great, so much so as almost to destroy the leak entirely; when, however, the potential-difference exceeded a certain value, the magnetic force produced little or no effect upon the leak. An example of this is shown by the results of the following experiment :—

The distance between the carbon filament and the plate connected with the electrometer was 3·5 millim., the strength of the magnetic field 170 C.G.S. units.

Difference of Potential between wire and plate, in volts.	Leak in 5 seconds.		Ratio of leaks.
	Without magnetic field.	With magnetic field.	
40	43	1	·023
80	170	50 .	·29
120	300	250	·83
140	345	345	1·0
160	400	430	1·07

Taking 140 volts as the critical value of the potential-difference, we find by equation (1) that

$$\frac{e}{m} = 7 \cdot 8 \times 10^6.$$

The results of this and similar experiments are given in the following table ; V denoting the critical potential-difference in C.G.S. units, and H the magnetic force :

d.	V.	H.	e/m.
·35	140×10^8	170	$7 \cdot 8 \times 10^6$
·35	220×10^8	220	$7 \cdot 5 \times 10^6$
·35	170×10^8	170	$9 \cdot 6 \times 10^6$
·35	130×10^8	170	$7 \cdot 2 \times 10^6$
·35	120×10^8	120	$11 \cdot 3 \times 10^6$

giving $8 \cdot 7 \times 10^6$ as the mean value of *e/m*. This value does not differ much from that found in the case of ultra-violet light.   In the case of the incandescent filament the ions are only produced at a small part of the plate, and not over the whole surface as in the case of ultra-violet light, so the conditions do not approximate so closely to those assumed in the theory.   We conclude that the particles which carry the negative electrification in this case are of the same nature as those which carry it in the cathode rays and in the electrification arising from the action of ultra-violet light.

The unipolar positive leak which occurs from an incandescent platinum wire in air or oxygen, and in which the moving bodies are positively electrified, was found not to be affected by a magnetic field of the order of that used in the experiments on the negative leak. This had already been observed by Elster and Geitel (Wied. *Ann.* xxxviii. p. 27).

On the theory of the effect given in this paper, the absence of magnetic effect on the positively charged carriers indicates that e/m is much smaller or m/e much larger for the positive ions than it is for the negative. I am engaged with some experiments on the effect of the magnetic field on the convection of electricity by positive ions, using very strong magnetic fields produced by a powerful electromagnet kindly lent to me by Professor Ewing. From the results I have already got, it is clear that m/e for the positive ions produced by an incandescent wire must be at least 1000 times the value for the negative ions, and this is only an inferior limit.

The positive and negative ions produced by incandescent solids show the same disproportion of mass as is shown by the positive and negative ions in a vacuum-tube at low pressures.

W. Wien (Wied. *Ann.* lxv. p. 440) and Ewers (Wied. *Ann.* lxix. p. 187) have measured the ratio of m/e for the positive ions in such a tube, and found that it is of the same order as the value of m/e in ordinary electrolysis; Ewers has shown that it depends on the metal of which the cathode is made. Thus the carriers of positive electricity at low pressures seem to be ordinary molecules, while the carriers of negative electricity are very much smaller.

Measurement of the Charge on the Ion produced by the Action of Utra-Violet Light on a Zinc Plate.

This charge was determined by the method used by me to measure the charge on the ions produced by the action of Röntgen rays on a gas (Phil. Mag. Dec. 1898); for the details of the method I shall refer to my former paper, and here give only an outline of the principle on which the method is based. Mr. C. T. R. Wilson (Phil. Trans. 1898) discovered that the ions produced by ultra-violet light act like those produced by Röntgen rays, in forming nuclei around which water will condense from dust-free air when the supersaturation exceeds a certain definite value.

Suppose, then, we wish to find the number of ions produced by ultra-violet light in a cubic centimetre of air. We cool the air by a sudden expansion until the supersaturation produced by the cooling is sufficient to form a cloud round the ions : the problem of finding the number of ions per cub. centim. is now reduced to finding the number of drops per cub. centim. in this cloud. We can do this in the following way :—If we know the amount of the expansion we can calculate the amount of water deposited per cub. centim. of the cloud; this water is deposited as drops, and if the drops are of equal size, the number of drops per cub. centim. will be equal to the volume of water per cub. centim. divided by the volume of one of the drops. Hence, if we know the size of the drops, we can calculate the number. The size of the drops in the cloud was determined by observing v, the velocity with which they fall under gravity, and then deducing a, the radius of the drop, by means of the equation

$$v = \frac{2}{9}\frac{ga^2}{\mu},$$

where μ is the coefficient of viscosity of the gas through which the drop falls.

In this way we can determine n the number of ions per cub. centim. : if e is the charge on an ion, v the velocity with which it moves under a known electric force, the quantity of electricity which crosses unit area in unit time under this force is equal to neu. We can determine this quantity if we allow the negative ions to fall on a plate connected with a condenser of known capacity and measure the rate at which the potential falls. We thus determine the product neu, and we already know n; u has been determined by Mr. Rutherford (Proc. Camb. Phil. Soc. ix. p. 401); for air at atmospheric pressure u is proportional to the potential gradient, and when this is one volt per centim., u is 1·5 centim. per second; for hydrogen at atmospheric pressure u is 4·5 centim. per second for the same potential gradient. Hence, as in the known product neu we know n and u, we can deduce the value of e the charge on the ion.

There are some features in the condensation of clouds by ultra-violet light which are not present in the clouds formed by the Röntgen rays. In the first place, the cloud due to the ultra-violet light is only formed in an electric field. When there is no electric field, the ions remain close to the surface of the illuminated plate, and are not diffused through the region in which the cloud has to be formed; to get the negative ions into this region we must electrify the plate negatively; when this is done, expansion produces a cloud. Again, if the ultra-violet light is very strong, Mr. C. T. R. Wilson has shown (Phil. Trans. 1899) that large nuclei are produced in the gas through which the light passes; these are distinct from those produced near a metal plate on which the light falls, and they can produce a cloud with very little supersaturation; these nuclei are not ions, for they do not move in an electric field, and the drops formed round these nuclei ought therefore not to be counted in estimating the number of negative ions. For this reason it is necessary to use ultra-violet light

Fig. 2.

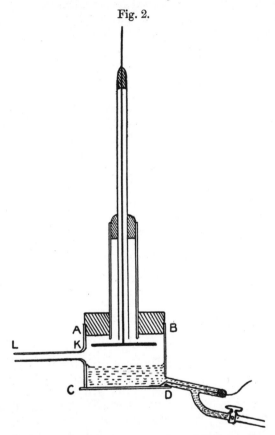

of small intensity, and there are in addition other reasons which make it impossible to work with strong light. I found when working with the ions produced by Röntgen rays, that it was impossible to get good results unless the rays were weak and the clouds therefore thin. If the rays were strong, one expansion was not sufficient to bring down all the ions by the cloud; sometimes as many as five or six expansions were required to remove the ions from the vessel. Another reason why the strong rays do not give good results is that there are slight convection-currents in the vessel after the expansion, for the walls of the vessel are warmer than the gas; this gives rise to convection-currents in the gas, the gas going up the sides and down the middle of the vessel. The velocity of the convection-current is added on to the velocity of the ions due to gravity; and if the velocity of the ions is very small, as it is when the rays are strong and the drops numerous, a very small convection-current will be sufficient to make the actual rate of fall of the drops very different from that of a drop of the same size falling through air at rest. All the reasons are operative in the case of ultra-violet light, and it is only when the intensity of the light is small that I have got consistent results.

The vessel in which the expansion took place is shown in fig. 2. AB is a glass tube about 3·6 cm. in diameter; the base CD is a quartz plate about ·5 cm. thick; on the top of this there is a layer of water in electrical connexion with the earth about 1 cm. in thickness; the illuminated zinc plate was 3·2 cm. in diameter, and was 1·2 cm. above the surface of the water. The ultra-violet light was produced by an arc about ·3 cm. long, between zinc terminals connected with an induction-coil; the arc was about 40 cm. below the lower face of the quartz plate. The space between the zinc plate and the water surface was illuminated by an arc-light so as to allow the rate of fall of the drops to be accurately measured. The tube LK connected this vessel with the apparatus used in the previous experiments; a figure of this is given in the Phil. Mag. Dec. 1898.

To observe the current of electricity through the gas, the illuminated plate was connected with one pair of quadrants of an electrometer, the other pair of quadrants being kept connected with the earth. The capacity C of the system, consisting of the plate, connecting wires and quadrants of the electrometer, was determined. The plate was then charged to a negative potential, and the deflexion of the electrometer-needles observed. The induction-coil was now set in action, and the ultra-violet light allowed to fall on the zinc plate: the deflexion of the electrometer-needle immediately began to decrease; the rate at which it decreased was determined by measuring the diminution of the deflexion in 30 seconds.

Let D be the original deflexion of the electrometer, let this correspond to a potential-difference equal to aD between the plate and the earth. If b is the distance between the zinc plate and the surface of the water, the potential gradient is aD/b. If A is the area of the plate, n the number of ions per cub. centim., e the charge on an ion, u_0 the velocity of the ion under unit potential gradient, then the quantity of negative electricity lost by the plate in one second is

$$A n e u_0 \alpha D / b.$$

But the plate is observed to fall in potential by αb per second, and the capacity of the system attached to the plate is C : hence the loss of electricity by the plate per second is

$$C \alpha d.$$

Equating these two expressions for the loss of electricity, we get

$$A n e u_0 \alpha D / b = C \alpha d$$

or
$$e = \frac{b}{n u_0} \frac{C}{A} \frac{d}{D}.$$

Hence knowing b, C, A, and u_0, if we measure n and d/D we can determine e.

To calculate n we begin by finding the volume of water deposited in consequence of the expansion in each cub. centim. of the expansion. In my previous paper I show how this can be determined if we know the ratio of the final to the initial volumes and the temperature before expansion. In the present experiments the final volume was 1·36 times the initial volume, and the temperature before expansion was 18°·5 C. It follows from this that 50×10^{-7} cub. centim. of water were deposited in each cub. centim. of the expansion chamber.

If a is the radius of one of the drops, the volume of a drop is $4\pi a^3/3$, and hence $n' = \dfrac{3 \times 50 \times 10^{-7}}{4\pi a^2}$: here n' is the number of ions per cub. centim. of the expanded gas.

If v is the velocity of fall

$$v = \frac{2}{9} \frac{g a^2}{\mu}.$$

Since for air $\mu = 1\cdot8 \times 10^{-4}$,   we find

$$a = \frac{v^{\frac{1}{2}}}{1\cdot1 \times 10^3},$$

and

$$\frac{4}{3}\pi a^3 = 3\cdot14\, v^{\frac{3}{2}} \times 10^{-9},$$

$$n' = \frac{5000}{3\cdot14\, v^{\frac{3}{2}}}.$$

This is the number in 1 cub. centim. of the expanded gas; the number in 1 cub. centim. of the gas before expansion is $1·36\,n'$. To find n the number of ions we must subtract from $1·36\,n'$ the number of drops which are formed when the ultra-violet light does not fall on the plate. With an expansion as large as $1·36$, Mr. Wilson has shown that a few drops are always formed in dust-free air, even when free from the influence of Röntgen rays or ultra-violet light. If V be the velocity with which these drops formed in the absence of the light fall, then the number of drops due to these nuclei is

$$\frac{1·36 \times 5000}{3·14\,\mathrm{V}^{\frac{3}{2}}}.$$

Subtracting this from $1·36\,n'$, we find

$$n = 2·07 \times 10^3 \left\{ \frac{1}{v^{\frac{3}{2}}} - \frac{1}{\mathrm{V}^{\frac{3}{2}}} \right\}.$$

In making this correction we have assumed that the clouds form round these nuclei even when the negative ions due to the ultra-violet light are present. If the cloud formed more readily about the negative ions than about the nuclei, the ions would rob the nuclei of their water, and we should not need the correction. The following table gives the result of some experiments; in making the observation on the cloud the same potential-difference between the plate and the water was used as when observing the value of d/D: u_0 was determined by Prof. Rutherford as $1·5 \times 3 \times 10^2$, and A was $\pi(1·6)^2$ throughout the experiments.

$b.$	C.	$d/\mathrm{D}.$	$v.$	V.	$e \times 10^{10}.$
1·2	62	·0017	·13	·3	7·9
1·2	62	·0019	·11	·3	7·3
·9	50	·0012	·14	·3	5·3
1·2	65	·0035	·08	·3	7·3
1·2	50	·0018	·11	·3	6
1·2	40	·0018	·14	·3	7

The mean value of e is $6·8 \times 10^{-10}$. The values differ a good deal, but we could not expect a very close agreement unless we could procure an absolutely constant source of ultra-violet light, as these experiments are very dependent on the constancy of the light; since the electrical part of the experiment measures the average intensity of the light over 30 seconds, while the observations on the cloud measure the intensity over an interval of a small fraction of a second.

The value of e found by me previously for the ions produced by Röntgen rays was $6·5 \times 10^{-8}$: hence we conclude that e for the ions produced by ultra-violet light is the same as e for the ions produced by the Röntgen rays; and as Mr. Townsend has shown that the charge on these latter ions is the same as the charge on an atom of hydrogen in electrolysis, we arrive at the result previously referred to, that the charge on the ion produced by ultra-violet light is the same as that on the hydrogen ion in ordinary electrolysis.

The experiments just described, taken in conjunction with previous ones on the value of m/e for the cathode rays (J. J. Thomson, Phil. Mag. Oct. 1897), show that in gases at low pressures negative electrification, though it may be produced by very different means, is made up of units each having a charge of electricity of a definite size; the magnitude of this negative charge is about 6×10^{-10} electrostatic units, and is equal to the positive charge carried by the hydrogen atom in the electrolysis of solutions.

In gases at low pressures these units of negative electric charge are always associated with carriers of a definite mass. This mass is exceedingly small, being only about $1·4 \times 10^{-3}$ of that of the hydrogen ion, the smallest mass hitherto recognized as capable of a separate existence. The production of negative electrification thus involves the splitting up of an atom, as from a collection of atoms something is detached whose mass is less than that of a single atom. We have not yet data for determining whether the mass of the negative atom is entirely due to its charge. If the charge is e, the apparent mass due to the charge supposed to be collected on a sphere of radius a is $\frac{1}{3}e^2/\mu a$: hence m/e in this case is $e/3\mu a$. Substituting the values of m/e and e found above, we find that a would be of the order 10^{-13} centim.

We have no means yet of knowing whether or not the mass of the negative ion is of electrical origin. We could probably get light on this point by comparing the heat produced by the bombardment by these negatively electrified particles of the inside of a vessel composed of a substance transparent to Röntgen rays, with the heat produced when the vessel was opaque to those rays. If the mass was "mechanical," and not electrical, the heat produced should be same in the two cases. If, on the other hand, the mass were electrical, the heat would be less in the first case than in the second, as part of the energy would escape through the walls.

Hitherto we have been considering only negative electrification; as far as our present knowledge extends positive electrification is never associated with masses as small as those which invariably accompany negative electrification in gases at low pressures. From W. Wien's experiments on the ratio of the mass to the electric charge for the carriers of positive electrification in a highly exhausted vacuum-tube (Wied. *Ann.* lxv. p. 440), it would seem that the masses with which positive electrification is associated are comparable with the masses of ordinary atoms. This is also in accordance with the experiments of Elster and Geitel (Wied. *Ann.* xxxviii. p. 27), which show that when positive ions are produced by an incandescent platinum wire in air they are not affected to anything like the same extent as negative ions produced by an incandescent carbon filament in hydrogen.

It is necessary to point out that the preceding statements as to the masses of the ions are only true when the pressure of the gas is very small, so small that we are able to determine the mass of the carriers before they have made many collisions with the surrounding molecules. When the pressure is too high for this to be the case, the electric charge, whether positive or negative, seems to act as a nucleus around which several molecules collect, just as dust collects round an electrified body, so that we get an aggregate formed whose mass is larger than that of a molecule of a gas.

The experiments on the velocities of the ions produced by Röntgen or uranium rays, by ultra-violet light, in flames or in the arc, show that in gases at pressures comparable with the atmospheric pressure, the electric charges are associated with masses which are probably several times the mass of a molecule of the gas, and enormously greater than the mass of a carrier of negative electrification in a gas at a low pressure.

There are some other phenomena which seem to have a very direct bearing on the nature of the process of ionizing a gas. Thus I have shown (Phil. Mag. Dec. 1898) that when a gas is ionized by Röntgen rays, the charges on the ions are the same whatever the nature of the gas: thus we get the same charges on the ions whether we ionize hydrogen or oxygen. This result has been confirmed by J. S. Townsend ("On the Diffusion of Ions," Phil. Trans. 1899), who used an entirely different method. Again, the ionization of a gas by Röntgen rays is in general an additive property; *i. e.*, the ionization of a compound gas AB, where A and B represent the atoms of two elementary gases, is one half the sum of the ionization of A_2 and B_2 by rays of the same intensity, where

A_2 and B_2 represent diatomic molecules of these gases (Proc. Camb. Phil. Soc. vol. x. p. 9). This result makes it probable that the ionization of a gas in these cases results from the splitting up of the atoms of the gas, rather than from a separation of one atom from the other in a molecule of the gas.

These results, taken in conjunction with the measurements of the mass of the negative ion, suggest that the ionization of a gas consists in the detachment from the atom of a negative ion; this negative ion being the same for all gases, while the mass of the ion is only a small fraction of the mass of an atom of hydrogen.

From what we have seen, this negative ion must be a quantity of fundamental importance in any theory of electrical action; indeed, it seems not improbable that it is the fundamental quantity in terms of which all electrical processes can be expressed. For, as we have seen, its mass and its charge are invariable, independent both of the processes by which the electrification is produced and of the gas from which the ions are set free. It thus possesses the characteristics of being a fundamental conception in electricity; and it seems desirable to adopt some view of electrical action which brings this conception into prominence. These considerations have led me to take as a working hypothesis the following method of regarding the electrification of a gas, or indeed of matter in any state.

I regard the atom as containing a large number of smaller bodies which I will call corpuscles; these corpuscles are equal to each other; the mass of a corpuscle is the mass of the negative ion in a gas at low pressure, *i. e.* about 3×10^{-26} of a gramme. In the normal atom, this assemblage of corpuscles forms a system which is electrically neutral. Though the individual corpuscles behave like negative ions, yet when they are assembled in a neutral atom the negative effect is balanced by something which causes the space through which the corpuscles are spread to act as if it had a charge of positive electricity equal in amount to the sum of the negative charges on the corpuscles. Electrification of a gas I regard as due to the splitting up of some of the atoms of the gas, resulting in the detachment of a corpuscle from some of the atoms. The detached corpuscles behave like negative ions, each carrying a constant negative charge, which we shall call for brevity the unit charge; while the part of the atom left behind behaves like a positive ion with the unit positive charge and a mass large compared with that of the negative ion. On this view, electrification essentially involves the splitting up of the atom, a part of the mass of the atom getting free and becoming detached from the original atom.

Phil. Mag. S. 5. Vol. 48. No. 295. *Dec.* 1899.   2 R

A positively electrified atom is an atom which has lost some of its " free mass," and this free mass is to be found along with the corresponding negative charge. Changes in the electrical charge on an atom are due to corpuscles moving from the atom when the positive charge is increased, or to corpuscles moving up to it when the negative charge is increased. Thus when anions and cations are liberated against the electrodes in the electrolysis of solutions, the ion with the positive charge is neutralized by a corpuscle moving from the electrode to the ion, while the ion with the negative charge is neutralized by a corpuscle passing from the ion to the electrode. The corpuscles are the vehicles by which electricity is carried from one atom to another.

We are thus led to the conclusion that the mass of an atom is not invariable : that, for example, if in the molecule of HCl the hydrogen atom has the positive and the chlorine atom the negative charge, then the mass of the hydrogen atom is less than half the mass of the hydrogen molecule H_2; while, on the other hand, the mass of the chlorine atom in the molecule of HCl is greater than half the mass of the chlorine molecule Cl_2.

The amount by which the mass of an atom may vary is proportional to the charge of electricity it can receive; and as we have no evidence that an atom can receive a greater charge than that of its ion in the electrolysis of solutions, and as this charge is equal to the valency of the ion multiplied by the charge on the hydrogen atom, we conclude that the variability of the mass of an atom which can be produced by known processes is proportional to the valency of the atom, and our determination of the mass of the corpuscle shows that this variability is only a small fraction of the mass of the original atom.

In the case of the ionization of a gas by Röntgen or uranium rays, the evidence seems to be in favour of the view that not more than one corpuscle can be detached from any one atom. For if more than one were detached, the remaining part of the atom would have a positive charge greater than the negative charge carried by each of the detached corpuscles. Now the ions, in virtue of their charges, act as nuclei around which drops of water condense when moist dust-free gas is suddenly expanded. If the positive charge were greater than the individual negative ones, the positive ions would be more efficient in producing cloudy condensation than the negative one, and would give a cloud with smaller expansion. As a matter of fact, however, the reverse is the case, as C. T. R. Wilson (Phil. Trans. 1899) has shown that it requires a considerably greater expansion to produce a cloud in dust-free air on positive ions than on negative ones when the ions are produced by Röntgen rays.

Though only a small fraction of the mass of an atom can be detached by any known process, it does not follow that the part left behind does not contain more corpuscles which could be detached by more powerful means than we have hitherto been able to use. For it is evident that it will require a greater expenditure of energy to tear two corpuscles from one atom than to tear two corpuscles one from each of two separate atoms; for when one corpuscle has been torn off from an atom the atom is positively electrified, and it will be more difficult to tear off a second negatively electrified corpuscle from this positively electrified atom, than it was to tear the first from the originally neutral atom. A reason for believing that there are many more corpuscles in the atom than the one or two that can be torn off, is afforded by the Zeeman effect. The ratio of the mass to the charge, as determined by this effect, is of the same order as that we have deduced from our measurements on the free corpuscles; and the charges carried by the moving particles, by which the Zeeman effect is explained, are all negatively electrified. Now, if there were only one or two of these corpuscles in the atom, we should expect that only one or two lines in the spectrum would show the Zeeman effect; for even if the coordinates fixing the position of the moving corpuscles were not " principal coordinates," though there might be a secondary effect on the periods of the other oscillations due to their connexion with these coordinates, yet we should expect this secondary effect to be of quite a different order from the primary one. As, however, there are a considerable number of lines in the spectrum which show Zeeman effects comparable in intensity, we conclude that there are a considerable number of corpuscles in the atom of the substance giving this spectrum.

I have much pleasure in thanking my assistant Mr. E. Everett for the help he has given me in making the experiments described in this paper.

On a Diffuse Reflection of the α-Particles.

By H. Geiger, Ph.D., John Harling Fellow, and E. Marsden, Hatfield Scholar, University of Manchester.

(Communicated by Prof. E. Rutherford, F.R.S. Received May 19,—Read June 17, 1909.)

When β-particles fall on a plate, a strong radiation emerges from the same side of the plate as that on which the β-particles fall. This radiation is regarded by many observers as a secondary radiation, but more recent experiments seem to show that it consists mainly of primary β-particles, which have been scattered inside the material to such an extent that they emerge again at the same side of the plate.* For α-particles a similar effect has not previously been observed, and is perhaps not to be expected on account of the relatively small scattering which α-particles suffer in penetrating matter.†

In the following experiments, however, conclusive evidence was found of the existence of a diffuse reflection of the α-particles. A small fraction of the α-particles falling upon a metal plate have their directions changed to such an extent that they emerge again at the side of incidence. To form an idea of the way in which this effect takes place, the following three points were investigated :—

(I) The relative amount of reflection from different metals.

(II) The relative amount of reflection from a metal of varying thickness.

(III) The fraction of the incident α-particles which are reflected.

* See Schmidt, 'Jahrbuch der Radioaktivität und Electronik,' vol. 5, p. 471, 1908.

† Rutherford, 'Phil. Mag.,' vol. 12, p. 143, 1906 ; H. Geiger, 'Roy. Soc. Proc.,' A, vol. 81, p. 174, 1908.

For the observation of the reflected particles the scintillation method was used in all experiments. With regard to the details of the method we refer to the papers of Regener* and of Rutherford and Geiger.†

On account of the fact that the amount of reflection is very small, it was necessary to use a very intense source of α-rays. A tube was employed similar to that which has been proved to be a suitable source in the scattering experiments of one of us.‡ This source consisted of a glass tube AB (fig. 1), drawn down conically and filled with radium emanation, the end B of the tube being closed airtight by means of a mica window. The thickness of the mica was equivalent to about 1 cm. of air, so that the α-particles could easily pass through it.

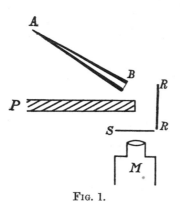

Fig. 1.

Since it is of importance that the gas pressure inside this tube should be as low as possible, the emanation was purified according to the methods developed by Prof. Rutherford.§ The tube contained an amount of emanation equivalent to about 20 milligrammes RaBr$_2$ at a pressure of a few centimetres. The number of α-particles expelled per second through the window was, therefore, very great, and, on account of the small pressure inside the tube, the different ranges of the α-particles from the three products (*i.e.* emanation, RaA, and RaC) were sharply defined.

The zinc sulphide screen S (fig. 1) was fixed behind the lead plate P, in such a position that no α-particles could strike it directly. When a reflector was placed in the position RR at about 1 cm. from the end of the tube, scintillations were at once observed. At the same time the screen brightened up appreciably on account of the reflected β-particles.

By means of a low power microscope, the number of scintillations per minute on a definite square millimetre of the screen was counted for reflectors of different materials. Care was taken that the different reflectors were always placed in exactly the same position.

It is, of course, to be expected that the number of α-particles reflected from the plate would be different in different directions, and would also depend on the angle of incidence. In our arrangement, however, no appreciable difference was found for different angles. This is due to the fact that,

* 'Verh. d. D. Phys. Ges.,' vol. 10, p. 78, 1908.
† 'Roy. Soc. Proc.,' A, vol. 81, p. 141, 1908.
‡ Geiger, 'Roy. Soc. Proc.,' A, vol. 81, p. 174, 1908.
§ 'Phil. Mag.,' August, p. 300, 1908.

owing to the necessity of having the tube very near to the reflector, the angle of incidence varied very much. An investigation of the variation of the effect with the angles of incidence and emergence would necessitate a parallel and very intense source of homogeneous α-rays, which can, however, not easily be realised.

In the following table the number of scintillations observed per minute are given in column 3; in column 4 the ratio to the atomic weight is calculated, and it can be seen that this ratio decreases with decreasing atomic weight. The case of lead appears to be an exception which may be due to slight impurities in the lead.

1. Metal.	2. Atomic weight, A.	3. Number of scintillations per minute, Z.	4. A/Z.
Lead	207	62	30
Gold	197	67	34
Platinum............	195	63	33
Tin	119	34	28
Silver	108	27	25
Copper..............	64	14·5	23
Iron	56	10·2	18·5
Aluminium	27	3·4	12·5

Even in the absence of any reflector about one scintillation per minute was observed. It was easy to show that this was due to a reflection from the air through which the α-particles passed. The numbers on the table are corrected for this effect.

It is interesting to note here that for β-particles the number of reflected particles also decreases with the atomic weight of the reflector.[*] But while for β-particles the number reflected from gold is only about twice as great as for aluminium, for α-particles the same ratio amounts to about twenty.

(II) We have already pointed out that the diffuse reflection of the α-particles is a consequence of their scattering. According to this point of view, the number of particles reflected must vary with the thickness of the reflecting screen. Since gold can be obtained in very thin and uniform foils, different numbers of these foils were used as reflectors. Each foil was equivalent in stopping power to about 0·4 mm. of air. It was necessary to mount the foils on glass plates, but the number reflected from the glass itself was found to be very small compared even with the number from one gold foil. The curve, fig. 2, gives the result of the measurements.

[*] McClelland, 'Dublin Trans.,' vol. 9, p. 9, 1906.

The number of scintillations which were due to the reflection from the air is subtracted from each reading. The first point on the curve represents the number of scintillations observed for a glass plate alone as reflector; the last point (marked 30) gives the number of scintillations when a thick gold plate was used.

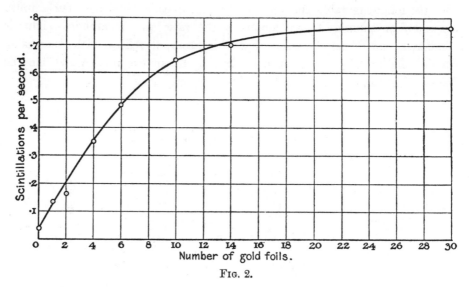

Fig. 2.

The curve is similar to those which have been obtained for the reflection of the β-particles.* It brings out clearly that the reflection is not a surface but a volume effect.

Compared, however, with the thickness of gold which an α-particle can penetrate, the effect is confined to a relatively thin layer. In our experiment, about half of the reflected particles were reflected from a layer equivalent to about 2 mm. of air. If the high velocity and mass of the α-particle be taken into account, it seems surprising that some of the α-particles, as the experiment shows, can be turned within a layer of 6×10^{-5} cm. of gold through an angle of 90°, and even more. To produce a similar effect by a magnetic field, the enormous field of 10^9 absolute units would be required.

(III) In the next experiment, an estimate of the total number of particles reflected was aimed at. For this purpose the emanation tube used in the previous experiments was unsuitable, firstly, on account of the difficulty of correctly ascertaining the number of α-particles emerging from the tube; and secondly, on account of the different ranges of the α-particles from the

* McClelland, 'Phil. Mag.,' vol. 9, p. 230, 1905; 'Ann. d. Phys.,' vol. 18, p. 974, 1905; Schmidt, 'Ann. d. Phys.,' vol. 23, p. 671, 1907; 'Phys. Zeit.,' vol. 8, p. 737, 1907.

three products: emanation, radium A, and radium C. Consequently, as radiating source, radium C, deposited on a plate of small dimensions, was used. The arrangement, which is sketched in fig. 3, was such that the α-particles from the plate A fell upon the platinum reflector R, of about 1 square centimetre area, at an average angle of 90°. The reflected particles were counted on different points of the screen S.

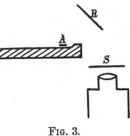

FIG. 3.

No appreciable variation of the number was found with different angles of emergence, the reason of which has already been explained above.

The amount of radium C deposited on the plate was determined by its γ-ray activity. Assuming that $3\cdot4 \times 10^{10}$ particles are expelled per second from an amount of RaC equivalent to 1 gramme Ra,* the number of α-particles expelled per second from the active plate was determined. The number falling on the platinum reflector was then easily calculated from its known distance and area. To find the whole number of reflected particles, it was assumed that they were distributed uniformly round a half sphere with the middle of the reflector as centre.

Three different determinations showed that of the incident α-particles about 1 in 8000 was reflected, under the described conditions.

A special experiment conducted at low pressure showed that in the case of grazing incidence the number of particles reflected at a very small angle to the reflector is largely in excess of the number calculated from the above ratio. This tangential scattering is of considerable importance in some experiments; for instance, if α-particles from a radio-active source are fired along a glass tube of appreciable length the conditions are very favourable for this effect. The number of scintillations counted on a screen sealed to the other end of the tube is made up not only of the particles striking the screen directly, but also of those which have been reflected from the glass walls of the tube.

The correction for the latter effect may be appreciable, and would be still greater in the case of a metal tube. In the counting experiments of Rutherford and Geiger this effect did not influence the final result, the arrangement being such that the reflected particles were prevented from entering the opening of the ionisation vessel by the narrow constriction of a stopcock.

It appears probable that the number of reflected particles depends also upon the velocity of the α-particles falling on the reflector. In our case

* Rutherford and Geiger, 'Roy. Soc. Proc.,' A, vol. 81, p. 162, 1908.

the particles from the radium C had to travel through a little over a centimetre of air before reaching the reflector. The reflected particles had still an appreciable velocity, since, by interposing an aluminium foil of thickness equivalent in stopping power to $\frac{1}{2}$ cm. of air, the number of scintillations counted was not changed. This might be expected from Experiment (II), which showed that the α-particles are reflected from a relatively thin surface layer of the reflector.

We are indebted to Prof. Rutherford for his kind interest and advice throughout this research.

LVII. *Scattering of α Particles by Gases.* *By* Professor
E. RUTHERFORD, *F.R.S., and* J. M. NUTTALL, *M.Sc.**

THE scattering of α particles by matter has been examined in detail by the scintillation method by Geiger† and by Geiger and Marsden‡. In the experiments of Geiger, the most probable angle through which an α particle was scattered was determined by the scintillation method for different thicknesses of a number of elements. It was found that the most probable angle of scattering for thicknesses of different elements, equivalent in stopping power of the α particle to one centimetre of air, was proportional to the atomic weight of the scattering element. A systematic investigation was later made by Geiger and Marsden of the "large angle scattering" by thin films of matter. The results were shown to be in complete accordance with the theory of "single" scattering advanced by Rutherford §. This theory supposes that the atom consists of a charged nucleus surrounded by a compensating distribution of electrons. The large angle scattering is due to the passage of the α particle through the intense electric field of the nucleus. It was deduced by Rutherford, and Geiger and Marsden, that the charge on the nucleus for atoms between carbon and gold was approximately proportional to the atomic weight, and was equal to $\frac{1}{2}Ae$, where A is the atomic weight in terms of that of hydrogen and e is the electronic charge. On this theory it is to be anticipated that hydrogen has a nucleus of one charge, helium of two, and carbon of about six.

As this deduction is of great importance in connexion with the constitution of the simpler atoms, experiments were undertaken to determine the scattering of α particles by the simple gases. The method employed by Geiger and Marsden for solids is not altogether suitable for gases; in addition, the large angle scattering to be expected for the light elements is exceedingly small, and would be difficult to measure with accuracy.

In some preliminary experiments, the α particles were made to pass between two parallel plates, placed a small distance apart, and the number of issuing particles were observed (1) in a vacuum and (2) when the space between the plates was filled with gas at a known pressure. The number of α particles was counted photographically, using a string electrometer. On account, however, of the probability

* Communicated by the Authors.
† H. Geiger, Proc. Roy. Soc. lxxxi. p. 174 (1908).
‡ H. Geiger and E. Marsden, Phil. Mag. xxv. p. 604 (1913).
§ E. Rutherford, Phil. Mag. xxi. p. 669 (1911).

variations, a very large number would have to be counted in order to obtain a reliable result. This would involve much time and labour, and it was consequently felt desirable to use a more indirect but rapid method.

The experimental arrangement finally adopted is shown in fig. 1. A narrow pencil of α particles was obtained by placing

Fig. 1.

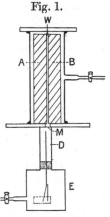

a thin platinum wire W (see fig. 1), coated with radium C, between two thick glass plates A and B, 14·5 cm. long and 2 cm. in width, and kept about 0·3 mm. apart by mica stops. After traversing the space between the glass plates, the beam passed through a mica window M, of stopping power equivalent to 1·9 cm. of air, and then into an ionization chamber D, consisting essentially of three parallel equidistant brass plates 5 cm. long and 3 cm. wide, 7 mm. apart. The outer plates were earthed and the central one insulated and connected to the gold-leaf system of an electroscope E. The latter was kept exhausted in order to diminish the ionization due to β and γ rays. The upper part of the apparatus, consisting of a cylindrical glass tube (with ground-glass ends) containing the plates A and B and the source of α rays W, could be completely exhausted and filled with any gas or vapour to any desired pressure, measured in the usual way by a mercury gauge. It was necessary to employ a strong source of α particles, and this was obtained by exposing about one centimetre length of thin platinum wire 0·2 mm. diameter to radium emanation for three hours as cathode in an electric field. A short time after removal from the emanation, radium C is the only α-ray product remaining on the wire, and since its curve of decay is accurately known, the amount of radium C present at any subsequent time can be readily calculated. Care was taken to remove any traces of emanation from the wire by washing it in absolute alcohol and heating it slightly.

The method of procedure in an experiment was as follows. An active wire was placed in position between the glass plates AB and the upper part of the apparatus was exhausted. The source W emitted a pencil of homogeneous α particles which passed through the mica window M, and the ionization they produced in chamber D was measured in the electroscope E. The whole issuing beam of α rays was completely absorbed in the chamber D, and the ionization due to β and γ rays was never more than 2 per cent. of the whole effect. If a gas is now introduced into the upper chamber, *i. e.* between the plates A and B, and the ionization current again measured, any decrease, when correction is made for decay of source, will be due either to partial absorption of α particles by the gas in the upper chamber or to the scattering of α particles against the faces of the plates resulting in a diminution in the number entering the ionization chamber. The decrease of ionization due to loss of range by absorption was measured in a separate experiment. For this purpose the plates AB forming the long narrow slit were removed, and the ionization current measured for various pressures of gas in the upper cylinder, the source W

Fig. 2.

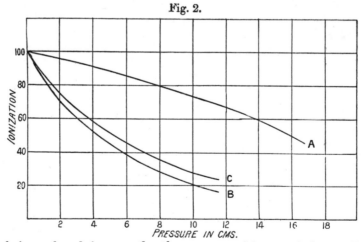

being placed in exactly the same position as before. In this way a curve can be obtained showing the relation between the pressure of the gas in the upper cylinder and the ionization produced by the source in the chamber D. A typical curve is shown in the curve A of fig. 2 *.

* Compare H. L. Bronson, Phil. Mag. xi. p. 806 (1906).

In the same figure, curve B gives the result of a typical experiment showing the effect of both scattering and absorption together. From the two curves A and B, a curve can be obtained which gives the effect of scattering alone. To obtain this, the ratios of the ordinates of the curves A and B at each pressure must be plotted. It is obvious that this ratio gives the fraction of α particles scattered by the gas at each particular pressure, and is independent of any change of ionization due to loss of range. Curve C obtained in this way indicates the amount of unscattered radiation passing between the plates at various pressures. It is seen that, over a certain range of the α particle at least, the amount of unscattered radiation passing between the plates varies nearly exponentially with the pressure of gas, *i. e.* if N_0 is the number of α particles at zero pressure and N_p the number at pressure p cm., then $N_p/N_0 = e^{-\lambda p}$, where λ may be called the "scattering coefficient" for the particular gas under the given conditions. It should be noted that this formula does not hold accurately when the pressure of the gas becomes so large that the velocity of the α particle is much reduced. For pressures of the gas, whereby the loss of range of the α particle is equivalent to more than 2 cm. of air at atmospheric pressure, the scattering will increase more rapidly. Indications of this were obtained in some of the experiments. Table I. gives the results of a typical experiment, air being used as the scattering gas.

TABLE I.

Pressure of Gas p.	Scattering and absorption.	Absorption alone.	Intensity N due to scattering alone.	$\dfrac{\log N_0/N_p}{p}$.
0 cm.	100	100	100	
·92	84·2	98·2	86·8	·66
1·9	72·6	96·5	75·2	·65
3·55	58·0	93·0	62·5	·58
5·10	45·9	88·6	51·9	·56
7·15	33·5	82·5	40·6	·55
9·00	24·6	76·5	32·0	·55

The numbers in the last column show that the radiation is scattered approximately according to an exponential law over a considerable range of pressure.

Variation of scattering with the distance between the plates.

A few experiments were made to determine approximately the variation of scattering with the distance between the plates. The latter distance was varied from ·173 mm. to ·89 mm.; the corresponding least angles of scattering to deflect the α particles against the faces of the plates varying from 0°·069 to 0°·356.

The collected results are shown in Table II. The relative scattering coefficients are compared by observing from the curves the pressure of gas required to scatter 50 per cent. of the initial number of α particles.

TABLE II.

Distance d apart of plates.	Relative scattering coefficient λ.	$\lambda \cdot d^{5/4}$.
·172 mm.	·562	·618
·325	·256	·627
·586	·126	·643
·890	·0712	·615

Within the limits employed, the scattering appears to vary rather more rapidly than the inverse of the linear distance d between the plates and to be nearly proportional to $d^{-5/4}$.

It will be shown later that the scattering coefficient increases rapidly with decrease of velocity of the α particle. A correction has consequently to be applied to reduce the amount of scattering to a standard velocity. This correction has been made in the results of Table II.

Variation of scattering with atomic weight.

The gases whose scattering coefficients were compared were as follows:—air, hydrogen, helium, methane, carbon dioxide, and sulphuretted hydrogen. A few experiments were made on the scattering produced by the heavy vapours, methyl iodide and ethyl bromide, but they are not included in this paper. In all cases two sets of experiments were performed: (1) experiments on the scattering and absorption combined, and (2) experiments on the absorption alone. The latter were in agreement with the stopping powers of the gases as calculated by Bragg's* square-root law.

The distance between the plates was kept constant during

* W. H. Bragg, Phil. Mag. x. p. 318 (1905).

the course of these experiments, and the scattering of each gas was compared with air as a standard. The scattering curve for air, which was repeated before and after each experiment, was found to be unchanged throughout the investigation. The logarithmic curves for the different gases are shown in fig. 3. The pressures of gas are plotted as

Fig. 3.

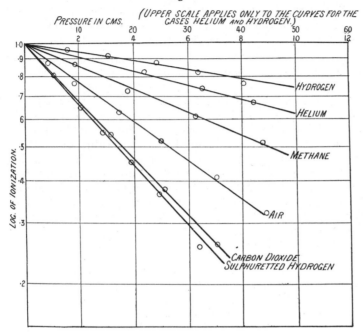

abscissæ, and the logarithms of the intensity of the unscattered radiation passing between the plates as ordinates.

A few details of the method of preparation and purification of the gases are given.

Hydrogen. This was prepared electrolytically and dried carefully. It contained about 1 per cent. of impurity, chiefly oxygen. A correction was made for this in the curve of fig. 3, which is the mean of several experiments.

Helium. The helium was purified by passing over charcoal immersed in liquid air. This removed all traces of air and other impurities, except possibly the last traces of hydrogen.

Methane. This was prepared by acting on aluminium carbide with water and passing through cuprous sulphate to remove the acetylene. The resulting impure methane was condensed by liquid air, and pure methane obtained by fractional distillation.

Carbon dioxide was obtained from a cylinder of compressed gas, which on analysis was found to be of 99·7 per cent. purity.

Sulphuretted hydrogen was prepared by action of sulphuric acid on calcium sulphide. It was analysed and found to be of 99·8 per cent. purity.

From the results obtained in these experiments, the relative atomic coefficients of scattering were deduced for hydrogen, helium, carbon, air, oxygen, and sulphur. In the case of complex molecules, it was assumed that the scattering coefficient of the molecule was the sum of the values for each of its individual components. For example, the coefficient for carbon was deduced from the value of methane (CH_4) by subtracting from the observed value the scattering coefficient due to four atoms of hydrogen. In a similar way, the value for oxygen was deduced from CO_2 and sulphur from H_2S. A correction was required in each case to allow for the variation of scattering with velocity of the α particle. The reduction in velocity of the α particle in passing through a sufficient pressure of gas to scatter half the α particles was deduced from the loss of range of the α particle in the gas, using the relation between velocity and range found by Geiger. In making this correction it was assumed, as will

TABLE III.

Gas.	Corrected pressure to scatter half of incident radiation.	Relative scattering coefficient.	Atomic weight.	Remarks.
Air	5·32 cm.	1·00	14·4	Diatomic.
Carbon (from CH_4).	13·32 ,,	·40	12·0	Monatomic.
Carbon dioxide......	3·64 ,,			
Oxygen	5·00 ,,	1·064	15·99	Diatomic.
Sulphur	3·36 ,,	1·61	32·0	Monatomic.
Hydrogen*............	46·3 ,,	·0353	1·0	Diatomic.
Helium*	26·2 ,,	·064	3·99	Monatomic.

* In the cases of hydrogen and helium the pressures given are those required to cut down the incident radiation to 80 per cent. of its initial value, and they are compared with the pressure of air required to scatter to the same extent, viz. 1·68 cm. of mercury.

be seen later, that the scattering coefficient varied inversely
as the fourth power of the velocity. In practice, the value
of the pressure was corrected so as to give the scattering
observed, assuming that the velocity was equal throughout
to the initial value for the α particle.

Variation of scattering with velocity.

Geiger found that the most probable angle of scattering of
α particles by solid matter increased rapidly with decrease
of velocity of the α particle. This also holds for light gases.
The initial velocity of the α particle was diminished by
placing a sheet of aluminium foil of known stopping power
under the active wire. The results are shown in fig. 4,

Fig. 4.

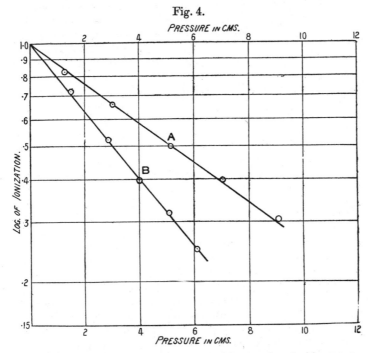

where the logarithm of the corrected ionization in the testing
vessel is plotted as ordinates and pressures as abscissæ. In
curve A, the initial velocity was the maximum velocity of
α particles from radium C, whilst in curve B the initial
velocity was ·893 of the maximum velocity. The scattering
coefficients observed in the two cases were in the ratio
1 : 1·66. The scattering thus varied approximately as the

Phil. Mag. S. 6. Vol. 26. No. 154. Oct. 1913. 3 B

inverse fourth power of the velocity. This is the law of scattering with velocity found by Geiger and Marsden in their experiments on " single " scattering.

Consideration of the Results.

In drawing deductions from these experiments, it is of importance to decide whether the scattering coefficient observed is to be ascribed to " single " or " compound " scattering. If the reduction in the number of α particles in passing between the glass plates is due mainly to " single " scattering, we should expect the scattering to vary directly as the pressure of the gas and inversely as the fourth power of the velocity—results observed experimentally. On the other hand, if the reduction in number is due mainly to " compound " scattering, we should expect that the scattering should be proportional to the square root of the pressure, and to vary as the inverse square of the velocity. It is thus clear from the experiments that the scattering coefficient observed is a consequence mainly of " single " scattering. This conclusion is still further strengthened by the rapid variation of the scattering with atomic weight between carbon and sulphur. No doubt " compound " scattering produces some effect, but the main part of the scattering is to be ascribed to the scattering of individual atoms resulting from the passage of the α particle through the intense field close to the electrons and the nucleus. If we consider the atom to be composed of a nucleus with a charge ne and a compensating distribution of n electrons, the scattering due to the n electrons is proportional to n, and the scattering due to the nucleus is proportional to n^2. Mr. C. Darwin kindly examined this question mathematically for us, and concluded that if the electrons and the nucleus were a sufficient distance apart so as not to interfere seriously with the electric fields close to them, the scattering for simple atoms should be proportional to $n + n^2$ or $n(n+1)$, where ne is the charge on the atomic nucleus. For deflexions through a small angle, such as are involved in the experimental arrangement employed in this paper, we should expect the scattering in the heavy atoms to be proportional to $n + kn^2$, where k is less than unity. This is borne out by the fact that under the experimental conditions the scattering due to heavy atoms like bromine and iodine was found to be less than the theoretical values when k is taken as unity. Assuming the simple formula found by Darwin as applicable to light atoms, the scattering coefficient λ is proportional to $n(n+1)$ or $\lambda = cn(n+1)$, where c is a constant.

It should be noted that Geiger and Marsden found that the "single" scattering per atom was proportional to the square of the atomic weight. This undoubtedly holds in the case of heavy elements for large angles of scattering, where the α particle passes close to the nucleus. It is a different matter, however, when the scattering angle is only about 1/10 of a degree, as in the present experiment. It is to be anticipated that under such conditions this simple law would be widely departed from, especially in the case of heavy atoms for which the number of electrons is large.

The following table gives the observed and calculated scattering coefficient for an *atom* of each of the elements examined. The value of n, the number of electronic charges assumed for the nucleus, is given in the second column. For a comparison of the calculated with the experimental values, carbon is assumed in both to have a scattering coefficient of ·40 on the arbitrary scale. The scattering coefficient for nitrogen is deduced on the assumption that air is composed of 80 per cent. of N with 20 per cent of O.

Gas.	Assumed value of n.	Relative scattering per atom.	
		Calculated values.	Experimental values.
H atom ...	1	·0190	·0176
He ,, ...	2	·057	·064
C ,, ...	6	·40	·40
N ,, ...	7	·53	·48
O ,, ...	8	·69	·53
S ,, ...	16	2·58	1·61

Considering the difficulty of determining with accuracy the scattering by the light gases, the agreement between the simple theory and experiment is as close as could be expected for hydrogen, helium, and carbon. The probable explanation of the divergence between theory and experiment for the heavier atoms, like sulphur, has already been outlined. From the experiments of Geiger and Marsden (*loc. cit.*) on the large angle scattering of α particles by carbon, it is clear that the carbon atom behaves as if the nucleus carries a charge of about six units. Assuming this value of n for carbon, the results indicate that the hydrogen nucleus has a charge of *one* fundamental unit and the helium nucleus of *two* units. This value for helium is to be anticipated from

3 B 2

the observed fact that the α particle in its flight carries two unit positive charges.

The observations on the scattering of α particles by matter in general afford strong experimental evidence for the theory that the atom consists of a positively charged nucleus of minute dimensions surrounded by a compensating distribution of negative electrons. The charge on the nucleus for heavy atoms is approximately $\frac{1}{2}Ae$, where A is the atomic weight and e the electronic charge. The experiments in this paper on the scattering of simple gases indicate that the hydrogen atom has the simplest possible structure of a nucleus with one unit charge, and helium comes next with a nucleus of two unit charges. This simple structure for hydrogen and helium atoms has been assumed by Bohr* in a recent interesting paper on the constitution of atoms, and has been shown by him to yield very promising results.

We desire to express our thanks to Dr. Pring for his assistance in preparing and purifying the gases employed.

University of Manchester,
    July 1913.

LXI. *The Laws of Deflexion of α Particles through Large Angles*.   By* Dr. H. Geiger *and* E. Marsden †.

IN a former paper ‡ one of us has shown that in the passage of α particles through matter the deflexions are, on the average, small and of the order of a few degrees only.   In the experiments a narrow pencil of α particles fell on a zinc-sulphide screen in vacuum, and the distribution of the scintillations on the screen was observed when different metal foils were placed in the path of the α particles.   From the distribution obtained, the most probable angle of scattering could be deduced, and it was shown that the results could be explained on the assumption that the deflexion of a single α particle is the resultant of a large number of very small deflexions caused by the passage of the α particle through the successive individual atoms of the scattering substance.

* Communicated to *k. d.-k. Akad. d. Wiss. Wien.*
† Communicated by Prof. E. Rutherford, F.R.S.
‡ H. Geiger, Roy. Soc. Proc. vol. lxxxiii. p. 492 (1910); vol. lxxxvi. p. 235 (1912).

In an earlier paper [*], however, we pointed out that α particles are sometimes turned through very large angles. This was made evident by the fact that when α particles fall on a metal plate, a small fraction of them, about 1/8000 in the case of platinum, appears to be diffusely reflected. This amount of reflexion, although small, is, however, too large to be explained on the above simple theory of scattering. It is easy to calculate from the experimental data that the probability of a deflexion through an angle of 90° is vanishingly small, and of a different order to the value found experimentally.

Professor Rutherford [†] has recently developed a theory to account for the scattering of α particles through these large angles, the assumption being that the deflexions are the result of an intimate encounter of an α particle with a single atom of the matter traversed. In this theory an atom is supposed to consist of a strong positive or negative central charge concentrated within a sphere of less than about 3×10^{-12} cm. radius, and surrounded by electricity of the opposite sign distributed throughout the remainder of the atom of about 10^{-8} cm. radius. In considering the deflexion of an α particle directed against such an atom, the main deflexion-effect can be supposed to be due to the central concentrated charge which will cause the α particle to describe an hyperbola with the centre of the atom as one focus.

The angle between the directions of the α particle before and after deflexion will depend on the perpendicular distance of the initial trajectory from the centre of the atom. The fraction of the α particles whose paths are sufficiently near to the centre of the atom will, however, be small, so that the probability of an α particle suffering a large deflexion of this nature will be correspondingly small. Thus, assuming a narrow pencil of α particles directed against a thin sheet of matter containing atoms distributed at random throughout its volume, if the scattered particles are counted by the scintillations they produce on a zinc-sulphide screen distance r from the point of incidence of the pencil in a direction making an angle ϕ with it, the number of α particles falling on unit area of the screen per second is deduced to be equal to

$$\frac{Qntb^2 \operatorname{cosec}^4 \phi/2}{16r^2},$$

where Q is the number of α particles per second in the

[*] H. Geiger and E. Marsden, Roy. Soc. Proc. vol. lxxxii. p. 495 (1909).

[†] E. Rutherford, Phil. Mag. vol. xxi. p. 669 (1911).

original pencil, n the number of atoms in unit volume of the material, and t the thickness of the foil. The quantity

$$b = \frac{2NeE}{mu^2},$$

where Ne is the central charge of the atom, and m, E, and u are the respective mass, charge, and velocity of the α particle.

The number of deflected α particles is thus proportional to (1) $\operatorname{cosec}^4 \phi/2$, (2) thickness of scattering material t if the thickness is small, (3) the square of the central charge Ne of the atoms of the particular matter employed to scatter the particles, (4) the inverse fourth power of the velocity u of the incident α particles.

At the suggestion of Prof. Rutherford, we have carried out experiments to test the main conclusions of the above theory. The following points were investigated :—

(1) Variation with angle.
(2) Variation with thickness of scattering material.
(3) Variation with atomic weight of scattering material.
(4) Variation with velocity of incident α particles.
(5) The fraction of particles scattered through a definite angle.

The main difficulty of the experiments has arisen from the necessity of using a very intense and narrow source of α particles owing to the smallness of the scattering effect. All the measurements have been carried out by observing the scintillations due to the scattered α particles on a zinc-sulphide screen, and during the course of the experiments over 100,000 scintillations have been counted. It may be mentioned in anticipation that all the results of our investigation are in good agreement with the theoretical deductions of Prof. Rutherford, and afford strong evidence of the correctness of the underlying assumption that an atom contains a strong charge at the centre of dimensions, small compared with the diameter of the atom.

(1) *Variation of Scattering with Angle.*

We have already pointed out that to obtain measurable effects an intense pencil of α particles is required. It is further necessary that the path of the α particles should be in an evacuated chamber to avoid complications due to the absorption and scattering of the air. The apparatus used is shown in fig. 1, and mainly consisted of a strong cylindrical metal box B, which contained the source of α particles R.

the scattering foil F, and a microscope M to which the zinc-sulphide screen S was rigidly attached. The box was fastened down to a graduated circular platform A, which could be rotated by means of a conical airtight joint C. By rotating the platform the box and microscope moved with it, whilst the scattering foil and radiating source remained in position, being attached to the tube T, which was fastened to the standard L. The box B was closed by the ground-glass plate P, and could be exhausted through the tube T.

Fig. 1.

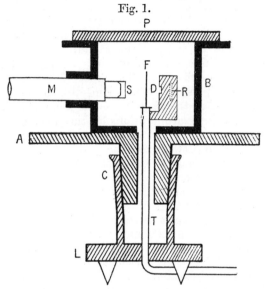

The source of α particles employed was similar to that used originally by Rutherford and Royds * in their experiments on the nature of the α particle. It consisted of a small thin-walled glass tube about 1 mm. in diameter, containing a large quantity of well purified radium emanation. The α particles emitted by the emanation and its active deposit could pass through the glass walls without much reduction of range. For these experiments the unhomogeneity of the source, due to the different α particles from the emanation, Ra A and Ra C, does not interfere with the application of the law of scattering with angle as deduced from the theory, as each group of α particles is scattered according to the same law.

By means of a diaphragm placed at D, a pencil of α particles was directed normally on to the scattering foil F. By

* E. Rutherford and T. Royds, Phil. Mag. vol. xvii. p. 281 (1909).

rotating the microscope the α particles scattered in different directions could be observed on the screen S. Although over 100 millicuries of radium emanation were available for the experiments, the smallness of the effect for the larger angles of deflexion necessitated short distances of screen and source from the scattering foil. In some experiments the distance between the source and scattering foil was 2·5 cm., and the screen moved in a circle of 1·6 cm. radius, while in other experiments these distances were increased. Observations were taken in various experiments for angles of deflexion from 5° to 150°. When measuring the scattering through large angles the zinc-sulphide screen had to be turned very near to the source, and the β and γ rays produced a considerable luminescence on it, thus making countings of the scintillations difficult. The effect of the β rays was reduced as far as possible by enclosing the source in a lead box shown shaded in the diagram. The amount of lead was, however, limited by considerations of the space taken up by it, and consequently observations could not be made for angles of deflexion between 150° and 180°.

In the investigation of the scattering through relatively small angles the distances of source and screen from the scattering foil were increased considerably in order to obtain beams of smaller solid angle.

The number of particles scattered through different angles was found to decrease extremely rapidly with increase of angle, and as it is not possible to count with certainty more than 90 scintillations per minute or less than about 5 per minute, measurements could only be made over a relatively small range of angles at the same time. The number of α particles scattered through large angles was first measured, and as the emanation decayed it was possible to take measurements for smaller and smaller angles, and from the known decay of the emanation measurements taken at different times could be corrected for the decrease of activity.

Even when no scattering foil was used a few scintillations were always observed on the screen. They were obviously due to scattered radiation from the walls of the vessel and from the edge of the diaphragm limiting the beam. The effect was reduced as far as possible by lining the box with paper and by using a substance of low atomic weight, viz. aluminium, for the diaphragm. The number of stray α particles was determined for different positions of the microscope by removing the scattering foil so that the necessary corrections could be applied with certainty.

In order to make the best use of the emanation available,

measurements were made simultaneously with different foils. These foils were attached to frames which fitted into a slot in the tube T in such a way that they could be exchanged and accurately replaced in position. Table I. gives an example of a particular set of countings, when a silver foil was used to scatter the α particles.

TABLE I.—Variation of Scattering with Angle. (Example of a set of measurements.) Silver Foil. Time elapsed since filling of emanation tube, 51 hours. Correction for decay, 0·683.

Angle ϕ.	Scintillations per minute.				$\dfrac{1}{\sin^4 \phi/2}$	$N \times \sin^4 \phi/2$.
	Without foil.	With foil.	Corrected for effect without foil.	Corrected for decay, N.		
150°...	0·2	4·95	4·75	6·95	1·15	6·0
135 ..	2·6	8·3	5·7	8·35	1·38	6·1
120...	3·8	10·3	6·5	9·5	1·79	5·3
105...	0·6	10·6	10·0	14·6	2·53	5·8
75...	0·0	28·6	28·6	41·9	7·25	5·8
60...	0·3	69·2	68·9	101	16·0	6·3

In this set about 2500 scintillations were counted. After a few days had elapsed the measurements for the smaller angles were repeated and the range of angles extended. Proceeding in this way the whole range of angles was investigated in the course of a few weeks. When measuring relatively large angles of deflexion a wide beam of about 15° radius had to be used in order to obtain a suitable number of scintillations, but for the smaller angles the aperture of the diaphragm confining the beam was reduced considerably, so that the angle at which the scintillations were counted was always large compared with the angular radius of the beam. When changing over from one diaphragm to another comparative measurements for different angles were made so as to obtain an accurate value of the reduction constant.

Table II. gives the collected results for two series of experiments with foils of silver and gold. The thicknesses of the foils were in the first series equivalent to 0·45 and 0·3 cm. air, and in the second series 0·45 and 0·1 cm. air for silver and gold respectively. Col. I. gives the values of the

Phil. Mag. S. 6. Vol. 25. No. 148. *April* 1913.   2 T

TABLE II.

Variation of Scattering with Angle.   (Collected results.)

I. Angle of deflexion, ϕ.	II. $\dfrac{1}{\sin^4 \phi/2}$	III. SILVER. Number of scintillations, N.	IV. $\dfrac{N}{\sin^4 \phi/2}$	V. GOLD. Number of scintillations, N.	VI. $\dfrac{N}{\sin^4 \phi/2}$
150	1·15	22·2	19·3	33·1	28·8
135	1·38	27·4	19·8	43·0	31·2
120	1·79	33·0	18·4	51·9	29·0
105	2·53	47·3	18·7	69·5	27·5
75	7·25	136	18·8	211	29·1
60	16·0	320	20·0	477	29·8
45	46·6	989	21·2	1435	30·8
37·5	93·7	1760	18·8	3300	35·3
30	223	5260	23·6	7800	35·0
22·5	690	20300	29·4	27300	39·6
15	3445	105400	30·6	132000	38·4
30	223	5·3	0·024	3·1	0·014
22·5	690	16·6	0·024	8·4	0·012
15	3445	93·0	0·027	48·2	0·014
10	17330	508	0·029	200	0·0115
7·5	54650	1710	0·031	607	0·011
5	276300	...	...	3320	0·012

angles ϕ between the direction of the beam and the direction in which the scattered α particles were counted. Col. II. gives the values of $\dfrac{1}{\sin^4 \phi/2}$. In Cols. III. and V. the numbers of scintillations are entered which were observed for the silver and gold respectively. Corrections are made for the decay of the emanation, for the natural effect, and for change of diaphragm. For the smaller angles corrections have been applied (in no case exceeding 20 per cent.) owing to the fact that the beam of α particles was of finite dimensions and not negligible compared with the angle of deflexion. These corrections were calculated from geometrical considerations. In Cols. IV. and VI. the ratios of the numbers of scintillations to $\dfrac{1}{\sin^4 \phi/2}$ are entered. It will be seen that in both sets the values are approximately constant. The deviations are somewhat systematic, the ratio increasing with decreasing angle. However, any slight asymmetry in the apparatus and other causes would affect the results in a systematic way so that, fitting on the two sets of observations and considering the enormous variation in the numbers of scattered particles, from 1 to 250,000, the deviations from constancy of the ratio are probably well within the experimental error. The experiments, therefore, prove that the number of α particles scattered in a definite direction varies as cosec⁴ φ/2.

Variation with Thickness of Material.

In investigating the variation of scattering with thickness of material, it seemed necessary to use a homogeneous source of α particles, for according to the theory the effect of the change of velocity with increasing thickness will be very appreciable for α particles of low velocity. In the experiments on " compound scattering " by one of us, a source was used consisting of Ra C deposited from radium emanation *in situ* in a small conical tube fitted with a mica window, the emanation being withdrawn when measurements were taken by expanding into a large volume connected to it. In our first experiments we used such a source, but the observations eventually showed it to be unsuitable. After expansion some emanation remains clinging to the walls of the glass tube. This emanation and the Ra A associated with it gives α particles of considerably lower velocity than the α particles of Ra C, and although the number of α particles so contributed was of the order of only a few per cent. of the number from the Ra C, yet owing to the fact that the amount of scattering increases very rapidly with decreasing velocity, the disturbances caused by the slower α particles were so large as to render the source unsuitable for the present work.

Fig. 2.

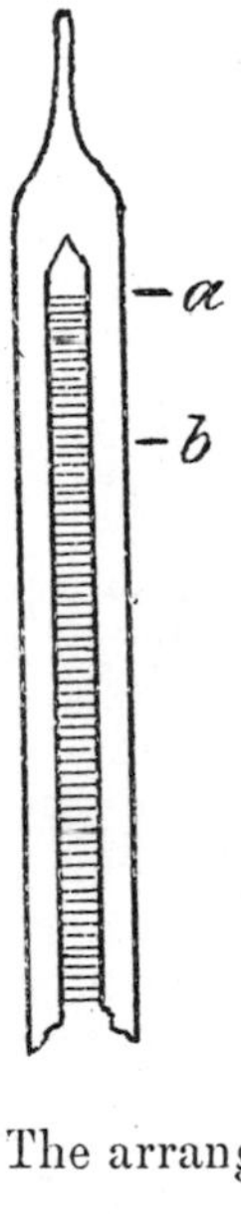

The source finally adopted was prepared as shown in fig. 2. About 80 millicuries of radium emanation were very highly purified and pressed into the conical end of the glass tube T of about 1 mm. internal diameter. After the emanation had remained in position for a sufficient time to attain equilibrium with Ra C, it was expanded into a bulb below, and a small part of the capillary tube was drawn off at *b*. About 1 mm. of the end of the tube which was coated with the Ra C was then cut off (at *a*) and freed from occluded emanation by washing with alcohol and by heating. The resulting source of Ra C was used in the experiments, and with due care its decay was found to be in agreement with theory, at least for the first 80 minutes.

The arrangement used for the comparison of the scattering

2 T 2

of different thicknesses of metal foils is shown diagrammatically in fig. 3. It consists essentially of a source of α radiation R, a diaphragm D, a scattering foil F, and a zinc-sulphide screen Z on which the scattered α particles were observed. The main part of the apparatus was enclosed in a cylindrical brass ring A, the ends of which were planed so that they could be closed airtight by the two glass plates B and C. The depth of the ring was 3·5 cm., and its internal and external diameters 5·5 and 7·5 cm. respectively. Two holes were drilled through the glass plate B, one in the centre and the other 1·65 cm. excentric. The source of radiation R was placed directly against a sheet of mica which was waxed over and closed the opening E. By placing the source outside the apparatus, any small amount of emanation associated with it was prevented from entering the chamber and disturbing the measurements.

Fig. 3.

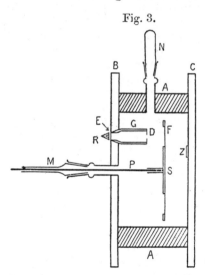

By means of the diaphragm D a narrow pencil of α particles could be directed on to the scattering foil. The different foils were attached to the disk S and covered five of six holes drilled through it at equal distances from its centre. The uncovered opening was used to determine the natural effect. The disk could be fitted on to the rod P, which was fastened to the ground-glass joint M so that it could be rotated and the different foils brought in front of the diaphragm. The scattered α particles were observed by means of a microscope on the zinc-sulphide screen Z fixed inside the glass plate.

In making the observations the disk carrying the foils was placed in position about 1·2 cm. from the glass plate C. The apparatus was then completely exhausted through a tube not shown in the diagram, charcoal cooled by liquid air being used for the final exhaustion.   After the source of radiation had been placed in position, the microscope was adjusted at that part of the zinc-sulphide screen where the scintillations appeared at a rate convenient for counting. With a source of 30 millicuries of Ra C this was usually the case for an angle of deflexion of from 20° to 30°.   The area of the screen visible through the microscope was about 1 sq. mm., whilst the main beam of α particles covered an area of about 3 sq. mm.

As soon as the Ra A in the source had decayed completely (*i. e.* after 20 minutes) countings were commenced. Measurements were first taken with the layers of foils of smaller thickness, and as the source decayed they were extended to the thicker foils.   From the known decay of the active deposit of radium the measurements could all be corrected for the variation in activity of the source, the results being verified by making observations on the same foils at different times.   An experiment generally extended for about 80 minutes.   After that time the decay corrections for the source were not always reliable owing to small quantities of radium emanation associated with it, as has been mentioned above.   Owing to the relatively short time available in each experiment for the completion of the measurements, only about 100 to 200 scintillations could be counted with each foil.

As in the experiments on the variation of scattering with angle, some scintillations appeared on the zinc-sulphide screen even when no scattering foil was interposed.   It was found that these scintillations were due to α particles which had been scattered from the edges of the diaphragm limiting the beam.   Experiments were made with paper diaphragms and with aluminium diaphragms of only $\frac{1}{10}$ mm. thickness, whilst a diaphragm D′ (fig. 4) was also introduced to prevent scattering from the inside of the glass tube G carrying the main diaphragm D.   Even with these precautions the effect was still so large that accurate experiments with foils of low atomic weight would have been impossible.   The difficulty was, however, successfully overcome by intercepting the stray α particles by a screen K, which could be turned by means of a ground-glass joint (N in fig. 3) about a vertical axis passing through A so as to be just outside the main pencil.   The adjustment was made by observation of the scintillations produced by the main beam on the zinc-sulphide screen Z, which was temporarily placed at Z'. The magnitude of the effect may be judged from the following figures obtained in a particular experiment with an aluminium diaphragm :—The number of scintillations without both the screen K and the scattering foil F was 60 per minute, whilst by bringing the screen K into position the number was reduced to 0·5 per minute. With the screen K in position and an aluminium foil equivalent to 0·5 cm. air as scattering foil, the number of scintillations was 14 per minute, or about one quarter the effect without screen or scattering foil.

Fig. 4.

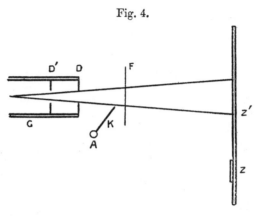

In the following table the results of an experiment with gold foils are tabulated. Column I. gives the number of foils and column II. the thicknesses expressed as the stopping power of α particles in centimetres of air as determined by the scintillation method. The figures given in column III. represent the number of scintillations observed on the zinc-sulphide screen. These figures are corrected for the variation of activity with time of the source. A slight correction has been made due to the increase of scattering on account of the decrease of velocity of the α particles in passing through the foils. The magnitude of this correction could be calculated from the results given in the last section of the present paper, and amounted to 9 per cent. in this experiment for the thickest foil used. The last column of the table gives the ratio of the corrected number of scintillations to the thickness. The values are constant within the limits of the experimental error. The variations exhibited by the figures are well within the probability errors, owing to the relatively small number of scintillations which could be counted in the time available.

TABLE III.

Gold.—Variation of Scattering with Thickness.

I.	II.	III.	IV.
Number of Foils.	Air equivalent. T in cm.	Number N of scintillations per minute.	Ratio $\frac{N}{T}$.
1	0·11	21·9	200
2	0·22	38·4	175
5	0·51	84·3	165
8	0·81	121·5	150
9	0·90	145	160

Similar experiments were carrried out with foils of tin, silver, copper, and aluminium. In each set about 1000 scintillations were counted. The results are plotted in fig. 5, where the abscissæ represent the thickness of the scattering foil expressed in centimetres of air equivalent and the ordinates the number of scattered particles. Similar corrections to the above have been introduced in each case.

Fig. 5.

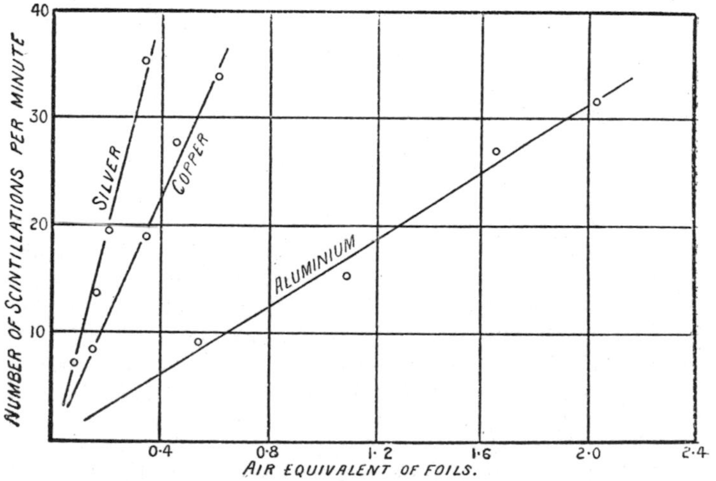

For all the metals examined the points lie on straight lines which pass through the origin. The experiments therefore prove that for small thicknesses of matter the scattering is proportional to the thickness. If there is any appreciable diminution in velocity of the α particles in passing through the foils, the number of scattered particles increases somewhat more rapidly than the thickness.

Variation with Atomic Weight.

Assuming that the magnitude of the central charge of the atom is proportional to the atomic weight A, Professor Rutherford has shown that the number of α particles scattered by different foils containing the same number of atoms should be proportional to A^2. With the thin foils which had to be used experimentally, it was found impracticable to calculate the number of atoms per unit area by weighing the foils. It proved much more reliable to deduce the required number of atoms from the air equivalent as found by the reduction of the range of α particles by the scintillation method. This method had the advantage that the thickness was determined at the exact part of the foil which served to scatter the α particles, thus eliminating any errors due to variations in the thickness of the foils. Bragg and others have given numbers connecting the thicknesses of foils of various materials and their stopping power, and it has been shown that for different foils of the same air equivalent the numbers of atoms per unit area are inversely proportional to the square roots of the atomic weights. Consequently if the scattering per atom of atomic weight A is proportional to A^2, the scattering per centimetre air equivalent will be proportional to $A^2 \times A^{-\frac{1}{2}}$, *i. e.* to $A^{3/2}$.

In the experimental investigation the same apparatus was used as in the previous experiments on the variation of scattering with thickness of material. The openings in the disk S were covered with thin foils of different materials, and their thicknesses chosen in such a way that they gave approximately the same effect of scattering. A number of different sets of experiments were made, the foils being varied in each experiment. The results in a particular experiment are given in Table IV. Columns I. and II. give the foils used and their respective atomic weights. In column III. the air equivalents of the foils are entered. Column IV. gives the number of scintillations observed after correction for the variation in activity of the source and the loss of velocity of the α particles in the foil. Column V. gives the number of scintillations per unit air equivalent of material. In column VI. the values of $A^{3/2}$ are given, and in column VII. the ratios of the numbers of scintillations to $A^{3/2}$ are calculated. The figures are constant within the experimental error.

TABLE IV.

Variation of Scattering with Atomic Weight. (Example of a set of measurements.)

I. Substance.	II. Atomic weight. A.	III. Air equivalent in cm.	IV. Number of scintillations per minute corrected for decay.	V. Number N of scintillations per cm. air equivalent.	VI $A^{3/2}$.	VII. $N \times A^{2/3}$.
Gold	197	·229	133	581	2770	0·21
Tin	119	·441	119	270	1300	0·21
Silver	107·9	·262	51·7	198	1120	0·18
Copper	63·6	·616	71	115	507	0·23
Aluminium..	27·1	2·05	71	34·6	141	0·24

The combined results of four experiments are given in Table V. In the last column are given the ratios of the numbers of scintillations per centimetre equivalent to $A^{3/2}$. This ratio should be constant according to theory. The experimental values show a slight increase with decreasing atomic weight.

TABLE V.

Variation of Scattering with Atomic Weight. (Collected results using Ra C.)

Substance.	Total number of scintillations counted for each material.	$A^{3/2}$.	Ratio of scintillations per cm. air equivalent to $A^{3/2}$ *.
Gold	850	2770	95
Platinum	200	2730	99
Tin	700	1300	96
Silver	800	1120	98
Copper	600	507	104
Aluminium	700	144	110

* *Note* 1.—Since these experiments were carried out, Richardson and one of us (Phil. Mag. vol. xxv. p. 184 (1913)) have determined the masses per unit area per cm. air equivalent for different metals, using the scintillation method. Introducing the results, and calculating the values of the ratio of the scattering per atom divided by A^2, the following are obtained:—Au 3·4, Pt 3·2, Sn 3·3, Ag 3·6, Cu 3·7, Al 3·6. These numbers show better agreement than those in the last column above, which are calculated on the assumption of Bragg's law.

On account of the importance of these experiments further measurements were made under somewhat different conditions.   The main difficulty in the previous experiments arose from the fact, that owing to the rapid decay of the source it was impossible to count in each case a sufficient number of scintillations to obtain a true average value.   In the following set of measurements radium emanation in equilibrium with its active deposit was used as source of radiation.   The source consisted of a conical glass tube (fig. 6) of about 1½ mm. internal diameter at its widest part, the height of the cone being about 2·5 mm.

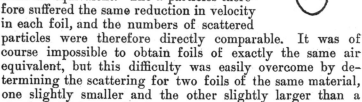

Fig. 6.

The end of the tube was closed airtight by a sheet of mica of 0·62 cm. air equivalent. This tube was filled with about 30 milli-curies of highly purified emanation and placed at R (fig. 3, p. 612) directly against the mica window E, the air equivalent of which was also 0·62 cm.

The difficulty introduced by the employ-ment of α particles of different velocities (emanation, Ra A, and Ra C) was elimi-nated by using foils of approximately the same air equivalent.   The α particles there-fore suffered the same reduction in velocity in each foil, and the numbers of scattered particles were therefore directly comparable.   It was of course impossible to obtain foils of exactly the same air equivalent, but this difficulty was easily overcome by de-termining the scattering for two foils of the same material, one slightly smaller and the other slightly larger than a standard thickness of 0·6 cm. air equivalent.

Owing to the large variation with atomic weight of the amount of scattering, the foils could not be all directly com-pared with each other at the same angle.   They were there-fore compared in sets, the angle being chosen smaller for the sets of lower atomic weight.   Column VI. in the following table gives the mean results of the ratio of the number of scattered particles to $A^{3/2}$.

The scattering of carbon was obtained by using thin sheets of paraffin wax which contained about 85·2 per cent. carbon and 14·8 per cent. hydrogen.   The air equivalent of the carbon was calculated from Bragg's law to be about 78 per cent. of the whole stopping power, and on account of the low atomic weight of hydrogen all the scattering effect was assumed due to the carbon.   The measurements of the scattering were made by comparison with that due to aluminium foils of the same air equivalent.

Table VI.

Variation of Scattering with Atomic Weight. (Collected results using Radium emanation.)

I. Substance.	II. Air equivalents of foils used.	III. Total number of scintillations counted for each substance.	IV. Number N of scintillations at same angle and for same air equivalent.	V. $A^{3/2}$.	VI. $N \times A^{2/3}$
Gold	·52, ·68	1200	2400	2770	·85
Platinum	·54, ·625	1000	2900	2730	1·05
Tin	·51, 1·15	1400	1290	1300	·99
Silver	·38, ·435	600	1060	1120	·95
Copper	·495, ·61	1300	570	507	1·12
Aluminium ...	·45, ·52, 1·06	1600	151	144	1·05
Carbon	·55, ·57	400	57	41·6	1·37

Note 2.—Introducing the new data for the mass per unit area of foils of the same air equivalent, as in note 1, the following are the values for the ratio of the scattering per atom divided by A^2:—Au 3·1, Pt 3·4, Sn 3·4, Ag 3·4, Cu 3·95, Al 3·4.

It will be seen from the table that, although the experimental conditions were very different from those in the previous experiments, the results are similar, and indicate the essential correctness of the assumption that the scattering per atom is proportional to the square of the atomic weight. The deviations from constancy of the ratio (see notes 1 and 2) are nearly within the experimental error.

The measurements have not so far been extended to substances of lower atomic weight than carbon. When the atomic weight is small and comparable with the mass of the α particle, the laws of scattering will require some modification to take into account the relative motion of the atom itself when a collision occurs.

Variation of Scattering with Velocity.

In order to determine the variation of scattering with velocity the apparatus was somewhat modified. A conical glass tube coated with active deposit was again used as source of radiation. This source was placed about 1 mm. from the mica window (E, fig. 3), so that it was possible to insert additional sheets of mica between the source and the window to reduce the velocity of the α particles. Mica sheets were used for this purpose on account of their uniformity of thickness in comparison with metal foils. The micas were attached to a cardboard disk which could be rotated to bring the different sheets successively in position. The α particles were scattered by a foil of gold or silver, of stopping power about 3 mm. of air, which was attached to a rod passing through the ground glass N. This made it possible to turn the foil away from the main beam during an experiment in order to test the natural effect. The disk S, in this case, rotated in a plane very close to the glass plate C and carried sheets of mica of different thicknesses. By rotating the ground-glass joint the micas could be placed directly in front of the zinc-sulphide screen, making it possible to test the homogeneity of the α particles after they had been scattered.

The results are given in Table VII. Column I. gives the number of mica sheets which were interposed in addition to the mica window, and column II. the ranges of the α particles incident on the scattering foil. The values of the velocities v were calculated from these ranges R by use of the formula $v^3 = a$R previously found by one of us *. The relative values

TABLE VII.

Variation of Scattering with Velocity.

I. Number of sheets of mica.	II. Range R of α particles after leaving mica.	III. Relative values of $1/v^4$.	IV. Number N of scintillations per minute.	V. Nv^4.
0	5·5	1·0	24·7	25
1	4·76	1·21	29·0	24
2	4·05	1·50	33·4	22
3	3·32	1·91	44	23
4	2·51	2·84	81	28
5	1·84	4·32	101	23
6	1·04	9·22	255	28

of $1/v^4$ are given in column III. The number of scintillations per minute N are entered in column IV., and in column V. relative values of $N \times v^4$ are given. Over the range examined the number of scintillations varies in the ratio 1 : 10, while it will be seen that the product Nv^4 remains sensibly constant. Several experiments were made, and in every case

* H. Geiger, Roy. Soc. Proc. A. vol. lxxxiii. p. 506 (1910).

the scattering was found to vary at a rate more nearly proportional to the inverse fourth power of the velocity than to any other integral power. Owing to the comparative uncertainty of the values of the velocity for small ranges, however, the error of experiment may be somewhat greater than appears from column V. of the table.

In these experiments it proved essential to use a source possessing a high degree of homogeneity. In earlier experiments, where we were not able to fulfil this condition, the scattering apparently increased much more rapidly than the inverse fourth power of the velocity of the Ra C α particles. Even with a source of Ra C with which only a small quantity of emanation was associated, the amount of scattering first rapidly increased on interposing the sheets of mica, then showed a slight decrease, and finally increased again. This irregularity was due to the α particles of the emanation and Ra A, which are of shorter range than those of Ra C, and therefore more easily scattered.

The measurements could not easily be extended to α particles of lower velocity than corresponds to a range of about 1 centimetre, owing to the difficulty of observing the faint scintillations at lower ranges. However, in one particular experiment, by adding sheets of mica to cut down the velocity the number of scattered α particles appearing on the screen was increased 25 times, showing how easily the α particles of low velocity are scattered.

The results of the examination of the homogeneity of the scattered α particles showed that at least in the case of gold they remained practically homogeneous after the scattering. Experiments of this nature in the case of scattering foils of low atomic weight would be very interesting, but are somewhat difficult.

Determination of Absolute Number of Scattered α Particles.

In the previous sections we have completely verified the theory given by Prof. Rutherford. Since, according to this theory, the large deflexion of an α particle is the result of a close encounter with a single atom of matter, it is possible to calculate the magnitude of the central charge of the atom when the fraction of α particles scattered under definite conditions is determined. We have made several attempts under different conditions to obtain a quantitative estimate of the scattered particles, but the results so far have only given us an approximate value. The main difficulty arises from the fact that the scattered particles consist of such a small fraction of the original beam that different methods of measurement have to be employed in the two cases. The number of scattered α particles was determined from the number of scintillations observed on the zinc-sulphide screen, a correction being necessary owing to the fact that with the particular screens used only about 85 per cent. of the incident α particles produce scintillations. The number of α particles in the main beam was in one case in which an emanation tube was used (as shown in fig. 1, p. 607) determined directly by the scintillation method, several weeks being allowed to elapse, so that the emanation had decayed to a small value. In other experiments Ra C deposited on the inside of a conical glass tube (as in fig. 2, p. 611) was used, and the number of α particles was calculated from its γ-ray activity and the distance and area of the diaphragm determining the beam.

The results showed that, using a gold foil of air equivalent 1 mm. (actual thickness $2 \cdot 1 \times 10^{-5}$ cm.), the fraction of incident Ra C α particles ($v = 2 \cdot 06 \times 10^9$ cm./sec.) scattered through an angle of $45°$ and observed on an area of 1 sq. mm. placed normally at a distance of 1 cm. from the point of incidence of the beam, was $3 \cdot 7 \times 10^{-7}$. Substituting this value in the equation given at the commencement of this paper, it can be calculated that the value of the number of elementary electric charges composing the central charge of the gold atom is about half the atomic weight. This result is probably correct to 20 per cent., and agrees with the deduction of Prof. Rutherford from the less definite data given in our previous paper.

From the results of this and the previous sections it is possible to calculate the probability of an α particle being scattered through any angle under any specified conditions. For materials of atomic weight greater than that of aluminium, it is sufficiently accurate to put N equal to half the atomic weight in the equation given at the commencement of the paper.

It will be seen that the laws of "single scattering" found in this paper are quite distinct from the laws of "compound scattering" previously deduced by Geiger. It must be remembered, however, that the experiments are not directly comparable. In the present paper we are dealing with very thin sheets of matter, and are measuring the very small fraction of α particles which are deflected by single collisions through relatively large angles. The experiments of Geiger, however, deal with larger thicknesses of scattering foils and angles of deflexion of a few degrees only. Under these conditions the scattering is due to the combination of a large number of deflexions not only by the central charges of the atoms, but probably also by the electronic charges distributed throughout the remainder of their volumes.

Summary.

The experiments described in the foregoing paper were carried out to test a theory of the atom proposed by Prof. Rutherford, the main feature of which is that there exists at the centre of the atom an intense highly concentrated electrical charge. The verification is based on the laws of scattering which were deduced from this theory. The following relations have been verified experimentally :—

(1) The number of α particles emerging from a scattering foil at an angle ϕ with the original beam varies as $1/\sin^4 \phi/2$, when the α particles are counted on a definite area at a constant distance from the foil. This relation has been tested for angles varying from 5° to 150°, and over this range the number of α particles varied from 1 to 250,000 in good agreement with the theory.

(2) The number of α particles scattered in a definite direction is directly proportional to the thickness of the scattering foil for small thicknesses. For larger thicknesses the decrease of velocity of the α particles in the foil causes a somewhat more rapid increase in the amount of scattering.

(3) The scattering per atom of foils of different materials varies approximately as the square of the atomic weight. This relation was tested for foils of atomic weight from that of carbon to that of gold.

(4) The amount of scattering by a given foil is approximately proportional to the inverse fourth power of the velocity of the incident α particles. This relation was tested over a range of velocities such that the number of scattered particles varied as 1 : 10.

(5) Quantitative experiments show that the fraction of α particles of Ra C, which is scattered through an angle of 45° by a gold foil of 1 mm. air equivalent ($2 \cdot 1 \times 10^{-5}$ cm.), is $3 \cdot 7 \times 10^{-7}$ when the scattered particles are counted on a screen of 1 sq. mm. area placed at a distance of 1 cm. from the scattering foil. From this figure and the foregoing results, it can be calculated that the number of elementary charges composing the centre of the atom is equal to half the atomic weight.

We are indebted to Prof. Rutherford for his kind interest in these experiments, and for placing at our disposal the large quantities of radium emanation necessary. We are also indebted to the Government Grant Committee of the Royal Society for a grant to one of us, out of which part of the expenses has been paid.

XCIII. *The High-Frequency Spectra of the Elements.*
By H. G. J. Moseley, *M.A.**

[Plate XXIII.]

IN the absence of any available method of spectrum analysis, the characteristic types of X radiation, which an atom emits when suitably excited, have hitherto been described in terms of their absorption in aluminium †. The interference phenomena exhibited by X rays when scattered by a crystal have now, however, made possible the accurate determination of the frequencies of the various types of radiation. This was shown by W. H. and W. L. Bragg‡, who by this method analysed the line spectrum emitted by the platinum target of an X-ray tube. C. G. Darwin and the author § extended this analysis and also examined the continuous spectrum, which in this case constitutes the greater part of the radiation. Recently Prof. Bragg ‖ has also determined the wave-lengths of the strongest lines in the spectra of nickel, tungsten, and rhodium. The electrical methods which have hitherto been employed are, however, only successful where a constant source of radiation is available. The present paper contains a description of a method of photographing these spectra, which makes the analysis of the X rays as simple as any other branch of spectroscopy. The author intends first to make a general survey of the principal types of high-frequency radiation, and then to examine the spectra of a few elements in greater detail and with greater accuracy. The results already obtained show that such data have an important bearing on the question of

* Communicated by Prof. E. Rutherford, F.R.S.
† *Cf.* Barkla, Phil. Mag. xxii. p. 396 (1911).
‡ Proc. Roy. Soc. A. lxxxviii. p. 428 (1913).
§ Phil. Mag. xxvi. p. 210 (1913).
‖ Proc. Roy. Soc, A. lxxxix. p. 246 (1913).

the internal structure of the atom, and strongly support the views of Rutherford[*] and of Bohr[†].

Kaye[‡] has shown that an element excited by a stream of sufficiently fast cathode rays emits its characteristic X radiation. He used as targets a number of substances mounted on a truck inside an exhausted tube. A magnetic device enabled each target to be brought in turn into the line of fire. This apparatus was modified to suit the present work. The cathode stream was concentrated on to a small area of the target, and a platinum plate furnished with a fine vertical slit placed immediately in front of the part bombarded. The tube was exhausted by a Gaede mercury pump, charcoal in liquid air being also sometimes used to remove water vapour. The X rays, after passing through the slit marked S in fig. 1,

Fig. 1.

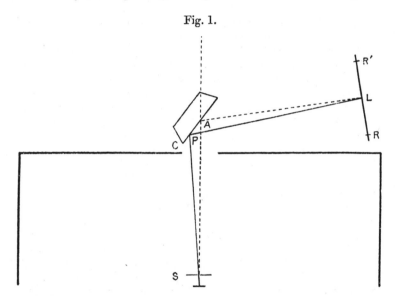

emerged through an aluminium window ·02 mm. thick. The rest of the radiation was shut off by a lead box which surrounded the tube. The rays fell on the cleavage face, C, of a crystal of potassium ferrocyanide which was mounted on the prism-table of a spectrometer. The surface of the crystal was vertical and contained the geometrical axis of the spectrometer.

[*] Phil. Mag. xxi. p. 669 (1911).
[†] Phil. Mag. xxvi. pp. 1, 476, & 857 (1913).
[‡] Phil. Trans. Roy. Soc. A. ccix. p. 123 (1909).

Now it is known* that X rays consist in general of two types, the heterogeneous radiation and characteristic radiations of definite frequency. The former of these is reflected from such a surface at all angles of incidence, but at the large angles used in the present work the reflexion is of very little intensity. The radiations of definite frequency, on the other hand, are reflected only when they strike the surface at definite angles, the glancing angle of incidence θ, the wavelength λ, and the "grating constant" d of the crystal being connected by the relation

$$n\lambda = 2d \sin \theta, \quad \ldots \quad \ldots \quad (1)$$

where n, an integer, may be called the "order" in which the reflexion occurs. The particular crystal used, which was a fine specimen with face 6 cm. square, was known to give strong reflexions in the first three orders, the third order being the most prominent.

If then a radiation of definite wave-length happens to strike any part P of the crystal at a suitable angle, a small part of it is reflected. Assuming for the moment that the source of the radiation is a point, the locus of P is obviously the arc of a circle, and the reflected rays will travel along the generating lines of a cone with apex at the image of the source. The effect on a photographic plate L will take the form of the arc of an hyperbola, curving away from the direction of the direct beam. With a fine slit at S, the arc becomes a fine line which is slightly curved in the direction indicated.

The photographic plate was mounted on the spectrometer arm, and both the plate and the slit were 17 cm. from the axis. The importance of this arrangement lies in a geometrical property, for when these two distances are equal the point L at which a beam reflected at a definite angle strikes the plate is independent of the position of P on the crystal surface. The angle at which the crystal is set is then immaterial so long as a ray can strike some part of the surface at the required angle. The angle θ can be obtained from the relation $2\theta = 180° - \mathrm{SPL} = 180° - \mathrm{SAL}$.

The following method was used for measuring the angle SAL. Before taking a photograph a reference line R was made at both ends of the plate by replacing the crystal by a lead screen furnished with a fine slit which coincided with the axis of the spectrometer. A few seconds' exposure to the X rays then gave a line R on the plate, and so defined on it

* Moseley and Darwin, *loc. cit.*

the line joining S and A. A second line R′ was made in the same way after turning the spectrometer arm through a definite angle. The arm was then turned to the position required to catch the reflected beam and the angles LAP for any lines which were subsequently found on the plate deduced from the known value of RAP and the position of the lines on the plate. The angle LAR was measured with an error of not more than $0°\cdot1$, by superposing on the negative a plate on which reference lines had been marked in the same way at intervals of $1°$. In finding from this the glancing angle of reflexion two small corrections were necessary in practice, since neither the face of the crystal nor the lead slit coincided accurately with the axis of the spectrometer. Wave-lengths varying over a range of about 30 per cent. could be reflected for a given position of the crystal.

In almost all cases the time of exposure was five minutes. Ilford X-ray plates were used and were developed with rodinal. The plates were mounted in a plate-holder, the front of which was covered with black paper. In order to determine the wave-length from the reflexion angle θ it is necessary to know both the order n in which the reflexion occurs and the grating constant d. n was determined by photographing every spectrum both in the second order and the third. This also gave a useful check on the accuracy of the measurements ; d cannot be calculated directly for the complicated crystal potassium ferrocyanide. The grating constant of this particular crystal had, however, previously * been accurately compared with d', the constant of a specimen of rocksalt. It was found that

$$d = 3d' \frac{\cdot 1988}{\cdot 1985}.$$

Now W. L. Bragg † has shown that the atoms in a rocksalt crystal are in simple cubical array. Hence the number of atoms per c.c.

$$2\frac{N\sigma}{M} = \frac{1}{(d')^3}:$$

N, the number of molecules in a gram-mol., $= 6\cdot05 \times 10^{23}$, assuming the charge on an electron to be $4\cdot89 \times 10^{-10}$; σ, the density of this crystal of rocksalt, was $2\cdot167$, and M the molecular weight $= 58\cdot46$.

* Moseley & Darwin, *loc. cit.*
† Proc. Roy. Soc. A. lxxxix. p. 248 (1913).

TABLE I.

Element.	Line.	θ_2.	λ.	θ_3.	λ.	$\lambda_\alpha/\lambda_\beta$.	$Q=(\nu/\tfrac{3}{4}\nu_0)^{\tfrac{1}{2}}$.	N atomic number.	Atomic weight.
CALCIUM.	α ...	23·4°	3·357×10⁻⁸	36·7°	3·368×10⁻⁸	1·089	19·00	20	40·09
	β ...	21·4	3·085	33·3	3·094				
SCANDIUM.	...	...	...	...	...	...	...	21	44·1
TITANIUM.	α ...	19·1	2·766	29·3	2·758	1·093	20·99	22	48·1
	β ...	17·4	2·528	26·6	2·524				
VANADIUM.	α ...	17·35	2·521	26·55	2·519	1·097	21·96	23	51·06
	β ...	15·8	2·302	24·05	2·297				
CHROMIUM.	α ...	15·75	2·295	24·1	2·301	1·100	22·98	24	52·0
	β ...	14·3	2·088	21·8	2·093				
MANGANESE.	α ...	14·5	2·117	22·0	2·111	1·101	23·99	25	54·93
	β ...	13·15	1·923	19·9	1·918				
IRON.	α ...	13·3	1·945	20·2	1·946	1·103	24·99	26	55·85
	β ...	12·05	1·765	18·25	1·765				
COBALT.	α ...	12·25	1·794	18·6	1·798	1·104	26·00	27	58·97
	β ...	11·15	1·635	16·8	1·629				
NICKEL.	α ...	11·35	1·664	17·15	1·662	1·104	27·04	28	58·68
	β ...	10·25	1·504	15·5	1·506				
COPPER.	α ...	10·55	1·548	15·95	1·549	1·105	28·01	29	63·57
	β ...	9·55	1·403	14·4	1·402				
ZINC.	α ...	9·85	1·446	14·85	1·445	1·106	29·01	30	65·37
	β ...	not found		13·4	1·306				

This gives $d' = 2 \cdot 814 \times 10^{-8}$ and $d = 8 \cdot 454 \times 10^{-8}$ cm. It is seen that the determination of wave-length depends on $e^{\frac{1}{3}}$, so that the effect of uncertainty in the value of this quantity will not be serious. Lack of homogeneity in the crystal is a more likely source of error, as minute inclusions of water would make the true density greater than that found experimentally.

Twelve elements have so far been examined. The ten given in Table I. were chosen as forming a continuous series with only one gap. It was hoped in this way to bring out clearly any systematic results. The inclusion of nickel was of special interest owing to its anomalous position in the periodic system. Radiations from these substances are readily excited, and the large angles of reflexion make it easy to measure the wave-lengths with accuracy. Calcium alone gave any trouble. In this case, owing to the high absorption coefficient of the principal radiation—about 1200 cm.$^{-1}$ in aluminium—the X-ray tube was provided with a window of goldbeaters' skin and the air between the crystal and the photographic plate displaced by hydrogen. The layer of lime which covered the surface of the metal gave off such a quantity of gas that the X rays could only be excited for a second or two at a time. Brass was substituted for zinc to avoid volatilization by the intense heat generated at the point struck by the cathode rays. Ferro-vanadium (35 per cent. V) and ferro-titanium (23 per cent. Ti), for which I am indebted to the International Vanadium Co., proved convenient substitutes for the pure elements, which are not easily obtained in the solid form.

Plate XXIII. shows the spectra in the third order placed approximately in register. Those parts of the photographs which represent the same angle of reflexion are in the same vertical line. The actual angles can be taken from Table I. It is to be seen that the spectrum of each element consists of two lines. Of these the stronger has been called α in the table, and the weaker β. The lines found on any of the plates besides α and β were almost certainly all due to impurities. Thus in both the third and second order the cobalt spectrum shows Ni α very strongly and Fe α faintly. In the third order the nickel spectrum shows Mn α_2 faintly. The brass spectra naturally show α and β both of Cu and of Zn, but Zn β_2 has not yet been found. In the second order the ferro-vanadium and ferro-titanium spectra show very intense third-order Fe lines, and the former also shows Cu α_3 faintly. The Co contained Ni and $0 \cdot 8$ per cent. Fe, the Ni $2 \cdot 2$ per cent. Mn,

and the V only a trace of Cu. No other lines have been
found ; but a search over a wide range of wave-lengths
has been made only for one or two elements, and perhaps
prolonged exposures, which have not yet been attempted,
will show more complex spectra. The prevalence of lines
due to impurities suggests that this may prove a powerful
method of chemical analysis. Its advantage over ordinary
spectroscopic methods lies in the simplicity of the spectra
and the impossibility of one substance masking the radiation
from another. It may even lead to the discovery of missing
elements, as it will be possible to predict the position of
their characteristic lines.

It will be seen from Table I. that the wave-lengths calculated from the two orders are in good agreement. The third
order gives the stronger reflexion, and as the angles dealt
with are the larger these results are the more accurate.
The similarity of the different spectra is shown by the fact
that the two lines α and β remain approximately constant,
not only in relative intensity but also in relative wave-
length. The frequency of β increases, however, slightly
faster than that of α. The same two lines α strong and β
weak constitute the rhodium spectrum examined by Bragg [*],
and they are obviously in some way closely related.
One or two photographs taken with the radiation from
platinum gave results in good agreement with those obtained
by the electrical method, and no trace of the elaborate system
of bands described by de Broglie [†] in the reflexion from rocksalt was encountered. The three lines found by Herveg [‡] in
the reflexion from selenite doubtless represent part of the
Pt spectrum in the second order. The actual breadth of the
lines and certain minute details in their structure will not
be considered here, as discussion would take too much
space and more experiments are needed. The only other
element examined was tantalum. In this case the radiation
belongs to the L series, and the spectrum consists of a strong
line of wave-length $1 \cdot 525 \times 10^{-8}$ cm., two others of less
intensity at $1 \cdot 330$ and $1 \cdot 287 \times 10^{-8}$ cm., and probably some
very faint lines also.

A discussion will now be given of the meaning of the
wave-lengths found for the principal spectrum-line α. In
Table I. the values are given of the quantity

$$Q = \sqrt{\frac{\nu}{\frac{3}{4}\nu_0}},$$

[*] Proc. Roy. Soc. A. lxxxix. p. 277 (1913).
[†] *Le Radium*, x. pp. 186 & 245 (1913).
[‡] *Deutsch. Phys. Ges. Verh.* xv. 13, p. 555 (1913).

ν being the frequency of the radiation α, and ν_0 the fundamental frequency of ordinary line spectra. The latter is obtained from Rydberg's wave-number, $N_0 = \dfrac{\nu}{c} = 109,720$.

The reason for introducing this particular constant will be given later. It is at once evident that Q increases by a constant amount as we pass from one element to the next, using the chemical order of the elements in the periodic system. Except in the case of nickel and cobalt *, this is also the order of the atomic weights. While, however, Q increases uniformly the atomic weights vary in an apparently arbitrary manner, so that an exception in their order does not come as a surprise. We have here a proof that there is in the atom a fundamental quantity, which increases by regular steps as we pass from one element to the next. This quantity can only be the charge on the central positive nucleus, of the existence of which we already have definite proof. Rutherford has shown, from the magnitude of the scattering of α particles by matter, that this nucleus carries a $+$ charge approximately equal to that of $\dfrac{A}{2}$ electrons, where A is the atomic weight. Barkla, from the scattering of X rays by matter, has shown that the number of electrons in an atom is roughly $\dfrac{A}{2}$, which for an electrically neutral atom comes to the same thing. Now atomic weights increase on the average by about 2 units at a time, and this strongly suggests the view that N increases from atom to atom always by a single electronic unit. We are therefore led by experiment to the view that N is the same as the number of the place occupied by the element in the periodic system. This atomic number is then for H 1 for He 2 for Li 3 ... for Ca 20 ... for Zn 30, &c. This theory was originated by Broek † and since used by Bohr ‡. We can confidently predict that in the few cases in which the order of the atomic weights A clashes with the chemical order of the periodic system, the chemical properties are governed by N; while A is itself probably a complicated function of N. The very close similarity between the X-ray spectra of the different elements shows that these radiations originate inside the atom, and have no direct connexion with the complicated light-spectra and chemical properties which are governed by the structure of its surface.

* *Cf.* Barkla, Phil. Mag. xiv. p. 408 (1907).
† *Phys. Zeit.* xiv. p. 32 (1913).   ‡ *Loc. cit.*

We will now examine the relation

$$Q = \sqrt{\frac{\nu}{\frac{3}{4}\nu_0}}$$

more closely. So far the argument has relied on the fact that Q is a quantity which increases from atom to atom by equal steps. Now Q has been obtained by multiplying $\nu^{\frac{1}{2}}$ by a constant factor so chosen as to make the steps equal to unity. We have, therefore,

$$Q = N - k,$$

where k is a constant. Hence the frequency ν varies as $(N-k)^2$. If N for calcium is really 20 then $k=1$.

There is good reason to believe that the X-ray spectra with which we are now dealing come from the innermost ring of electrons *. If these electrons are held in equilibrium by mechanical forces, the angular velocity ω with which they are rotating and the radius r of their orbit are connected by

$$m\omega^2 r = \frac{e^2}{r^2}(N - \sigma_n),$$

where σ_n is a small term arising from the influence of the n electrons in the ring on each other, and $\sigma_2 = 0.25$, $\sigma_4 = 0.96$, $\sigma_6 = 1.83$, $\sigma_8 = 2.81$. In obtaining this simple expression the very small effect of other outside rings has been neglected. If then, as we pass from atom to atom, the number of electrons in the central ring remains unaltered,

$$(\omega^2 r^3)_{N+1} - (\omega^2 r^3)_N \text{ remains constant};$$

but these experiments have shown that

$$\nu^{\frac{1}{2}}_{N+1} - \nu^{\frac{1}{2}}_N \text{ is also constant,}$$

and therefore

$$\frac{\omega^2 r^3}{\nu^{\frac{1}{2}}} \text{ is constant.}$$

For the types of radiation considered by Bohr, provided the ring moves from one stationary state to another as a whole, and for the ordinary transverse vibrations of the ring, provided the influence of outer rings can be neglected, ν is proportional to ω.

This gives $\omega^{\frac{3}{2}}r^3$ and therefore $m\omega r^2$, the angular momentum of an electron, the same for all the different atoms. Thus we

* J. J. Thomson, Phil. Mag. xxiii. p. 456 (1912).

have an experimental verification of the principle of the constancy of angular momentum which was first used by Nicholson *, and is the basis of Bohr's theory of the atom.

It is evident that $k = \sigma_n$. If then $k = 1$, it is suggested that the ring contains 4 electrons, for $\sigma_4 = 0 \cdot 96$.

We are now justified in making a quantitative comparison between the frequency of α and that of the fundamental radiation from such a ring calculated from the theory of Bohr.

We have obtained the experimental result,

$$\nu = \tfrac{3}{4}\nu_0 (N - \sigma_n)^2.$$

On his theory, making the assumption that the ring moves as a whole from stationary state 2 to state 1, the frequency of the principal radiation emitted is

$$\nu = \left(\frac{1}{1^2} - \frac{1}{2^2}\right)\frac{2\pi^2 e^4 m}{h^3}(N - \sigma_n)^2,$$

where e is the charge on an electron, m its mass, and h Planck's constant.

The numerical agreement between these two constants ν_0 and $\dfrac{2\pi^2 e^4 m}{h^3}$ is known to be very close, while Bohr's explanation of the Balmer series for hydrogen assumes them to be identical. This numerical agreement between the experimental values and those calculated from a theory designed to explain the ordinary hydrogen spectrum is remarkable, as the wave-lengths dealt with in the two cases differ by a factor of about 2000. The assumption that the whole ring takes part in the radiation introduces, however, a grave difficulty from energy considerations, while no explanation of the faint line β has been forthcoming. Probably further experiments will show that the theory needs some modification.

The results hitherto obtained for the radiations of the L·series are too meagre to justify any explanation. As before, the line of longest wave-length is the most prominent, a result similar to that found in ordinary light-spectra. The wave-lengths found for this line in the case of tantalum and platinum suggest that possibly the frequency is here

$$\nu = \left(\frac{1}{2^2} - \frac{1}{3^2}\right)\nu_0(N - \sigma_n)^2.$$

Here N and σ_n are unknown, but it is evident from the periodic system that $N_{Pt} - N_{Ta} = 5$, while probably σ_n remains

* Monthly Notes Roy. Astr. Soc. June 1912.

1034

the same for all elements in the same column. The actual value found for $\nu_{Pt}^{\frac{1}{2}} - \nu_{Ta}^{\frac{1}{2}}$ is $1 \cdot 08 \times 10^8$, and the calculated value is $1 \cdot 07 \times 10^8$. Whether this relation really holds good can only be decided by further experiment.

In conclusion I wish to express my warm thanks to Prof. Rutherford for the kind interest which he has taken in this work.

Physical Laboratory,
University of Manchester.

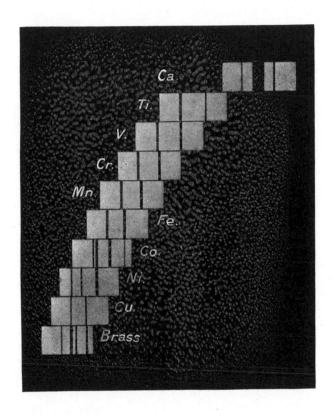

LXXX. *The High-Frequency Spectra of the Elements.*
Part II. *By* H. G. J. Moseley, *M.A.**

THE first part † of this paper dealt with a method of photographing X-ray spectra, and included the spectra of a dozen elements. More than thirty other elements have now been investigated, and simple laws have been found which govern the results, and make it possible to predict with confidence the position of the principal lines in the spectrum of any element from aluminium to gold. The present contribution is a general preliminary survey, which claims neither to be complete nor very accurate.

A somewhat different method of photographing these spectra has been developed independently by de Broglie ‡ and by Herveg §. The latter closely confirms the angles given by Moseley and Darwin ‖ for reflexion of Pt rays from selenite. De Broglie finds less satisfactory agreement for the reflexion from rocksalt. De Broglie has also examined the spectra of W and Au, and has obtained for Cu and Fe results similar to those given in Part I.

The general experimental method has remained unaltered, and need not be again described. The same crystal of potassium ferrocyanide has been used as analyser throughout. The sharpness of the lines of short wave-length has

* Communicated by the Author.
† Moseley, Phil. Mag. xxvi. p. 1024 (1913).
‡ De Broglie, *C. R.* 17 Nov., 22 Dec., 1913, 19 Jan., 2 Feb., 2 March, 1914.
§ Herveg, *Verh. d. D. Phys. Ges.* xvi. p. 73, Jan. 1914.
‖ Moseley & Darwin, Phil. Mag. xxvi. p. 210 (1913).

3 A 2

been much improved by reducing the breadth of the defining slit to about 0·2 mm. The most convenient type of X-ray tube is drawn to scale in fig. 1. The aluminium trolley which carries the targets can be drawn to and fro by means of silk fishing-line wound on brass bobbins. An iron screen S fastened to the rails is furnished with a fine vertical slit which defines the X-ray beam. The slit should be fixed exactly opposite the focus-spot of the cathode-stream, though a slight error can be remedied by deflecting the cathode rays with a magnet. The X rays escape by a side-tube $2\frac{1}{2}$ cm. diameter closed by an aluminium window 0·022 mm. thick. The X-ray tube, which has a capacity of over 3 litres, was exhausted with a Gaede mercury-pump, for the loan of which I am indebted to Balliol College.

Fig. 1.

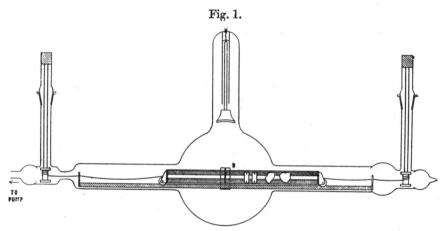

TO PUMP

The radiations of long wave-length cannot penetrate an aluminium window or more than a centimetre or two of air. The photographs had therefore in this case to be taken inside an exhausted spectrometer. Fig. 2 gives a vertical section to scale of the X-ray tube and spectrometer. The former consists of a bulb containing the cathode, joined by a very large glass T-piece to a long tube of 4 cm. diameter, in which are the rails R and the carriage C. S is the defining-slit and W a window of goldbeaters' skin which separates the tube from the spectrometer. This material, which is usually air-tight, though sometimes it may require varnishing, is extremely transparent to X rays. A circular window of 2 cm. diameter will easily withstand the pressure of the atmosphere if left undisturbed. In these experiments, however, the pressure was relieved every time the spectrometer was exhausted, and under such conditions the goldbeaters' skin had frequently to be renewed. The spectrometer, which was specially designed for this work, consists of a strong circular iron box of 30 cm. inside diameter and 8 cm. high, closed by a lid which, when the flange is greased, makes an air-tight joint. Two concentric grooves are cut in the floor of the box. The table A, which carries the plate-holder, rests on three steel balls, of which two run in the outer groove, while the third rests on the floor of the box. The position of the crystal-table B is controlled in like manner by the inner groove. This geometrical construction for a spectrometer is well

Fig. 2.

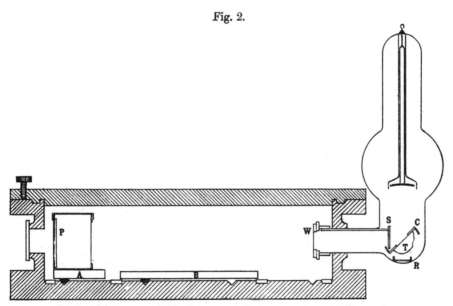

known. The scales are fixed to the box and the verniers to the tables. For these very soft rays the absorption by the black paper front of the plate-holder became serious, and two sheets of black tissue-paper were used instead. Lumps of the pure elements, usually several millimetres thick, were used as targets in the case of Mg, Al, Si, Mo, Ru, Pd, Ag, Sb, Ta. Foils such as Rh, W, Au were either silver-soldered or brazed onto copper. Os was used in the form of a thin chemical deposit on copper. The alloys used were ZrNi (70 per cent.), WFe (50 per cent.), NbTa (50 per cent.), and SnMn (50 per cent.). KCl and the oxides of the rare-earth elements were rubbed onto the surface of nickel plates roughened with coarse emery-powder. The only serious difficulty in the experiments is caused by the heat produced by the cathode ray bombardment, and the consequent liberation of gas and destruction of the surface of the target. This makes it necessary to use the element in a form which is not too volatile and prevents the employment of a very powerful discharge. The total time of an exposure, including rests, varied from three minutes for a substance such as ruthenium, which could safely be heated, to thirty minutes for the rare earth oxides. The importance of using an efficient high-tension valve may again be mentioned.

The oxides of Sa, Eu, Gd, Er were given me by Sir William Crookes, O.M., to whom I wish to express my sincere gratitude. For the loan of the Os and a button of Ru I am indebted to Messrs. Johnson Matthey. The alloys were obtained from the Metallic Compositions Co., and the oxides of La, Ce, Pr, Nd, and Er from Dr. Schuchardt, of Görlitz.

Almost every line was photographed in two different orders, and the double angles of reflexion measured as before to within $0°\cdot1$ and sometimes $0°\cdot05$. In some sets of experiments a small error caused by the crystal surface not being exactly on the spectrometer-axis gave rise to a systematic discrepancy in the results obtained from reflexion in different orders. It was found that this error, which never changed the reflexion-angle by more than $0°\cdot05$, could be measured more accurately from the amount of the discrepancy than from direct observation of the crystal. A more serious correction was necessary when using the long wave-length apparatus. In this case the slit and photograph are not equidistant from the crystal, and the position of the spectrum-lines on the plate is no longer independent of the angle at which the crystal is set. The necessary corrections were calculated geometrically, and verified by photographing the same line for both right-handed and left-handed reflexions and with the crystal set at various angles.

In the work on the very short wave-lengths, the reflexion of the general heterogeneous radiation gave some trouble. This is always an important part of the radiation from an X-ray tube, but with a hard tube it is analysed by reflexion mainly into constituents of very short wave-length, and so usually does not interfere with the line-spectra. It is only with an extremely soft tube, combined with precautions against absorption by the air, that constituents reflected at large angles become prominent. When examining such a spectrum as that of Ag in the K series, the general reflexion cannot be avoided. Unfortunately, when photographed it takes the form of irregular fringes, which effectually hide faint spectrum-lines. A change of target, with the position of slit and crystal unaltered, does not affect the appearance of the fringes, a fact which proves that they are due to the general heterogeneous radiation. It is easy to show that the fringes are merely a very foreshortened pattern of patches on the crystal surface which reflect exceptionally well. The way in which they move and spread out laterally as the crystal is turned provides a proof of this, and so does Barkla's * observation that when the crystal is moved sideways the fringes move with it. It is easy to devise methods for getting rid of the fringes. In the first place, narrowing the slit or increasing the distance from the crystal will diminish their intensity compared with that of the line-spectrum. In the second place, turning the crystal will move and blur the fringes, but leave the sharpness of the lines unaffected provided the slit and photograph are equidistant from the reflecting surface †. The quantitative measurements of Moseley and Darwin ‡ on the reflexion of the general radiation must have been little affected by these fringes, as the incident beam was restricted to a very narrow pencil which always impinged on the same part of the crystal.

The results obtained for radiations belonging to Barkla's K series are given in Table I., and for convenience the figures already given in Part I. are included. The wave-length λ has been calculated from the glancing angle of reflexion θ by means of the relation $n\lambda = 2d \sin \theta$, where d has been taken to be $8 \cdot 454 \times 10^{-8}$ cm. As before, the strongest line is called α and the next line β. The square root of the frequency of each line is plotted in fig. 3, and the wave-lengths can be read off with the help of the scale at the top of the diagram.

The spectrum of Al was photographed in the first order only. The very light elements give several other fainter lines, which have not yet been fully investigated, while the results for Mg and Na are quite complicated, and apparently depart from the simple relations which connect the spectra of the other elements. In the spectra from yttrium onwards only the α line has so far been measured, and further results in these directions will be given in a later paper. The

---

* Barkla and Martyn, Proc. Phys. Soc. London (1913).

† Moseley, *loc. cit.* p. 1025. See also W. H. and W. L. Bragg, Proc. Roy. Soc. A, lxxxviii. p. 428 (1913).

‡ Moseley and Darwin, *loc. cit.*

TABLE I.

	a line. $\lambda \times 10^8$ cm.	Q_K.	N. Atomic Number.	β line. $\lambda \times 10^8$.
Aluminium	8·364	12·05	**13**	7·912
Silicon	7·142	13·04	14	6·729
Chlorine	4·750	16·00	17	......
Potassium	3·759	17·98	19	3·463
Calcium	3·368	19·00	20	3·094
Titanium	2·758	20·99	22	2·524
Vanadium	2·519	21·96	23	2·297
Chromium	2·301	22·98	24	2·093
Manganese	2·111	23·99	25	1·818
Iron	1·946	24·99	26	1·765
Cobalt	1·798	26·00	27	1·629
Nickel	1·662	27·04	28	1·506
Copper	1·549	28·01	29	1·402
Zinc	1·445	29·01	30	1·306
Yttrium	0·838	38·1	39	......
Zirconium	0·794	39·1	40	......
Niobium	0·750	40·2	41	......
Molybdenum.........	0·721	41·2	42	......
Ruthenium	0·638	43·6	44	......
Palladium	0·584	45·6	46	......
Silver	0·560	46·6	47	......

spectra both of K and of Cl were obtained by means of a target of KCl, but it is very improbable that the observed lines have been attributed to the wrong elements. The *α* line for elements from Y onwards appeared to consist of a very close doublet, an effect previously observed by Bragg [*] in the case of rhodium.

The results obtained for the spectra of the L series are given in Table II. and plotted in fig. 3. These spectra contain five lines, *α*, *β*, *γ*, *δ*, *ε*, reckoned in order of decreasing wave-length and decreasing intensity. There is also always a faint companion *α'* on the long wave-length side of *α*, a rather faint line *ϕ* between *β* and *γ* for the rare earth elements at least, and a number of very faint lines of wave-length greater than *α*. Of these, *α*, *β*, *ϕ*, and *γ* have been systematically measured with the object of finding out how the spectrum alters from one element to another. The fact that often values are not given for all these lines merely indicates the incompleteness of the work. The spectra, so far as they have been examined, are so entirely similar that without doubt *α*, *β*, and *γ* at least always exist. Often *γ* was

[*] Bragg, 'Nature,' March 12, 1914.

Fig. 3.

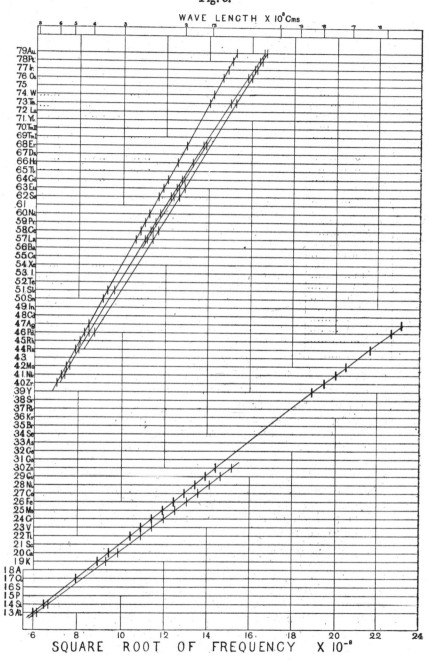

TABLE II.

	a line. $\lambda \times 10^8$ cm.	Q_L.	N. Atomic Number.	β line. $\lambda \times 10^8$.	ϕ line. $\lambda \times 10^8$.	γ line. $\lambda \times 10^8$.
Zirconium	6·091	32·8	40	......	......	......
Niobium	5·749	33·8	41	5·507	......	......
Molybdenum......	5·423	34·8	42	5·187	......	......
Ruthenium	4·861	36·7	44	4·660	......	......
Rhodium	4·622	37·7	45	......	......	......
Palladium	4·385	38·7	46	4·168	......	3·928
Silver	4·170	39·6	47	......	......	......
Tin	3·619	42·6	50	......	......	......
Antimony	3·458	43·6	51	3·245	......	......
Lanthanum	2·676	49·5	57	2·471	2·424	2·313
Cerium	2·567	50·6	58	2·360	2·315	2·209
Praseodymium ...	(2·471)	51·5	59	2·265	......	......
Neodymium	2·382	52·5	60	2·175	......	......
Samarium	2·208	54·5	62	2·008	1·972	1·893
Europium	2·130	55·5	63	1·925	1·888	1·814
Gadolinium	2·057	56·5	64	1·853	1·818	......
Holmium	1·914	58·6	66	1·711	......	......
Erbium	1·790	60·6	68	1·591	1·563	......
Tantalum	1·525	65·6	73	1·330	......	1·287
Tungsten	1·486	66·5	74	......	......	......
Osmium	1·397	68·5	76	1·201	......	1·172
Iridium	1·354	69·6	77	1·155	......	1·138
Platinum	1·316	70·6	78	1·121	......	1·104
Gold	1·287	71·4	79	1·092	......	1·078

not included in the limited range of wave-lengths which can be photographed on one plate. Sometimes lines have not been measured, either on account of faintness or of the confusing proximity of lines due to impurities.

Lines due to impurities were frequently present, but caused little trouble except in the rare earth group. Here two extreme cases occurred. The X-ray spectrum of the praseodymia showed that it consisted roughly of 50 per cent. La, 35 per cent. Ce, and 15 per cent. Pr. Unfortunately the position expected for the α line of Pr coincides with the known position of the β line of La, but the β line of Pr was quite conspicuous, and had precisely the wave-length anticipated. Two specimens of erbia were used. The specimen purchased contained 50 per cent. Er and 50 per cent. of another element, of which the X-ray spectrum coincides with the spectrum calculated for Ho. The erbia given by Sir William Crookes was evidently nearly pure, but showed the α and β lines of Ho quite faintly, and also faint lines agreeing with α and β of Ds and α of Tm I and of Tm II. The Nd was free from La, Ce, and Pr, but contained a fair proportion of Sm. The Sm, Eu, and Gd appeared to be pure. I hope soon to complete the examination of the spectra of this group.

Conclusions.

In fig. 3 the spectra of the elements are arranged on horizontal lines spaced at equal distances. The order chosen for the elements is the order of the atomic weights, except in the cases of A, Co, and Te, where this clashes with the order of the chemical properties. Vacant lines have been left for an element between Mo and Ru, an element between Nd and Sa, and an element between W and Os, none of which are yet known, while Tm, which Welsbach has separated into two constituents, is given two lines. This is equivalent to assigning to successive elements a series of successive characteristic integers. On this principle the integer N for Al, the thirteenth element, has been taken to be 13, and the values of N then assumed by the other elements are given on the left-hand side of fig. 3. This proceeding is justified by the fact that it introduces perfect regularity into the X-ray spectra. Examination of fig. 3 shows that the values of $\nu^{\frac{1}{2}}$ for all the lines examined both in the K and the L series now fall on regular curves which approximate to straight lines. The same thing is shown more clearly by comparing the values of N in Table I. with those of

$$Q_K = \sqrt{\frac{\nu}{\frac{3}{4}\nu_0}},$$

ν being the frequency of the α line and ν_0 the fundamental Rydberg frequency. It is here plain that $Q_K = N - 1$ very approximately, except for the radiations of very short wavelength which gradually diverge from this relation. Again, in Table II. a comparison of N with

$$Q_L = \sqrt{\frac{\nu}{\frac{5}{36}\nu_0}},$$

where ν is the frequency of the L α line, shows that $Q_L = N - 7\cdot4$ approximately, although a systematic deviation clearly shows that the relation is not accurately linear in this case.

Now if either the elements were not characterized by these integers, or any mistake had been made in the order chosen or in the number of places left for unknown elements, these

* Welsbach, *Monatsh.* xxxii. p. 373 (1911).

regularities would at once disappear. We can therefore conclude from the evidence of the X-ray spectra alone, without using any theory of atomic structure, that these integers are really characteristic of the elements.   Further, as it is improbable that two different stable elements should have the same integer, three, and only three, more elements are likely to exist between Al and Au.   As the X-ray spectra of these elements can be confidently predicted, they should not be difficult to find.   The examination of keltium * would be of exceptional interest, as no place has been assigned to this element.

Now Rutherford† has proved that the most important constituent of an atom is its central positively charged nucleus, and van den Broek ‡ has put forward the view that the charge carried by this nucleus is in all cases an integral multiple of the charge on the hydrogen nucleus.   There is every reason to suppose that the integer which controls the X-ray spectrum is the same as the number of electrical units in the nucleus, and these experiments therefore give the strongest possible support to the hypothesis of van den Broek. Soddy § has pointed out that the chemical properties of the radio-elements are strong evidence that this hypothesis is true for the elements from thallium to uranium, so that its general validity would now seem to be established.

From the approximate linear relation between $\nu^{\frac{1}{2}}$ and N for each line we obtain the general equation

$$\nu = A\,(N-b)^2,$$

where A and b are constants characteristic of each line.   For the K α line

$$A = \left(\frac{1}{1^2} - \frac{1}{2^2}\right)\nu_0 \quad \text{and} \quad b = 1.$$

For the L α line approximately

$$A = \left(\frac{1}{2^2} - \frac{1}{3^2}\right)\nu_0 \quad \text{and} \quad b = 7\cdot4.$$

The fact that the numbers and arrangement of the lines in the K and the L spectra are quite different, strongly suggests that they come from distinct vibrating systems, while the fact that b is much larger for the L lines than for the K lines

* Urbain, *C.R.* clii. p. 141 (1911).
† Rutherford, Phil. Mag. xxi. p. 669 (1911), and xxvii. p. 488 (1914).
‡ Van den Broek, *Phys. Zeit.* xiv. p. 32 (1913), and 'Nature,' Nov. 27, Dec. 25, 1913, March 5, 1914.
§ Soddy, *Jahrbuch Rad. und. Elect.* x. p. 193 (1913) ; 'Nature,' Dec. 4, Dec. 18 (1913).

suggests that the L system is situated the further from the nucleus.

It was shown in Part I. * that the linear relation between $\nu^{\frac{1}{2}}$ and $N-b$ was most naturally explained if the vibrating system was a ring of electrons rotating round the central nucleus with an angular momentum which was the same for the different elements. This view has been analysed and put in a more generalised form in a letter to 'Nature' †, written in answer to criticisms made by Lindemann ‡.

Summary.

1. Every element from aluminium to gold is characterized by an integer N which determines its X-ray spectrum. Every detail in the spectrum of an element can therefore be predicted from the spectra of its neighbours.

2. This integer N, the atomic number of the element, is identified with the number of positive units of electricity contained in the atomic nucleus.

3. The atomic numbers for all elements from Al to Au have been tabulated on the assumption that N for Al is 13.

4. The order of the atomic numbers is the same as that of the atomic weights, except where the latter disagrees with the order of the chemical properties.

5. Known elements correspond with all the numbers be-between 13 and 79 except three. There are here three possible elements still undiscovered.

6. The frequency of any line in the X-ray spectrum is approximately proportional to $A(N-b)^2$, where A and b are constants.

I wish to thank Prof. J. S. Townsend, F.R.S., for providing me with every facility for carrying on this work, which has been greatly assisted by a grant from the Institut International de Physique Solvay.

Electrical Laboratory,
    Oxford.

* *Loc. cit.* p. 1032.
† Moseley, 'Nature,' Jan. 15 (1914).
‡ F. A. Lindemann, 'Nature,' Jan. 1, Feb. 5, 1914.

LVII. *The Structure of the Atom.* By Sir ERNEST RUTHERFORD, *F.R.S., Professor of Physics, University of Manchester* *.

THE present paper and the accompanying paper by Mr. C. Darwin deal with certain points in connexion with the "nucleus" theory of the atom which were purposely omitted in my first communication on that subject (Phil. Mag. May 1911). A brief account is given of the later investigations which have been made to test the theory and of the deductions which can be drawn from them. At the same time a brief statement is given of recent observations on the passage of α particles through hydrogen, which throw important light on the dimensions of the nucleus.

In my previous paper (*loc. cit.*) I pointed out the importance of the study of the passage of the high speed α and β particles through matter as a means of throwing light on the internal structure of the atom. Attention was drawn to the remarkable fact, first observed by Geiger and Marsden †, that a small fraction of the swift α particles from radioactive substances were able to be deflected through an angle of more than 90° as the results of an encounter with a single atom. It was shown that the type of atom devised by Lord Kelvin and worked out in great detail by Sir J. J. Thomson was unable to produce such large deflexions unless the diameter of the positive sphere was exceedingly small. In order to account for this large angle scattering of α particles, I supposed that the atom consisted of a positively charged nucleus of small dimensions

---

* Communicated by the Author.
† Proc. Roy. Soc. A. lxxxii. p. 495 (1909).

in which practically all the mass of the atom was concentrated. The nucleus was supposed to be surrounded by a distribution of electrons to make the atom electrically neutral, and extending to distances from the nucleus comparable with the ordinary accepted radius of the atom. Some of the swift α particles passed through the atoms in their path and entered the intense electric field in the neighbourhood of the nucleus and were deflected from their rectilinear path. In order to suffer a deflexion of more than a few degrees, the α particle has to pass very close to the nucleus, and it was assumed that the field of force in this region was not appreciably affected by the external electronic distribution. Supposing that the forces between the nucleus and the α particle are repulsive and follow the law of inverse squares, the α particle describes a hyperbolic orbit round the nucleus and its deflexion can be simply calculated.

It was deduced from this theory that the number of α particles falling normally on unit area of a surface and making an angle ϕ with the direction of the incident rays is proportional to

(1) $\operatorname{cosec}^4 \phi/2$ or $1/\phi^4$ if ϕ be small ;
(2) the number of atoms per unit volume of the scattering material ;
(3) thickness of scattering material t provided this is small;
(4) square of the nucleus charge Ne ;
(5) and is inversely proportional to $(mu^2)^2$, where m is the mass of the α particle and u its velocity.

From the data of scattering on α particles previously given by Geiger [*], it was deduced that the value of the nucleus charge was equal to about half the atomic weight multiplied by the electronic charge. Experiments were begun by Geiger and Marsden [†] to test whether the laws of single scattering of α particles were in agreement with the theory. The general experimental method employed by them consisted in allowing a narrow pencil of α particles to fall normally on a thin film of matter, and observing by the scintillation method the number scattered through different angles. This was a very difficult and laborious piece of work involving the counting of many thousands of particles. They found that their results were in very close accord with the theory. When the thickness of the scattering film was very small, the amount of scattering was directly proportional

[*] Proc. Roy. Soc. A. lxxxiii. p. 492 (1910).
[†] Geiger and Marsden, Phil. Mag. xxv. p. 604 (1913).

to the thickness and varied inversely as the fourth power of the velocity of the incident α particles. A special study was made of the number of α particles scattered through angles varying between 5° and 150°. Although over this range the number decreased in the ratio 200,000 to 1, the relation between number and angle agreed with the theory within the limit of experimental error. They found that the scattering of different atoms of matter was approximately proportional to the square of the atomic weight, showing that the charge on the nucleus was nearly proportional to the atomic weight. By determining the number of α particles scattered from thin films of gold, they concluded that the nucleus charge was equal to about half the atomic weight multiplied by the electronic charge. On account of the difficulties of this experiment, the actual number could not be considered correct within more than 20 per cent.

The experimental results of Geiger and Marsden were thus in complete accord with the predictions of the theory, and indicated the essential correctness of this hypothesis of the structure of the atom.

In determining the magnitude of single scattering, I assumed in my previous paper, for simplicity of calculation, that the atom was at rest during an encounter with an α particle. In an accompanying paper, Mr. C. Darwin has worked out the relations to be expected when account is taken of the motion of the recoiling atom. He has shown that no sensible error has been introduced in this way even for atoms of such low atomic weight as carbon. Mr. Darwin has also worked out the scattering to be expected if the law of force is not that of the inverse square, and has shown that it is not in accord with experiment either with regard to the variation of scattering with angle or with the variation of scattering with velocity. The general evidence certainly indicates that the law of force between the α particle and the nucleus is that of the inverse square.

It is of interest to note that C. T. R. Wilson *, by photographing the trails of the α particle, later showed that the α particle occasionally suffers a sudden deflexion through a large angle. This affords convincing evidence of the correctness of the view that large deflexions do occasionally occur as a result of an encounter with a single atom.

On the theory outlined, the large deflexions of the α particle are supposed to be due to its passage close to the nucleus where the field is very intense and to be not appreciably affected by its passage through the external distribution of

* C. T. R. Wilson, Proc. Roy. Soc. A. lxxxvii. p. 277 (1912).

electrons. This assumption seems to be legitimate when we remember that the mass and energy of the α particle are very large compared with that of an electron even moving with a velocity comparable with that of light. Simple considerations show that the deflexions which an α particle would experience even in passing through the complex electronic distribution of a heavy atom like gold, must be small compared with the large deflexions actually observed. In fact, the passage of swift α particles through matter affords the most definite and straightforward method of throwing light on the gross structure of the atom, for the α particle is able to penetrate the atom without serious disturbance from the electronic distribution, and thus is only affected by the intense field associated with the nucleus of the atom.

This independence of the large angle scattering on the external distribution of electrons is only true for charged particles whose kinetic energy is very large. It is not to be expected that it will hold for particles moving at very much lower speeds and with much less energy—such, for example, as the ordinary cathode particles or the recoil atoms from active matter. In such cases it is probable that the external electronic distribution plays a far more prominent part in governing the scattering than in the case under consideration.

Scattering of β particles.

It is to be anticipated on the nucleus theory that swift β particles should suffer deflexions through large angles in their passage close to the nucleus. There seems to be no doubt that such large deflexions are actually produced, and I showed in my previous paper that the results of scattering of β particles found by Crowther * could be generally explained on the nucleus theory of atomic structure. It should be borne in mind, however, that there are several important points of distinction between the effects to be expected for an α particle and a β particle. Since the force between the nucleus and β particle is attractive, the β particle increases rapidly in speed in approaching the nucleus. On the ordinary electrodynamics, this entails a loss of energy by radiation, and also an increase of the apparent mass of the electron. Darwin† has worked out mathematically the result of these effects on the orbit of the electron, and has shown that, under certain conditions, the β particle does not escape from the atom but describes a spiral orbit ultimately

* Crowther, Proc. Roy. Soc. A. lxxxiv. p. 226 (1910).
† Darwin, Phil. Mag. xxv. p. 201 (1913).

falling into the nucleus. This result is of great interest, for it may offer an explanation of the disappearance of swift β particles in their passage through matter. In addition, it must be borne in mind that the swiftest β particle expelled from radium C possesses only about one-third of the energy of the corresponding α particle, while the average energy of the β particle is less than one-sixth of that of the α particle. It is thus to be anticipated that the large angle scattering of a β particle by the nucleus will take place in regions where the α particle will only suffer a small deflexion—regions for which the application of the simple theory may not have been accurately tested. For these reasons, it is of great importance to determine the laws of large angle scattering of β particles of different speeds in passing through matter, as it should throw light on a number of important points connected with atomic structure. Experiments are at present in progress in the laboratory to examine the scattering of such swift β particles in detail.

It is obvious that a β particle in passing close to an electron will occasionally suffer a large deflexion. The problem is mathematically similar to that for a close encounter of an α particle with a helium atom of the same mass, which is discussed by Mr. Darwin in the accompanying paper. Such large deflexions due to electronic encounter, however, should be relatively small in number compared with those due to the nucleus of a heavy atom.

Scattering in Hydrogen.

Special interest attaches to the effects to be expected when α particles pass through light gases like hydrogen and helium. In a previous paper by Mr. Nuttall and the author *, it has been shown that the scattering of α particles in hydrogen and helium is in good agreement with the view that the hydrogen nucleus has one positive charge, while the α particle, or helium, has two. Mr. Darwin has worked out in detail the simple scattering to be anticipated when α particles pass through hydrogen and helium. It is only necessary here to refer to the fact that on the nucleus theory a small number of hydrogen atoms should acquire, as the result of close encounters with α particles, velocities about 1·6 times that of the velocity of the α particle itself. On account of the fact that the hydrogen atom carries one positive charge while the α particle carries two, it can be calculated that some of the hydrogen atoms should have a range in hydrogen of nearly four times that of the α particle which sets them in motion.

* Rutherford and Nuttall, Phil. Mag. xxvi. p. 702 (1913).

Mr. Marsden has kindly made experiments for me to test whether the presence of such hydrogen atoms can be detected. A detailed account of his experiments will appear later, but it suffices to mention here that undoubted evidence has been obtained by him that some of the hydrogen atoms are set in such swift motion that they are able to produce a visible scintillation on a zinc sulphide screen and are able to travel through hydrogen a distance three or four times greater than the colliding α particle. The general method employed was to place a thin α-ray tube containing about 100 millicuries of purified emanation in a tube filled with hydrogen. The scintillations due to the α particle from the tube disappeared in air after traversing a distance of about 5 cm. When the air was displaced by hydrogen, the great majority of the scintillations disappeared at about 20 cm. from the source, which corresponds to the range of the α particle in hydrogen. A small number of scintillations, however, persisted in hydrogen up to a distance of about 90 cm. The scintillations were of less intensity than those due to the ordinary α particle. The number of scintillations observed is of the order of magnitude to be anticipated on the theory of single scattering, supposing that the nucleus in hydrogen and helium has such small dimensions, and that they behave like point charges for distances up to 10^{-13} cm.

There appears to be no doubt that the scintillations observed beyond 20 cm. are due to charged hydrogen atoms which are set in swift motion by a close encounter with an α particle. Experiments are at present in progress by Mr. Marsden to determine the number of hydrogen atoms set in motion, and the variation of the number with the scattering angle.

It does not appear possible to explain the appearance of such swift hydrogen atoms unless it be supposed that the forces of repulsion between the α particle and the hydrogen atom are exceedingly intense. Such intense forces can only arise if the positive nuclei have exceedingly small dimensions, so that a close approach between them is possible.

Dimensions and Constitution of the Nucleus.

In my previous paper I showed that the nucleus must have exceedingly small dimensions, and calculated that in the case of gold its radius was not greater than 3×10^{-12} cm. In order to account for the velocity given to hydrogen atoms by the collision with α particles, it can be simply calculated (see Darwin) that the centres of nuclei of helium and hydrogen must approach within a distance of $1 \cdot 7 \times 10^{-13}$ cm. of each other. Supposing for simplicity the nuclei to have dimensions and to be spherical in shape, it is clear that the sum of the radii of the hydrogen and helium nuclei is not greater than $1\cdot7\times10^{-13}$ cm. This is an exceedingly small quantity, even *smaller* than the ordinarily accepted value of the diameter of the electron, viz. 2×10^{-13} cm. It is obvious that the method we have considered gives a maximum estimate of the dimensions of the nuclei, and it is not improbable that the hydrogen nucleus itself may have still smaller dimensions. This raises the question whether the hydrogen nucleus is so small that its mass may be accounted for in the same way as the mass of the negative electron.

It is well known from the experiments of Sir J. J. Thomson and others, that no positively charged carrier has been observed of mass less than that of the hydrogen atom. The exceedingly small dimensions found for the hydrogen nucleus add weight to the suggestion that the hydrogen nucleus is the *positive electron*, and that its mass is entirely electromagnetic in origin. According to the electromagnetic theory, the electrical mass of a charged body, supposed spherical, is $\dfrac{2}{3}\dfrac{e^2}{a}$ where e is the charge and a the radius. The hydrogen nucleus consequently must have a radius about 1/1830 of the electron if its mass is to be explained in this way. There is no experimental evidence at present contrary to such an assumption.

The helium nucleus has a mass nearly four times that of hydrogen. If one supposes that the positive electron, *i. e.* the hydrogen atom, is a unit of which all atoms are composed, it is to be anticipated that the helium atom contains four positive electrons and two negative.

It is well known that a helium atom is expelled in many cases in the transformation of radioactive matter, but no evidence has so far been obtained of the expulsion of a hydrogen atom. In conjunction with Mr. Robinson, I have examined whether any other charged atoms are expelled from radioactive matter except helium atoms, and the recoil atoms which accompany the expulsion of α particles. The examination showed that if such particles are expelled, their number is certainly less than 1 in 10,000 of the number of helium atoms. It thus follows that the helium nucleus is a very stable configuration which survives the intense disturbances resulting in its expulsion with high velocity from the radioactive atom, and is one of the units, of which possibly the great majority of the atoms are composed. The radioactive evidence indicates that the atomic weight of successive products decreases by four units consequent on the expulsion of an α particle, and it has often been pointed out that the atomic weights of many of the permanent atoms differ by about four units.

It will be seen later that the resultant positive charge on the nucleus determines the main physical and chemical properties of the atom. The mass of the atom is, however, dependent on the number and arrangement of the positive and negative electrons constituting the atom. Since the experimental evidence indicates that the nucleus has very small dimensions, the constituent positive and negative electrons must be very closely packed together. As Lorentz has pointed out, the electrical mass of a system of charged particles, if close together, will depend not only on the number of these particles, but on the way their fields interact. For the dimensions of the positive and negative electrons considered, the packing must be very close in order to produce an appreciable alteration in the mass due to this cause. This may, for example, be the explanation of the fact that the helium atom has not quite four times the mass of the hydrogen atom. Until, however, the nucleus theory has been more definitely tested, it would appear premature to discuss the possible structure of the nucleus itself. The general theory would indicate that the nucleus of a heavy atom is an exceedingly complicated system, although its dimensions are very minute.

An important question arises whether the atomic nuclei, which all carry a positive charge, contain negative electrons. This question has been discussed by Bohr [*], who concluded from the radioactive evidence that the high speed β particles have their origin in the nucleus. The general radioactive evidence certainly supports such a conclusion. It is well known that the radioactive transformations which are accompanied by the expulsion of high speed β particles are, like the α ray changes, unaffected by wide ranges of temperature or by physical and chemical conditions. On the nucleus theory, there can be no doubt that the α particle has its origin in the nucleus and gains a great part, if not all, of its energy of motion in escaping from the atom. It seems reasonable, therefore, to suppose that a β ray transformation also originates from the expulsion of a negative electron from the nucleus. It is well known that the energy expelled in the form of β and γ rays during the transformation of radium C [†] is about one-quarter of the energy of the expelled α particle. It does not seem easy to explain this large

[*] Bohr, Phil. Mag. xxvi. p. 476 (1913).
[†] See Rutherford and Robinson, Phil. Mag. xxv. p. 301 (1913).

emission of energy by supposing it to have its origin in the electronic distribution. It seems more likely that a very high speed electron is liberated from the nucleus, and in its escape from the atom sets the electronic distribution in violent vibration, giving rise to intense γ rays and also to secondary β particles. The general evidence certainly indicates that many of the high speed electrons from radio-active matter are liberated from the electronic distribution in consequence of the disturbance due to the primary electron escaping from the nucleus.

Charge on the Nucleus.

We have seen that from an examination of the scattering of α particles by matter, it has been found that the positive charge on the nucleus is approximately equal to $\frac{1}{2}Ae$, when A is the atomic weight and *e* the unit charge. This is equivalent to the statement that the number of electrons in the external distribution is about half the atomic weight in terms of hydrogen. It is of interest to note that this is the value deduced by Barkla * from entirely different evidence, viz. the scattering of X rays in their passage through matter. This is founded on the theory of scattering given by Sir J. J. Thomson, which supposes that each electron in an atom scatters as an independent unit. It seems improbable that the electrons within the nucleus would contribute to this scattering, for they are packed together with positive nuclei and must be held in equilibrium by forces of a different order of magnitude from those which bind the external electrons.

It is obvious from the consideration of the cases of hydrogen and helium, where hydrogen has one electron and helium two, that the number of electrons cannot be exactly half the atomic weight in all cases. This has led to an interesting suggestion by van den Broek† that the number of units of charge on the nucleus, and consequently the number of external electrons, may be equal to the number of the elements when arranged in order of increasing atomic weight. On this view, the nucleus charges of hydrogen, helium, and carbon are 1, 2, 6 respectively, and so on for the other elements, provided there is no gap due to a missing element. This view has been taken by Bohr in his theory of the constitution of simple atoms and molecules.

Recently strong evidence of two distinct kinds has been

---

* Barkla, Phil. Mag. xxi. p. 648 (1911).
† van den Broek, *Phys. Zeit.* xiv. p. 32 (1913).

brought in support of such a contention. Soddy * has pointed out that the recent generalisation of the relation between the chemical properties of the elements and the radiations can be interpreted by supposing that the atom loses two positive charges by the expulsion of an α particle, and one negative by the expulsion of a high speed electron. From a consideration of the series of products of the three main radioactive branches of uranium, thorium, and actinium, it follows that some of the radioactive elements may be arranged so that the nucleus charge decreases by one unit as we pass from one element to another. It would thus appear that van den Broek's suggestion probably holds for some if not all of the heavy radioactive elements. Recently Moseley † has supplied very valuable evidence that this rule also holds for a number of the lighter elements. By examination of the wave-length of the characteristic X rays emitted by twelve elements varying in atomic weight between calcium (40) and zinc (65·4), he has shown that the variation of wave-length can be simply explained by supposing that the charge on the nucleus increases from element to element by exactly one unit. This holds true for cobalt and nickel, although it has long been known that they occupy an anomalous relative position in the periodic classification of the elements according to atomic weights.

There appears to be no reason why this new and powerful method of analysis, depending on an examination of the frequency of the characteristic X ray spectra of the elements, should not be extended to a large number of elements, so that further definite data on the point may be expected in the near future.

It is clear on the nucleus theory that the physical and chemical properties of the ordinary elements are for the most part dependent entirely on the charge of the nucleus, for the latter determines the number and distribution of the external electrons on which the chemical and physical properties must mainly depend. As Bohr has pointed out, the properties of gravitation and radioactivity, which are entirely uninfluenced by chemical or physical agencies, must be ascribed mainly if not entirely to the nucleus, while the ordinary physical and chemical properties are determined by the number and distribution of the external electrons. On this view, the nucleus charge is a fundamental constant of the atom, while the atomic mass of an atom may be a complicated function of the arrangement of the units which make up the nucleus.

* Soddy, *Jahr. d. Rad.* x. p. 188 (1913).
† Moseley, Phil. Mag. xxvi. p. 1024 (1913).

It should be borne in mind that there is no inherent impossibility on the nucleus theory that atoms may differ considerably in atomic weight and yet have the same nucleus charge. This is most simply illustrated by radioactive evidence. In the following table the atomic weight and nucleus charge are given for a few of the successive elements arising from the transformation of uranium. The actual nucleus charge of uranium is unknown, but for simplicity it is assumed to be 100.

uccessive Elements ..	$Ur_1 \rightarrow$	$Ur X_1 \rightarrow$	$UrX_2 \rightarrow$	$Ur_2 \rightarrow$	$Io \rightarrow$	Ra
Atomic weights	238·5	234·5	234·5	234·5	230·5	226·5
Charge on nucleus	100	98	99	100	98	96

Following the recent theories, it is supposed that the emission of an α particle lowers the nucleus charge by two units, while the emission of a β particle raises it by one unit. It is seen that Ur_1 and Ur_2 have the same nucleus charge although they differ in atomic weight by four units.

If the nucleus is supposed to be composed of a mixture of hydrogen nuclei with one charge and of helium nuclei with two charges, it is *a priori* conceivable that a number of atoms may exist with the same nucleus charge but of different atomic masses. The radioactive evidence certainly supports such a view, but probably only a few of such possible atoms would be stable enough to survive for a measurable time.

Bohr * has drawn attention to the difficulties of constructing atoms on the " nucleus " theory, and has shown that the stable positions of the external electrons cannot be deduced from the classical mechanics. By the introduction of a conception connected with Planck's quantum, he has shown that on certain assumptions it is possible to construct simple atoms and molecules out of positive and negative nuclei, *e. g.* the hydrogen atom and molecule and the helium atom, which behave in many respects like the actual atoms or molecules. While there may be much difference of opinion as to the validity and of the underlying physical meaning of the assumptions made by Bohr, there can be no doubt that the theories of Bohr are of great interest and importance to all physicists as the first definite attempt to construct simple atoms and molecules and to explain their spectra.

University of Manchester,
    February 1914.

* Bohr, Phil. Mag. xxvi. pp. 476, 857 (1913).

BAKERIAN LECTURE: *Nuclear Constitution of Atoms.*

By Sir E. RUTHERFORD, F.R.S., Cavendish Professor of Experimental Physics, University of Cambridge.

(Received June 3,—Lecture delivered June 3, 1920.)

Introduction.—The conception of the nuclear constitution of atoms arose initially from attempts to account for the scattering of α-particles through large angles in traversing thin sheets of matter.* Taking into account the large mass and velocity of the α-particles, these large deflexions were very remarkable, and indicated that very intense electric or magnetic fields exist within the atom. To account for these results, it was found necessary to assume† that the atom consists of a charged massive nucleus of dimensions very small compared with the ordinarily accepted magnitude of the diameter of the atom. This positively charged nucleus contains most of the mass of the atom, and is surrounded at a distance by a distribution of negative electrons equal in number to the resultant positive charge on the nucleus. Under these conditions, a very intense electric field exists close to the nucleus, and the large deflexion of the α-particle in an encounter with a single atom happens when the particle passes close to the nucleus. Assuming that the electric forces between the α-particle and the nucleus varied according to an inverse square law in the region close to the nucleus, the writer worked out the relations connecting the number of α-particles scattered through any angle with the charge on the nucleus and the energy of the α-particle. Under the central field of force, the α-particle describes a hyperbolic orbit round the nucleus, and the magnitude of the deflection depends on the closeness of approach to the nucleus. From the data of scattering of α-particles then available, it was deduced that the resultant charge on the nucleus was about $\frac{1}{2}Ae$, where A is the atomic weight and e the fundamental unit of charge. Geiger and Marsden‡ made an elaborate series of experiments to test the correctness of the theory, and confirmed the main conclusions. They found the nucleus charge was about $\frac{1}{2}Ae$, but, from the nature of the experiments, it was difficult to fix the actual value within about 20 per cent. C. G. Darwin§ worked out completely the deflexion of the α-particle and of the nucleus, taking into account the mass of the latter, and showed that the scattering

---

* Geiger and Marsden, 'Roy. Soc. Proc.,' A, vol. 82, p. 495 (1909).
† Rutherford, 'Phil. Mag.,' vol. 21, p. 669 (1911); vol. 27, p. 488 (1914).
‡ Geiger and Marsden, 'Phil. Mag.,' vol. 25, p. 604 (1913).
§ Darwin, 'Phil. Mag.,' vol. 27, p. 499 (1914).

experiments of Geiger and Marsden could not be reconciled with any law of central force, except the inverse square. The nuclear constitution of the atom was thus very strongly supported by the experiments on scattering of α-rays.

Since the atom is electrically neutral, the number of external electrons surrounding the nucleus must be equal to the number of units of resultant charge on the nucleus. It should be noted that, from the consideration of the scattering of X-rays by light elements, Barkla* had shown, in 1911, that the number of electrons was equal to about half the atomic weight. This was deduced from the theory of scattering of Sir J. J. Thomson, in which it was assumed that each of the external electrons in an atom acted as an independent scattering unit.

Two entirely different methods had thus given similar results with regard to the number of external electrons in the atom, but the scattering of α-rays had shown in addition that the positive charge must be concentrated on a massive nucleus of small dimensions. It was suggested by Van den Broek† that the scattering of α-particles by the atoms was not inconsistent with the possibility that the charge on the nucleus was equal to the atomic number of the atom, *i.e.*, to the number of the atom when arranged in order of increasing atomic weight. The importance of the atomic number in fixing the properties of an atom was shown by the remarkable work of Moseley‡ on the X-ray spectra of the elements. He showed that the frequency of vibration of corresponding lines in the X-ray spectra of the elements depended on the square of a number which varied by unity in successive elements. This relation received an interpretation by supposing that the nuclear charge varied by unity in passing from atom to atom, and was given numerically by the atomic number. I can only emphasise in passing the great importance of Moseley's work, not only in fixing the number of possible elements, and the position of undetermined elements, but in showing that the properties of an atom were defined by a number which varied by unity in successive atoms. This gives a new method of regarding the periodic classification of the elements, for the atomic number, or its equivalent the nuclear charge, is of more fundamental importance than its atomic weight. In Moseley's work, the frequency of vibration of the atom was not exactly proportional to N, where N is the atomic number, but to $(N-a)^2$, where a was a constant which had different values, depending on whether the K or L series of characteristic radiations were measured. It was supposed that this constant depended on the number and position of the electrons close to the nucleus.

* Barkla, ' Phil. Mag.,' vol. 21, p. 648 (1911).
† Van den Broek, ' Phys. Zeit.,' vol. 14, p. 32 (1913).
‡ Moseley, ' Phil. Mag.,' vol. 26, p. 1024 (1913) ; vol. 27, p. 703 (1914).

Charge on the Nucleus.—The question whether the atomic number of an element is the actual measure of its nuclear charge is a matter of such fundamental importance that all methods of attack should be followed up. Several researches are in progress in the Cavendish Laboratory to test the accuracy of this relation. The two most direct methods depend on the scattering of swift α- and β-rays. The former is under investigation, using new methods, by Mr. Chadwick, and the latter by Dr. Crowther. The results so far obtained by Mr. Chadwick strongly support the identity of the atomic number with the nuclear charge within the possible accuracy of experiment, viz., about 1 per cent.

It thus seems clear that we are on firm ground in supposing that the nuclear charge is numerically given by the atomic number of the element. Incidentally, these results, combined with the work of Moseley, indicate that the law of the inverse square holds with considerable accuracy in the region surrounding the nucleus. It will be of great interest to determine the extent of this region, for it will give us definite information as to the distance of the inner electrons from the nucleus. A comparison of the scattering of slow and swift β-rays should yield important information on this point. The agreement of experiment with theory for the scattering of α-rays between 5° and 150° shows that the law of inverse square holds accurately in the case of a heavy element like gold for distances between about 36×10^{-12} cm. and 3×10^{-12} cm. from the centre of the nucleus. We may consequently conclude that few, if any, electrons are present in this region.

An α-particle in a direct collision with a gold atom of nuclear charge 79 will be turned back in its path at a distance of 3×10^{-12} cm., indicating that the nucleus may be regarded as a point charge even for such a short distance. Until swifter α-particles are available for experiment, we are unable in the case of heavy elements to push further the question of dimensions of heavy atoms. We shall see later, however, that the outlook is more promising in the case of lighter atoms, where the α-particle can approach closer to the nucleus.

It is hardly necessary to emphasise the great importance of the nuclear charge in fixing the physical and chemical properties of an element, for obviously the number and the arrangements of the external electrons on which the great majority of the physical and chemical properties depend, is conditioned by the resultant charge on the nucleus. It is to be anticipated theoretically, and is confirmed by experiment, that the actual mass of the nucleus exercises only a second order effect on the arrangement of the external electrons and their rates of vibration.

It is thus quite possible to imagine the existence of elements of almost identical physical and chemical properties, but which differ from one another in mass, for, provided the resultant nuclear charge is the same, a number of possible stable modes of combination of the different units which make up a complex nucleus may be possible. The dependence of the properties of an atom on its nuclear charge and not on its mass thus offers a rational explanation of the existence of isotopes in which the chemical and physical properties may be almost indistinguishable, but the mass of the isotopes may vary within certain limits. This important question will be considered in more detail later in the paper in the light of evidence as to the nature of the units which make up the nucleus.

The general problem of the structure of the atom thus naturally divides itself into two parts :—

1. Constitution of the nucleus itself.

2. The arrangement and modes of vibration of the external electrons.

I do not propose to-day to enter into (2), for it is a very large subject in which there is room for much difference of opinion. This side of the problem was first attacked by Bohr and Nicholson, and substantial advances have been made. Recently, Sommerfeld and others have applied Bohr's general method with great success in explaining the fine structure of the spectral lines and the complex modes of vibration of simple atoms involved in the Stark effect. Recently, Langmuir and others have attacked the problem of the arrangement of the external electrons from the chemical standpoint, and have emphasised the importance of assuming a more or less cubical arrangement of the electrons in the atom. No doubt each of these theories has a definite sphere of usefulness, but our knowledge is as yet too scanty to bridge over the apparent differences between them.

I propose to-day to discuss in some detail experiments that have been made with a view of throwing light on the constitution and stability of the nuclei of some of the simpler atoms. From a study of radio-activity we know that the nuclei of the radio-active elements consist in part of helium nuclei of charge $2e$. We also have strong reason for believing that the nuclei of atoms contain electrons as well as positively charged bodies, and that the positive charge on the nucleus represents the excess positive charge. It is of interest to note the very different *rôle* played by the electrons in the outer and inner atom. In the former case, the electrons arrange themselves at a distance from the nucleus, controlled no doubt mainly by the charge on the nucleus and the interaction of their own fields. In the case of the nucleus, the electron forms a very close and powerful combination with the positively charged units and, as far as we know, there is a region just outside the nucleus where no electron is in stable equilibrium. While no doubt each of the external electrons acts as a point charge in considering the forces between it and the nucleus, this cannot be the case for the electron in the nucleus itself. It is to be anticipated that under the intense forces in the latter, the electrons are much deformed and the forces may be of a very different character from those to be expected from an undeformed electron, as in the outer atom. It may be for this reason that the electron can play such a different part in the two cases and yet form stable systems.

It has been generally assumed, on the nucleus theory, that electric forces and charges play a predominant part in determining the structure of the inner and outer atom. The considerable success of this theory in explaining fundamental phenomena is an indication of the general correctness of this point of view. At the same time if the electrons and parts composing the nucleus are in motion, magnetic fields must arise which will have to be taken into account in any complete theory of the atom. In this sense the magnetic fields are to be regarded as a secondary rather than a primary factor, even though such fields may be shown to have an important bearing on the conditions of equilibrium of the atom.

Dimensions of Nuclei.

We have seen that in the case of atoms of large nuclear charge the swiftest α-particle is unable to penetrate to the actual structure of the nucleus so that it is possible to give only a maximum estimate of its dimensions. In the case of light atoms, however, when the nucleus charge is small, there is so close an approach during a direct collision with an α-particle that we are able to estimate its dimensions and form some idea of the forces in operation. This is best shown in the case of a direct collision between an α-particle and an atom of hydrogen. In such a case, the H atom is set in such swift motion that it travels four times as far as the colliding α-particle and can be detected by the scintillation produced on a zinc sulphide screen.* The writer† has shown that these scintillations are due to hydrogen atoms carrying unit positive charge recoiling with the velocity to be expected from the simple collision theory, viz., 1·6 times the velocity of the α-particle. The relation between the number and velocity of these H atoms is entirely different from that to be expected if the α-particle and H atom are regarded as point charges for the distances under consideration. The result of the collision with swift α-particles is to produce H atoms which have a narrow range of velocity, and which travel nearly in the direction of the impinging particles. It was deduced that the law of inverse squares no longer holds when the nuclei

---

* Marsden, 'Phil. Mag.,' vol. 27, p. 824 (1914).
† Rutherford, 'Phil. Mag.,' vol. 37, I and II, pp. 538–571 (1919).

approach to within a distance of 3×10^{-13} cm. of each other. This is an indication that the nuclei have dimensions of this order of magnitude and that the forces between the nuclei vary very rapidly in magnitude and in direction for a distance of approach comparable with the diameter of the electron as ordinarily calculated. It was pointed out that in such close encounters there were enormous forces between the nuclei, and probably the structure of the nuclei was much deformed during the collision. The fact that the helium nucleus, which may be supposed to consist of four H atoms and two electrons, appeared to survive the collision is an indication that it must be a highly stable structure. Similar results* were observed in the collision between α-particles and atoms of nitrogen and oxygen for the recoil atoms appeared to be shot forward mainly in the direction of the α-particles and the region where special forces come into play is of the same order of magnitude as in the case of the collision of an α-particle with hydrogen.

No doubt the space occupied by a nucleus and the distance at which the forces become abnormal increase with the complexity of the nucleus structure. We should expect the H nucleus to be the simplest of all and, if it be the positive electron, it may have exceedingly small dimensions compared with the negative electron. In the collisions between α-particles and H atoms, the α-particle is to be regarded as the more complex structure.

The diameter of the nuclei of the light atoms except hydrogen are probably of the order of magnitude 5×10^{-13} cm. and in a close collision the nuclei come nearly in contact and may possibly penetrate each other's structure. Under such conditions, only very stable nuclei would be expected to survive the collision and it is thus of great interest to examine whether evidence can be obtained of their disintegration.

Long Range Particles from Nitrogen.

In previous papers, *loc. cit.*, I have given an account of the effects produced by close collisions of swift α-particles with light atoms of matter with the view of determining whether the nuclear structure of some of the lighter atoms could be disintegrated by the intense forces brought into play in such close collisions. Evidence was given that the passage of α-particles through dry nitrogen gives rise to swift particles which closely resembled in brilliancy of the scintillations and distance of penetration hydrogen atoms set in motion by close collision with α-particles. It was shown that these swift atoms which appeared only in dry nitrogen and not in oxygen or carbon dioxide could not be ascribed to the presence of water vapour or other

* Rutherford, 'Phil. Mag.,' vol. 37, III, p. 571 (1919).

hydrogen material, but must arise from the collision of α-particles with nitrogen atoms. The number of such scintillations due to nitrogen was small, viz., about 1 in 12 of the corresponding number in hydrogen, but was two to three times the number of natural scintillations from the source. The number observed in nitrogen was on an average equal to the number of scintillations when hydrogen at about 6 cm. pressure was added to oxygen or carbon dioxide at normal pressure.

While the general evidence indicated that these long range atoms from nitrogen were charged atoms of hydrogen, the preliminary experiments to test the mass of the particles by bending them in a strong magnetic field yielded no definite results.

From the data given in my previous paper (*loc. cit.*) several theories could be advanced to account for these particles. The calculated range of a singly charged atom set in motion by a close collision with an α-particle of range R cm. in air was shown to be for

Mass 1	....	Range 3·91 R
„ 2	....	„ 4·6 R
„ 3	....	„ 5·06 R
„ 4	....	„ 4·0 R

On account of the small number and weakness of the scintillations under the experimental conditions, the range of the swift atoms from nitrogen could not be determined with sufficient certainty to decide definitely between any of these possibilities. The likelihood that the particles were the original α-particles which had lost one of their two charges, *i.e.*, atoms of charge 1 and mass 4, was suggested by me to several correspondents, but there appeared to be no obvious reason why nitrogen, of all the elements examined, should be the only one in which the passage of a swift α-particle led to the capture of a single electron.

If, however, a sufficient number of scintillations could be obtained under the experimental conditions, there should be no inherent difficulty in deciding between the various possibilities by examining the deflexion of the swift atoms by a magnetic field. The amount of deflexion of charged atoms in a magnetic field perpendicular to the direction of flight is proportional to e/mu. Assuming that the particles were liberated by a direct collision with an α-particle, the relative values of this quantity for different recoiling masses are easily calculated. Taking values MV/E for the α-particle as unity, the corresponding values of mu/e for atoms of charge 1 and mass 1, 2, 3, and 4 are 1·25, 0·75, 0·58, and 0·50 respectively. Consequently the H atoms should be more bent than the α-particles which produced them while the atoms of mass 2 or 3, or 4 would be more difficult to deflect than the parent α-particle.

On my arrival in Cambridge, this problem was attacked in several ways. By the choice of objectives of wide aperture, the scintillations were increased in brilliancy and counting thus made easier. A number of experiments were also made to obtain more powerful sources of radiation with the radium at my command, but finally it was found best, for reasons which need not be discussed here, to obtain the active source of radiation of radium C in the manner described in my previous paper. After a number of observations with solid nitrogen compounds, described later, a simple method was finally devised to estimate the mass of the particle by the use of nitrogen in the gaseous state. The use of the gas itself for this purpose had several advantages over the use of solid nitrogen compounds, for not only was the number of scintillations greater, but the absence of hydrogen or other hydrogen compounds could be ensured.

The arrangement finally adopted is shown in fig. 1. The essential point

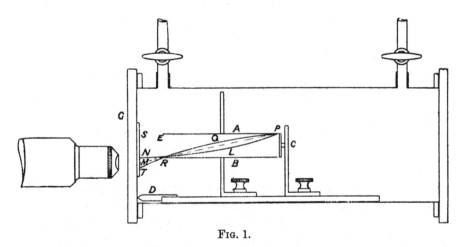

Fig. 1.

lay in the use of wide slits, between which the α-particles passed. Experiment showed that the ratio of the number of scintillations on the screen arising from the gas to the number of natural scintillations from the source, increased rapidly with increased depth of the slits. For plates 1 mm. apart this ratio was less than unity, but for slits 8 mm. apart the ratio had a value 2 to 3. Such a variation is to be anticipitated on theoretical grounds if the majority of the particles are liberated at an angle with the direction of the incident α-particles.

The horizontal slits A, B were 6·0 cm. long, 1·5 cm. wide, and 8 mm. deep, with the source, C of the active deposit of radium placed at one end and the zinc sulphide screen near the other. The carrier of the source and slits were placed in a rectangular brass box, through which a current of dry air or other gas was continuously passed to avoid the danger of radio-active contamination. The box was placed between the poles of a large electromagnet, so that the uniform field was parallel to the plane of the plates and perpendicular to their length. A distance piece, D, of length 1·2 cm., was added between the source and end of the slits, in order to increase the amount of deflexion of the radiation issuing from the slits. The zinc sulphide screen, S, was placed on a glass plate covering the end of the box. The distance between the source and the screen was 7·4 cm. The recoil atoms from oxygen or nitrogen of range 9 cm. could be stopped by inserting an aluminium screen of stopping power about 2 cm. of air placed at the end of the slits.

With such deep slits it was impossible to bend the wide beam of radiation to the sides, but the amount of deflexion of the radiation issuing near the bottom of the slit was measured. For this purpose it was essential to observe the scintillations at a fixed point of the screen near M. The method of fixing the position of the counting microscope was as follows: The source, C, was placed in position, and the air exhausted to a pressure of a few centimetres. Without the field, the bottom edge of the beam was fixed by the straight line PM cutting the screen at M. The microscope was adjusted so that the boundary line of scintillations appeared above the horizontal cross wire in the microscope, marking the centre of the field.

On exciting the magnet to bend the rays upward (called the + field), the

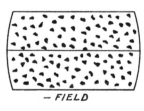

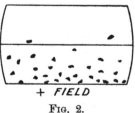

FIG. 2.

path of the limiting α-particles is marked by the curve PLRN cutting the screen at N, so that the boundary of the scintillations appears to be displaced downwards in the field of view. On reversing the field (called the − field), the path of the limiting α-particle PQRT cuts the screen at T, and the band of scintillations appears to be bent upwards. The strength of the magnetic field was adjusted so that, with a negative field, the scintillations were observed all over the screen, while, with a positive field, they were mainly confined below the cross wire. The appearance in the field of view of the microscope for the two fields is illustrated in fig. 2, where the dots represent approximately the density of distribution of the scintillations. The horizontal boundaries of the field of view were given by a rectangular opening in a plate fixed in the position of the cross wires. A horizontal wire, which bisected the field of view, was visible under the conditions of counting, and allowed the relative numbers of scintillations in the two halves of the field to be counted if required. Since the number of scintillations in the actual experiments with nitrogen was much too small to mark directly the boundary of the scintillations, in order to estimate the bending of the rays, it was necessary to determine the ratio of the number of scintillations with the + and − field.

The position of the microscope and the strength of the magnetic field were in most experiments so adjusted that this ratio was about one-third. Preliminary observations showed that this ratio was sensitive to changes of the field and it thus afforded a suitable method for estimating the relative bending of any radiations under examination.

After the position of the microscope was fixed, air was let in, and a continuous flow of dry air maintained through the apparatus. The absorbing screen was introduced at E to stop the atoms from N and O of range 9 cm. The number of scintillations was then systematically counted for the two directions of the field, and a correction, if required, made for any slight radio-active contamination of the screen. The deflexion due to the unknown radiation was directly compared with that produced by a known radiation of α-rays. For this purpose, after removal of the source and absorbing screen, a similar plate, coated with a weak distribution of the active deposit of thorium, was substituted for the radium source. The α-particles from thorium C of range 8·6 cm. produced bright scintillations in the screen after traversing the 7·4 cm. of air in their path. The ratio of the number of scintillations with + and − fields was determined as before.

An example of such comparison is given below. For a current of 4·0 amp. through the electromagnet, the ratio for particles from nitrogen was found to be 0·33. The corresponding ratio for α-particles from thorium C was 0·44 for a current of 4 amp. and 0·31 for a current of 5 amp. It is thus seen that on the average, the particles from nitrogen are more bent in a given field than the α-particles from thorium C. In order, however, to make a quantitative comparison, it is necessary to take into account the reduction in velocity of the radiations in passing through the air. The value mu/e for the α-ray of range 8·6 cm. from thorium C is known to be $4·28 \times 10^5$. Since the rays pass through 7·4 cm. of air in a uniform field before striking the screen, it can be calculated that the actual deflection corresponds to α-rays in a vacuum for which $mu/e = 3·7 \times 10^5$, about. Taking the deflection of the α-particles for a current of 4·8 amp. to be the same as for the nitrogen particles for a field of 4 amp.—ratio of fields 1·17—it is seen that the average deflexion of the

2 E 2

nitrogen particles under the experimental conditions corresponds to a radiation in a vacuum for which the value of $mu/e = 3\cdot1 \times 10^5$.

Bearing in mind that the particles under examination are produced throughout the volume of the gas between the slits, and that their distribution is unknown, and also that the particles are shot forward on an average at an angle with the incident α-particles, the experimental data are quite insufficient to calculate the average value of mu/e to be expected under the experimental conditions for any assumed mass of projected particles. It seems probable that the majority of the particles which produce scintillations are generated in the first few centimetres of the air next the source. The actual deflection of a given particle by the magnetic field will depend on the distance of its point of origin from the source. These factors will obviously tend to make the average deflection of the particles to appear less than if they were all expelled with constant velocity from the source itself. Assuming that the correction for reduction of velocity of the long range particles in traversing the gas is 10 per cent., the average value of mu/e is about $3\cdot4 \times 10^5$. Since the value of MV/E for the α-particle from radium C is $3\cdot98 \times 10^5$, it is seen that under the experimental conditions the average value of mu/e for the nitrogen particles is less than that of the α-particles which produce them.

From the data given earlier in the paper, this should only be true if the particles are comparable in mass with an atom of hydrogen, for singly charged particles of mass 2, 3, or 4 should suffer less deflexion than the α-particles. For example, if we assume that the particles were helium atoms carrying one charge, we should expect them to be deflected to about one-half of the extent of the α-particle. The experimental results thus afford strong presumptive evidence that the particles liberated from nitrogen are atoms of hydrogen.

A far more decisive test, however, can be made by comparing the deflexion of the nitrogen particles with that of H atoms under similar conditions. For this purpose, a mixture of about one volume of hydrogen to two of carbon dioxide was stored in a gas-holder and circulated in place of air through the testing apparatus. The proportions of the two gases were so adjusted that the stopping power of the mixture for α-rays was equal to that of air. Under these conditions, the H atoms, like the nitrogen particles, are produced throughout the volume of the gas, and probably the relative distribution of H atoms along the path of the α-rays is not very different from that of the nitrogen particles under examination. If the nitrogen particles are H atoms, we should expect the average deflexion to be nearly the same as for the H atoms liberated from the hydrogen mixture. A number of careful experiments showed that the ratio of the number of scintillations in + and − fields of equal value was so nearly identical in the two cases that the experiments were unable to distinguish between them. Since the two experiments were carried out under as nearly as possible identical conditions, the equality of the ratio shows that the long range particles liberated from nitrogen are atoms of hydrogen. The possibility that the particles may be of mass 2, 3, or 4 is definitely excluded.

In a previous paper I have given evidence that the long range particles observed in dry air and pure nitrogen must arise from the nitrogen atoms themselves. It is thus clear that some of the nitrogen atoms are disintegrated by their collision with swift α-particles and that swift atoms of positively charged hydrogen are expelled. It is to be inferred that the charged atom of hydrogen is one of the components of which the nucleus of nitrogen is built up.

While it has long been known that helium is a product of the spontaneous transformation of some of the radio-active elements, the possibility of disintegrating the structure of stable atoms by artificial methods has been a matter of uncertainty. This is the first time that evidence has been obtained that hydrogen is one of the components of the nitrogen nucleus.

It should be borne in mind that the amount of disintegration effected in nitrogen by the particles is excessively small, for probably on an average only one α-particle in about 300,000 is able to get near enough to the nitrogen nucleus to liberate the atom of hydrogen with sufficient energy to be detected by the scintillation method. Even if the whole α-radiation from 1 gramme of radium were absorbed in nitrogen gas, the volume of hydrogen set free would be only about 1/300000 of the volume of helium due to the collected α-particles, viz., about 5×10^{-4} cub. mm. per year. It may be possible that the collision of an α-particle is effective in liberating the hydrogen from the nucleus without necessarily giving it sufficient velocity to be detected by scintillations. If this should prove to be the case, the amount of disintegration may be much greater than the value given above.

Experiments with Solid Nitrogen Compounds.

A brief account will now be given of experiments with solid nitrogen compounds. Since the liberation of the particle from nitrogen is a purely atomic phenomenon, it was to be expected that similar particles would be liberated from nitrogen compounds in number proportional to the amount of nitrogen. To test this point, and also the nature of the particles, a number of compounds rich in nitrogen were examined. For this purpose

I have employed the following substances, which were prepared as carefully as possible to exclude the presence of hydrogen in any form :—

1. Boron nitride, kindly prepared for me by W. J. Shutt, in Manchester University.

2. Sodium nitride, titanium nitride and para-cyanogen, kindly prepared for me by Sir William Pope and his assistants.

The apparatus used was similar in form to that given in fig. 1, except that the plates were 4 cm. long. By means of a fine gauze, the powdered material was sifted as uniformly as possible on a thin aluminium plate about 2 sq. cm. in area. The weight of the aluminium plate was about 6 mgrm. per square centimetre, and usually about 4 to 5 mgrm. of the material per square centimetre was used. The stopping power of the aluminium plate for α-particles corresponded to about 3·4 cm. of air, and it was usually arranged that the average stopping power of the material was about the same as for the aluminium. In order to make the material adhere tightly to the plate, a layer of alcohol was first brushed on and the material rapidly sifted into position, and the plate then dried.

Experiment showed that no detectable hydrogen contamination was introduced by the use of alcohol in this way. The zinc sulphide screen was placed outside the box close to an aluminium plate of stopping power equal to 5·2 cm. of air which covered an opening in the end of the brass box. The aluminium carrier was then placed in position to cover the end of the slits near the source, care being taken not to shake off any material. The air was exhausted and the number of scintillations on the screen counted.

1. With material facing the source.

2. With plate reversed.

In the former case, the α-particles were fired directly into the material under examination; in the latter case the α-particles only fell on the material when their range was reduced to about half, when their power of liberating swift atoms is much reduced. This method of reversal had the great advantage that no correction was necessary for unequal absorption of the H-particles from the source in different experiments.

In this way it was found that all the nitrogen compounds examined gave a larger number of scintillations in position (1). The nature of these particles was examined by a method similar to that employed in the case of nitrogen and a direct comparison was made of the deflexion of the particles with that of H atoms liberated from a film of paraffin put in place of the nitrogen compound. In all experiments, the particles were found to be deflected to the same degree as H atoms from the paraffin and no trace of particles of mass 2, 3 or 4 was detected.

For films of equal average stopping power for α-rays, it can readily be calculated from Bragg's rule that the relative stopping power of the nitrogen in the compounds is 0·67 for B.N., 0·74 for C_2N_2, 0·40 for titanium nitride, taking the stopping power of sodium nitride as unity. Since the expulsion of long range nitrogen particles must be an atomic phenomenon, it was to be expected that the number of scintillations under the experimental conditions, after correction for the natural effect from the source, should be proportional to the relative values of stopping power given above. The observations with sodium nitride and titanium nitride were very consistent and the number of long range nitrogen particles was in the right proportion and about the same as that to be expected from the experiments with nitrogen gas. On the other hand, boron nitride and para-cyanogen gave between 1·5 and 2 times the number to be expected theoretically. In these experiments every precaution was taken to get rid of hydrogen and water vapour. Before use, the aluminium plates were heated in an exhausted quartz tube in an electric furnace nearly to its melting point to get rid of hydrogen and other gases. The films under examination were kept in a dessicator and heated in the electric furnace just before use and transferred at once to the testing vessel. Several control experiments were made, using preparations not containing nitrogen, viz., pure graphite and silica which had been kindly prepared for me by Sir William Pope. In both of these cases, the number of scintillations observed with the material facing the α-rays was actually less than when the plate was reversed. This showed that some H atoms were liberated by the α-rays from the heated aluminium. The control experiments were thus very satisfactory in showing that H atoms were not present in materials not containing nitrogen. Incidentally, they show that H atoms do not arise in appreciable numbers from carbon, silicon, or oxygen.

The increased effect in boron nitride and para-cyanogen naturally led to the suspicion that these preparations contained some hydrogen although every precaution was taken to avoid such a possibility. In the case of boron nitride there is also the uncertainty whether boron itself emits H atoms. This point has not yet been properly examined. On account of these uncertainties, experiments on solid nitrogen compounds were abandoned for the time, and experiments already described made directly on gaseous nitrogen.

It is of interest to note that a considerable contamination with hydrogen is required to produce the number of H atoms observed in these compounds. In the case of sodium nitride at least 50 c.c. of hydrogen must be present per gram of material. I am inclined to think that the H atoms liberated by the α-rays from sodium nitride is due mainly, if not entirely to the nitrogen, and in the case of para-cyanogen, part of the effect is probably due to the presence of hydrogen or other hydrogen compound. It is hoped to examine this question in more detail later.

Short Range Atoms from Oxygen and Nitrogen.

In addition to the long range H atoms liberated from nitrogen, the passage of α-particles through oxygen as well as through nitrogen gives rise to much more numerous swift atoms, which have a range in air of about 9·0 cm. compared with that of 7·0 cm. for the colliding α-particles. The method of determining the range and number of these atoms has been explained in a previous paper.* It is there shown that these projected atoms arise from the passage of the α-particles through the gas. Just beyond the range of the α-particles from radium C, the scintillations are much brighter than those due to H atoms, and more resemble α-particles.

In the absence of definite information as to the nature of these atoms, it was provisionally assumed that they were atoms of oxygen or nitrogen carrying a single charge set in swift motion by close collisions with α-particles, for the observed range of these particles was in approximate accord with that calculated on these assumptions. At the same time it was pointed out that the agreement of the ranges of the atoms set free in N and O was rather surprising, for it was to be anticipated that the range of the swifter N atoms should be about 19 per cent. greater than for the slower O atoms. The possibility that these swift atoms might prove to be fragments of disintegrated atoms was always present, but up till quite recently, I did not see any method of settling the question.†

As soon as the use of wide slits had proved successful in deciding the nature of the long range particles from nitrogen, experiments were made with the same apparatus and method to test the nature of the short range particles in O and N.

First consider the relative deflexion to be expected for an O atom which is set in motion by a direct impact with an α-particle. The velocity of the O atom after the collision is 2/5 V, where V is the velocity of the incident α-particle. The value of mu/e for the O atom carrying a single charge is easily seen to be 3·1 times that of the α-particle before impact. Consequently the O atom with a single charge should be much more difficult to deflect than the α-particle, and this is the case even if the former carries two charges.

* Rutherford, 'Phil. Mag.,' vol. 37, III, p. 571 (1919).

† Mr. G. S. Fulcher, of the National Research Council, U.S.A., sent me, in November, 1919, a suggestion that these atoms might prove to be α-particles.

To test these points, the apparatus was the same as that shown in fig. 1. The source was 7·4 cm. distant from the zinc sulphide screen, the end pieces, 1·2 cm. long, being used as before to increase the deflexion of the rays. During an experiment, dried air or oxygen was circulated slowly through the apparatus to avoid radio-active contamination of the screen. In the case of oxygen, the scintillations observed on the screen were due to the O atoms with a small proportion of H atoms from the source. In the case of air, the scintillations on the screen were due partly to N atoms, some O atoms, and H atoms from the source and nitrogen. The actual number of short range N atoms appeared to be less than the number of O atoms under similar conditions.

The position of the microscope was fixed as before to give a convenient ratio for the number of scintillations on reversing the magnetic field. This ratio varied with the position of the microscope, and in the actual experiments had values between 0·2 and 0·4.

It was at once obvious that the atoms from O instead of being *less* deflected than the α-particles, as they should be if they were O atoms, were *more* deflected. This at once excluded the possibility that the atoms from oxygen were actual atoms of oxygen carrying either one or two charges. Since helium is expelled in so many radio-active changes, it might be expected to be one of the components of light atoms, liberated by the intense collision. The deflexion of the atoms from O was, however, much too large to be accounted for in this way. To test this point, at the conclusion of the experiments with oxygen, a plate which had been exposed to thorium emanation was substituted for the radium source, and the bending of the rays of range 8·6 cm. from thorium C was examined in a similar way. If an α-particle were ejected from an O atom near the source, it would be bent like an α-particle of range 9·0 cm. ; if produced near the end of the range of α-rays, the amount of bending could not be more than for an α-particle of range 7·0 cm., *i.e.*, about 9 per cent. more than in the first case. Even supposing the particles were liberated uniformly along the path of the α-rays and moved in the same line as the colliding particle, the average bending would not differ by 5 per cent. from that of the α-particle from thorium C. If, as seems probable, some of the atoms are liberated at an angle with the incident particles, the average amount of bending of the beam would be less than the above, and in all probability less than for the α-particles from thorium C. Actually the bending observed was about 20 per cent. greater, showing that the hypothesis that the atoms from O are charged atoms of helium is quite untenable.

If the atoms from O were H atoms, they would be more bent than the α-particles, but would have a maximum range of 28 cm. instead of the

9·0 cm. observed. It thus seemed clear from this evidence that the atom must be of mass intermediate between 1 and 4, while from consideration of the range of the particles and their amount of deflexion it was clear that the atom carried two units of charge.

In order to make a more decisive test, the deflexion of O atoms in a positive and negative field of given value was directly compared with the deflexion of H atoms from a mixture of hydrogen and carbonic acid, in the ratio of about 1 to 2 in volume. In order to absorb completely the O atoms from CO_2, aluminium foil was placed over the zinc sulphide screen, so that the total absorption between the source and screen corresponded to slightly more than 9 cm. of air. In both experiments, the atoms under examination are produced in the gas between the slits, and probably the relative distribution along the path of the α-rays is not markedly different in the two cases.

The ratios for reversing the field in the two experiments were found to be nearly equal; but, as an average of a number of experiments, the H atoms were slightly more bent than the atoms from O. From a number of experiments it was concluded that the difference in deflexion did not on the average amount to more than 5 per cent., although from the nature of the observations it was difficult to fix the difference with any certainty.

From these data and the range of the atoms from O in air, we can deduce the mass of the particle liberated from oxygen.

Let m = mass of the atom from O,
u = its maximum velocity near the source,
E = charge

Let M, V, E be the corresponding values for the incident α-particles and $m'u'e$ the values for the H atoms liberated close to the source.

Taking into account that the particle from O of range 9 cm. is steadily reduced in velocity in passing through the 7·4 cm. of oxygen between the source and screen, it can easily be calculated that its average deflexion by the magnetic field is proportional to 1·14 E/mu in place of E/mu in a vacuum.

In a similar way, the deflexion of the H atom is proportional to 1·05 $e/m'u'$, the correction in this case for change of velocity being smaller, and estimated to be about 5 per cent. Now we have seen that the experimental results showed that the atoms from O were bent about 5 per cent. less than the H atoms. Consequently

$$1 \cdot 14 \, E/mu = \frac{1 \cdot 05}{1 \cdot 05} \, e/m'u' = 1 \cdot 25 \, E/mv,$$

or $$1 \cdot 14 \, MV = 1 \cdot 25 \, mu, \qquad (1)$$

since it has been calculated and verified by experiment that the deflexion of the H atom in a magnetic field is 1·25 times that of the α-particle which sets it in motion (see Paper II, *loc. cit.*). Also in a previous paper, III, I have given reasons for believing that the range x of mass m and initial velocity u, carrying a double charge, is given by

$$\frac{x}{R} = \frac{m}{M}\left(\frac{u}{V}\right)^3,$$

where R is the range of the α-particle of mass M and velocity V. Since $x = 9\cdot0$ cm. for the atoms from O set in motion by collision with α-particles from radium C of range 7 cm.,

$$\frac{x}{R} = 1\cdot29,$$

and taking M = 4 $$mu^3 = 5\cdot16\,v^3. \qquad (2)$$

A formula of this type has been shown to account for the range of the H atom, and there is every reason to believe it is fairly accurate over such a short difference of range.

From (1) and (2) $$\underline{u = 1\cdot19\,V},$$

$$\underline{m = 3\cdot1}.$$

Considering the difficulty of obtaining accurate data, the value $m = 3\cdot1$ indicates that the atom has a mass about 3 and this value will be taken as the probable value in later discussions.

When air was substituted for oxygen it was not possible to distinguish any difference between the bending of the short range atoms in the two cases. Since the short range atoms from air arise mainly from the nitrogen, we may consequently conclude that the short range atoms liberated by the passage of particles through oxygen or nitrogen consist of atoms of mass 3, carrying a double charge, and initially projected with a velocity 1·19 V, where V is the velocity of the colliding α-particle.

There seems to be no escape from the conclusion that these atoms of mass 3 are liberated from the atoms of oxygen or nitrogen as a result of an intense collision with an α-particle. It is thus reasonable to suppose that atoms of mass 3 are constituents of the structure of the nuclei of the atoms of both oxygen and nitrogen. We have shown earlier in the paper that hydrogen is also one of the constituents of the nitrogen nucleus. It is thus clear that the nitrogen nucleus can be disintegrated in two ways, one by the expulsion of an H atom and the other by the expulsion of an atom of mass 3 carrying two charges. Since now these atoms of mass 3 are five to ten times as numerous as the H atoms, it appears that these two forms of disintegration are independent and not simultaneous. From the rareness of the collisions it is highly improbable that a single atom undergoes both types of disintegration.

Since the particles ejected from O and N are not produced at the source, but along the path of the α-particles, it is difficult to determine their mass and velocity with the precision desired. To overcome this drawback, attempts were made to determine the deflection of O atoms released from a mica plate placed over the source. In consequence of hydrogen in combination in the mica, the H atoms falling on the screen were so numerous compared with the O particles, and their deflexion under the experimental conditions so nearly alike, that it was difficult to distinguish between them.

Energy Considerations.

In close collisions between an α-particle and an atom, the laws of conservation of energy and of momentum appear to hold,* but, in cases where the atoms are disintegrated, we should not necessarily expect these laws to be valid, unless we are able to take into account the change of energy and momentum of the atom in consequence of its disintegration.

In the case of the ejection of a hydrogen atom from the nitrogen nucleus, the data available are insufficient, for we do not know with certainty either the velocity of the H atom or the velocity of the α-particle after the collision.

If we are correct in supposing that atoms of mass 3 are liberated from O and N atoms, it can be easily calculated that there is a slight gain of energy as a result of the disintegration. If the mass is 3 exactly, the velocity of escape of the atom is 1·20 V, where V is the velocity of the impinging α-particle.

Thus, $$\frac{\text{energy of liberated atom}}{\text{energy of } \alpha\text{-particle}} = \frac{3 \times 1\cdot44}{4} = 1\cdot08,$$

or there is a gain of 8 per cent. in energy of motion, even though we disregard entirely the subsequent motion of the disintegrated nucleus or of the colliding α-particle. This extra energy must be derived from the nitrogen or oxygen nucleus in the same way that the α-particle gains energy of motion in escaping from the radio-active atom.

For the purpose of calculation, consider a direct collision between an α-particle and an atom of mass 3. The velocity of the latter is 8/7 V, where V is the velocity of the α-particle, and its energy is 0·96 of the initial energy of the α-particle. No doubt, in the actual case of a collision with the O or N atom, in which the atom of mass 3 is liberated, the

* Rutherford, 'Phil. Mag.,' vol. 37, p. 562 (1919).

α-particle comes under the influence of the main field of the nucleus, as well as of that of the part of mass 3 immediately in its path. Under such conditions, it is not to be expected that the α-particle can give 0·96 of its energy to the escaping atom, but the latter acquires additional energy due to the repulsive field of the nucleus.

In our ignorance of the constitution of the nuclei and the nature of the forces in their immediate neighbourhood, it is not desirable to enter into speculations as to the mechanism of the collision at this stage, but it may be possible to obtain further information by a study of the trails of α-particles through oxygen or nitrogen by the well-known expansion method of C. T. R. Wilson. In a previous paper,[*] I discussed the photograph obtained by Mr. Wilson, in which there is a sudden change of 43° in the direction of the trail, with the appearance of a short spur at the fork. Evidence was given that the relative length of the tracks of the α-particle and of the spur were in rough accord with the view that the spur was due to the recoiling oxygen atom. This is quite probably the case, for the general evidence shows that the atoms of mass 3, after liberation, travel nearly in the direction of the α-particle, and an oblique collision may not result in the disintegration of the atom.

Recently, Dr. Shimizu, of the Cavendish Laboratory, has devised a modification of the Wilson expansion apparatus, in which expansions can be periodically produced several times a second, so that the trails of many particles can be inspected in a reasonable time. Under these conditions, both Shimizu and myself saw on several occasions what appeared to be branching trails of an α-particle in which the lengths of the two tracks were comparable. Eye observations of this kind are too uncertain to regard them with much confidence, so arrangements are being made by Mr. Shimizu to obtain photographs, so that the tracks can be examined in detail at leisure. In this way we may hope to obtain valuable information as to the conditions which determine the disintegration of the atoms, and on the relative energy communicated to the three systems involved, viz., the α-particle, the escaping atom, and the residual nucleus.

So far no definite information is available as to the energy of the α-particle required to produce disintegration, but the general evidence indicates that fast α-particles, of range about 7 cm. in air, are more effective than α-particles of range about 4 cm. This may not be connected directly with the actual energy required to effect the disintegration of the atom itself, but rather to the inability of the slower α-particle under the repulsive field to approach close enough to the nucleus to be effective in disrupting it. Possibly the

* Rutherford, 'Phil. Mag.,' vol. 37, p. 577 (1919).

actual energy required to disintegrate the atom is small compared with the energy of the α-particle.

If this be the case, it may be possible for other agents of less energy than the α-particle to effect the disintegration. For example, a swift electron may reach the nucleus with sufficient energy to cause its disintegration, for it moves in an attractive and not a repulsive field as in the case of the α-particle. Similarly, a penetrating γ-ray may have sufficient energy to cause disintegration. It is thus of great importance to test whether oxygen or nitrogen or other elements can be disintegrated under the action of swift cathode rays generated in a vacuum tube. In the case of oxygen and nitrogen, this could be tested simply by observing whether a spectrum closely resembling helium is given by the gas in the tube, after an intense bombardment of a suitable substance, by electrons. Experiments of this type are being undertaken by Dr. Ishida in the Cavendish Laboratory, every precaution being taken by the heating of the vacuum tube of special glass and electrodes to a high temperature to ensure the removal of any occluded helium which may be initially in the material. Helium has previously been observed by several investigators in vacuum tubes and is known to be released from substances by bombardment with cathode rays. The proof of the actual production of helium in such cases is exceedingly difficult, but the recent improvements in vacuum tube technique may make it easier to give a decisive answer to this important question.

Properties of the new Atom.

We have shown that atoms of mass about 3 carrying two positive charges are liberated by α-particles both from nitrogen and oxygen, and it is natural to suppose that these atoms are independent units in the structure of both gases. Since probably the charged atom during its flight is the nucleus of a new atom without any external electrons, we should anticipate that the new atom when it has gained two negative electrons should have physical and chemical properties very nearly identical with those of helium, but with a mass 3 instead of 4. We should anticipate that the spectrum of helium and this isotope should be nearly the same, but on account of the marked difference in the relative masses of the nuclei, the displacement of the lines should be much greater than in the case of isotopes of heavy elements like lead.

It will be remembered that Bourget, Fabry, and Buisson,[*] from an examination of the width of the lines in the spectrum of nebulæ, conclude that the spectrum arises from an element of atomic mass about 2·7 or 3 in round

[*] Bourget, Fabry and Buisson, 'C. R.,' April 6, May 18 (1914).

numbers. It is difficult, however, on modern views to suppose that the spectrum of the so-called "nebulium" can be due to an element of nuclear charge 2 unless the spectrum under the conditions existing in nebulæ are very different from those observed in the laboratory. The possible origin of the spectrum of nebulium has been discussed at length by Nicholson[*] on quite other lines, and it is not easy at the moment to see how the new atoms from oxygen or nitrogen can be connected with the nebular material.

Since probably most of the helium in use is derived, either directly or indirectly, from the transformation of radio-active materials, and these, as far as we know, always give rise to helium of mass 4, the presence of an isotope of helium of mass 3 is not likely to be detected in such sources. It would, however, be of great interest to examine whether the isotope may be present in cases where the apparent presence of helium is difficult to connect with radio-active material; for example, in beryl, drawn attention to by Strutt.[†] This is based on the assumption that the atom of mass 3 is stable. The fact that it survives the intense disturbance of its structure due to a close collision with an α-particle is an indication that it is a structure difficult to disintegrate by external forces.

Constitution of Nuclei and Isotopes.

In considering the possible constitution of the elements, it is natural to suppose that they are built up ultimately of hydrogen nuclei and electrons. On this view the helium nucleus is composed of four hydrogen nuclei and two negative electrons with a resultant charge of two. The fact that the mass of the helium atom 3·997 in terms of oxygen 16 is less than the mass of four hydrogen atoms, viz., 4·032, has been generally supposed to be due to the close interaction of the fields in the nucleus resulting in a smaller electromagnetic mass than the sum of the masses of the individual components. Sommerfeld[‡] has concluded from this fact that the helium nucleus must be a very stable structure which would require intense forces to disrupt it. Such a conclusion is in agreement with experiment, for no evidence has been obtained to show that helium can be disintegrated by the swift α-particles which are able to disrupt the nuclei of nitrogen and oxygen. In his recent experiments on the isotopes of ordinary elements Aston[§] has shown that within the limit of experimental accuracy the masses of all the isotopes examined are given by whole numbers when oxygen is taken as 16. The only exception is hydrogen, which has a mass 1·008 in agreement

[*] Nicholson, 'Roy. Ast. Soc.,' vol. 72, No. 1, p. 49 (1911); vol. 74, No. 7, p. 623 (1914).
[†] Strutt, 'Roy. Soc. Proc.,' A, vol. 80, p. 572 (1908).
[‡] Sommerfeld, 'Atombau und Spektrallinien,' p. 538. Vieweg and Son, 1919.
[§] Aston, 'Phil. Mag.,' December, 1919: April and May, 1920.

with chemical observations. This does not exclude the probability that hydrogen is the ultimate constituent of which nuclei are composed, but indicates that either the grouping of the hydrogen nuclei and electrons is such that the average electromagnetic mass is nearly 1, or, what is more probable, that the secondary units, of which the atom is mainly built up, *e.g.*, helium or its isotope, have a mass given nearly by a whole number when O is 16.

The experimental observations made so far are unable to settle whether the new atom has a mass exactly 3, but from the analogy with helium we may expect the nucleus of the new atom to consist of three H nuclei and one electron, and to have a mass more nearly 3 than the sum of the individual masses in the free state.

If we are correct in this assumption it seems very likely that one electron can also bind two H nuclei and possibly also one H nucleus. In the one case, this entails the possible existence of an atom of mass nearly 2 carrying one charge, which is to be regarded as an isotope of hydrogen. In the other case, it involves the idea of the possible existence of an atom of mass 1 which has zero nucleus charge. Such an atomic structure seems by no means impossible. On present views, the neutral hydrogen atom is regarded as a nucleus of unit charge with an electron attached at a distance, and the spectrum of hydrogen is ascribed to the movements of this distant electron. Under some conditions, however, it may be possible for an electron to combine much more closely with the H nucleus, forming a kind of neutral doublet. Such an atom would have very novel properties. Its external field would be practically zero, except very close to the nucleus, and in consequence it should be able to move freely through matter. Its presence would probably be difficult to detect by the spectroscope, and it may be impossible to contain it in a sealed vessel. On the other hand, it should enter readily the structure of atoms, and may either unite with the nucleus or be disintegrated by its intense field, resulting possibly in the escape of a charged H atom or an electron or both.

If the existence of such atoms be possible, it is to be expected that they may be produced, but probably only in very small numbers, in the electric discharge through hydrogen, where both electrons and H nuclei are present in considerable numbers. It is the intention of the writer to make experiments to test whether any indication of the production of such atoms can be obtained under these conditions.

The existence of such nuclei may not be confined to mass 1 but may be possible for masses 2, 3, or 4, or more, depending on the possibility of combination between the doublets. The existence of such atoms seems almost necessary to explain the building up of the nuclei of heavy elements; for unless we suppose the production of charged particles of very high velocities it is difficult to see how any positively charged particle can reach the nucleus of a heavy atom against its intense repulsive field.

We have seen that so far the nuclei of three light atoms have been recognised experimentally as probable units of atomic structure, viz.,

$$\overset{+}{H_1}, \quad \overset{++}{X_3}, \quad \overset{++}{He_4},$$

where the subscript represents the mass of the element.

In considering the possible ways in which nuclei can be built up, difficulties at once arise, for many combinations of these units with negative electrons are possible to give an element of the required nuclear charge and mass. In our complete ignorance of the laws of force close to the nuclei, no criterion is available as to the stability or relative probability of the theoretical systems. With the exception of a few elements which can exist in the gaseous state, the possible isotopes of the elements have not yet been settled. When further information is available as to the products of the disintegration of other elements than the two so far examined, and more complete data have been obtained as to the number and mass of the isotopes, it may be possible to deduce approximate rules which may serve as a guide to the mode in which the nuclei are built up from the simpler units. For these reasons it seems premature at this stage to attempt to discuss with any detail the possible structure of even the lighter and presumably less complex atoms. It may, however, be of some interest to give an example to illustrate a possible method of the formation of isotopes in the case of the lighter elements. This is based on the view that probably in many cases a helium nucleus of mass 4 may be substituted in the complex structure for the corresponding nucleus of mass 3 without seriously interfering with the stability of the system. In such a case, the nuclear charge remains unchanged but the masses differ by unity.

For example, take the case of lithium of nuclear charge 3 and atomic mass about 7. It is natural to suppose that the nucleus is composed of helium or its isotope of mass 3 with one binding electron. The three possible combinations are shown in fig. 3 (p. 398).

On this view, at least three isotopes of lithium of mass 6, 7, and 8 are theoretically probable, but even if the combinations were equally stable, the question of their relative abundance in the element lithium on the earth will be dependent on many factors of which we know nothing; for example, the mode of actual formation of such nuclei, the relative amount of the combining units present, and the probability of their combinations.

The experimental results given in the paper support, as far as they go, the view that the atoms of hydrogen and of mass 3 are important units in the nuclear structure of nitrogen and oxygen. In the latter case, one could

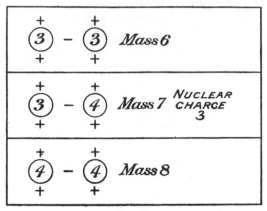

Fig. 3.

a priori have supposed that oxygen was in some way a combination of four helium nuclei of mass 4. It seems probable that the mass 3 is an important unit of the nuclei of light atoms in general, but it is not unlikely, with increasing complexity of the nuclei and corresponding increase of the electric field, the structures of mass 3 suffer a rearrangement and tend to revert to the presumably more stable nucleus of mass 4. This may be the reason why helium of mass 4 always appears to be expelled from the radio-active atoms, while the isotope of mass 3 arises in the artificial disintegration of lighter atoms like oxygen and nitrogen. It has long been known that for many of the elements the atomic weights can be expressed by the formula $4n$ or $4n+3$, where n is an integer, suggesting that atoms of mass 3 and 4 are important units of the structure of nuclei.*

Structure of Carbon, Oxygen, and Nitrogen Nuclei.

In the light of the present experiments, it may be of interest to give some idea, however crude, of the possible formation of the above atoms to account for the experimental facts. It will be remembered that nitrogen alone gives rise to H atoms while carbon and oxygen do not. Both nitrogen and oxygen give rise to atoms of mass 3, while carbon has not

* From these and other considerations, Harkins ('Phys. Rev.,' vol. 15, p. 73 (1920)) has proposed a constitutional formula for all the elements. The combining units employed by him are electrons and atoms of mass 1, 3, and 4 of nuclear charges 1, 1 and 2, respectively. The unit of mass 3 is taken by him to have a nucleus charge of 1 and not 2, and is thus to be regarded as an isotope of hydrogen and not an isotope of helium.

yet been investigated from this point of view.   A possible structure is shown in fig. 4 when the masses and charges of the combining units are indicated.   Negative electrons are represented by the symbol —.

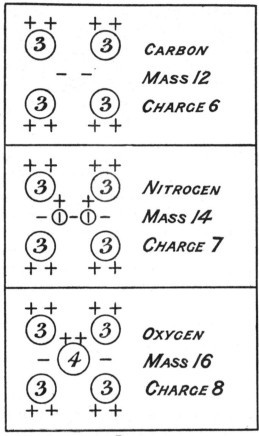

Fig. 4.

The carbon nucleus is taken to consist of four atoms of mass 3 and charge 2, and two binding electrons.   The change to nitrogen is represented by the addition of two H atoms with a binding electron and an oxygen nucleus by the substitution of a helium nucleus in place of the two H atoms.

We can see from this type of structure that the chance of a direct collision with one of the four atoms of mass 3 in nitrogen is much greater than the chance of removing an H atom, for it is to be anticipated that the main nucleus would screen the H atom from a direct collision except in restricted regions facing the H atoms.   This serves to illustrate why the number of H atoms of mass 3 liberated from nitrogen should be much

2 F 2

greater than the number of H atoms released under corresponding conditions. It should be borne in mind that the structures outlined are purely illustrative and no importance is attached to the particular arrangement employed.

It is natural to inquire as to the nature of the residual atoms after the disintegration of oxygen and nitrogen, supposing that they survive the collision and sink into a new stage of temporary or permanent equilibrium.

The expulsion of an H atom carrying one charge from nitrogen should lower the mass by 1 and the nuclear charge by 1. The residual nucleus should thus have a nuclear charge 6 and mass 13, and should be an isotope of carbon. If a negative electron is released at the same time, the residual atom becomes an isotope of nitrogen.

The expulsion of a mass 3 carrying two charges from nitrogen, probably quite independent of the release of the H atom, lowers the nuclear charge by 2 and the mass by 3. The residual atom should thus be an isotope of boron of nuclear charge 5 and mass 11. If an electron escapes as well, there remains an isotope of carbon of mass 11. The expulsion of a mass 3 from oxygen gives rise to a mass 13 of nuclear charge 6, which should be an isotope of carbon. In case of the loss of an electron as well, there remains an isotope of nitrogen of mass 13. The data at present available are quite insufficient to distinguish between these alternatives.

It is intended to continue experiments, to test whether any evidence can be obtained of the disintegration of other light atoms besides nitrogen and oxygen. The problem is more difficult in the case of elements which cannot be conveniently obtained in the gaseous state, since it is not an easy matter to ensure the absence of hydrogen or to prepare uniform thin films of such substances. For these reasons, and the strain involved in counting scintillations under difficult conditions, further progress is not likely to be rapid.

I am indebted to my assistant, G. A. R. Crowe, for the preparation of the radio-active sources and his help in counting; also to Mr. J. Chadwick and Dr. Ishida for assistance in counting scintillations in some of the later experiments.

Letters to the Editor

[The Editor does not hold himself responsible for opinions expressed by his correspondents. Neither can he undertake to return, nor to correspond with the writers of, rejected manuscripts intended for this or any other part of NATURE. *No notice is taken of anonymous communications.]*

Possible Existence of a Neutron

IT has been shown by Bothe and others that beryllium when bombarded by α-particles of polonium emits a radiation of great penetrating power, which has an absorption coefficient in lead of about $0\cdot3$ (cm.)$^{-1}$. Recently Mme. Curie-Joliot and M. Joliot found, when measuring the ionisation produced by this beryllium radiation in a vessel with a thin window, that the ionisation increased when matter containing hydrogen was placed in front of the window. The effect appeared to be due to the ejection of protons with velocities up to a maximum of nearly 3×10^9 cm. per sec. They suggested that the transference of energy to the proton was by a process similar to the Compton effect, and estimated that the beryllium radiation had a quantum energy of 50×10^6 electron volts.

I have made some experiments using the valve counter to examine the properties of this radiation excited in beryllium. The valve counter consists of a small ionisation chamber connected to an amplifier, and the sudden production of ions by the entry of a particle, such as a proton or α-particle, is recorded by the deflexion of an oscillograph. These experiments have shown that the radiation ejects particles from hydrogen, helium, lithium, beryllium, carbon, air, and argon. The particles ejected from hydrogen behave, as regards range and ionising power, like protons with speeds up to about $3\cdot2 \times 10^9$ cm. per sec. The particles from the other elements have a large ionising power, and appear to be in each case recoil atoms of the elements.

If we ascribe the ejection of the proton to a Compton recoil from a quantum of 52×10^6 electron volts, then the nitrogen recoil atom arising by a similar process should have an energy not greater than about 400,000 volts, should produce not more than about 10,000 ions, and have a range in air at N.T.P. of about $1\cdot3$ mm. Actually, some of the recoil atoms in nitrogen produce at least 30,000 ions. In collaboration with Dr. Feather, I have observed the recoil atoms in an expansion chamber, and their range, estimated visually, was sometimes as much as 3 mm. at N.T.P.

These results, and others I have obtained in the course of the work, are very difficult to explain on the assumption that the radiation from beryllium is a quantum radiation, if energy and momentum are to be conserved in the collisions. The difficulties disappear, however, if it be assumed that the radiation consists of particles of mass 1 and charge 0, or neutrons. The capture of the α-particle by the Be^9 nucleus may be supposed to result in the formation of a C^{12} nucleus and the emission of the neutron. From the energy relations of this process the velocity of the neutron emitted in the forward direction may well be about 3×10^9 cm. per sec. The collisions of this neutron with the atoms through which it passes give rise to the recoil atoms, and the observed energies of the recoil atoms are in fair agreement with this view. Moreover, I have observed that the protons ejected from hydrogen by the radiation emitted in the opposite direction to that of the exciting α-particle appear to have a much smaller range than those ejected by the forward radiation.

This again receives a simple explanation on the neutron hypothesis.

If it be supposed that the radiation consists of quanta, then the capture of the α-particle by the Be^9 nucleus will form a C^{13} nucleus. The mass defect of C^{13} is known with sufficient accuracy to show that the energy of the quantum emitted in this process cannot be greater than about 14×10^6 volts. It is difficult to make such a quantum responsible for the effects observed.

It is to be expected that many of the effects of a neutron in passing through matter should resemble those of a quantum of high energy, and it is not easy to reach the final decision between the two hypotheses. Up to the present, all the evidence is in favour of the neutron, while the quantum hypothesis can only be upheld if the conservation of energy and momentum be relinquished at some point.

J. CHADWICK.

Cavendish Laboratory,
Cambridge, Feb. 17.

The Existence of a Neutron.

By J. CHADWICK, F.R.S.

(Received May 10, 1932.)

§ 1. It was shown by Bothe and Becker* that some light elements when bombarded by α-particles of polonium emit radiations which appear to be of the γ-ray type. The element beryllium gave a particularly marked effect of this kind, and later observations by Bothe, by Mme. Curie-Joliot† and by Webster‡ showed that the radiation excited in beryllium possessed a penetrating power distinctly greater than that of any γ-radiation yet found from the radioactive elements. In Webster's experiments the intensity of the radiation was measured both by means of the Geiger-Müller tube counter and in a high pressure ionisation chamber. He found that the beryllium radiation had an absorption coefficient in lead of about $0 \cdot 22$ cm.$^{-1}$ as measured under his experimental conditions. Making the necessary corrections for these conditions, and using the results of Gray and Tarrant to estimate the relative contributions of scattering, photoelectric absorption, and nuclear absorption in the absorption of such penetrating radiation, Webster concluded that the radiation had a quantum energy of about 7×10^6 electron volts. Similarly he found that the radiation from boron bombarded by α-particles of polonium consisted in part of a radiation rather more penetrating than that from beryllium, and he estimated the quantum energy of this component as about 10×10^6 electron volts. These conclusions agree quite well with the supposition that the radiations arise by the capture of the α-particle into the beryllium (or boron) nucleus and the emission of the surplus energy as a quantum of radiation.

The radiations showed, however, certain peculiarities, and at my request the beryllium radiation was passed into an expansion chamber and several photographs were taken. No unexpected phenomena were observed though, as will be seen later, similar experiments have now revealed some rather striking events. The failure of these early experiments was partly due to the weakness of the available source of polonium, and partly to the experimental arrangement, which, as it now appears, was not very suitable.

* ' Z. Physik,' vol. 66, p. 289 (1930).
† I. Curie, ' C. R. Acad. Sci. Paris,' vol. 193, p. 1412 (1931).
‡ ' Proc. Roy. Soc.,' A, vol. 136, p. 428 (1932).

Quite recently, Mme. Curie-Joliot and M. Joliot* made the very striking observation that these radiations from beryllium and from boron were able to eject protons with considerable velocities from matter containing hydrogen. In their experiments the radiation from beryllium was passed through a thin window into an ionisation vessel containing air at room pressure. When paraffin wax, or other matter containing hydrogen, was placed in front of the window, the ionisation in the vessel was increased, in some cases as much as doubled. The effect appeared to be due to the ejection of protons, and from further experiment they showed that the protons had ranges in air up to about 26 cm., corresponding to a velocity of nearly 3×10^9 cm. per second. They suggested that energy was transferred from the beryllium radiation to the proton by a process similar to the Compton effect with electrons, and they estimated that the beryllium radiation had a quantum energy of about 50×10^6 electron volts. The range of the protons ejected by the boron radiation was estimated to be about 8 cm. in air, giving on a Compton process an energy of about 35×10^6 electron volts for the effective quantum.†

There are two grave difficulties in such an explanation of this phenomenon. Firstly, it is now well established that the frequency of scattering of high energy quanta by electrons is given with fair accuracy by the Klein-Nishina formula, and this formula should also apply to the scattering of quanta by a proton. The observed frequency of the proton scattering is, however, many thousand times greater than that predicted by this formula. Secondly, it is difficult to account for the production of a quantum of 50×10^6 electron volts from the interaction of a beryllium nucleus and an α-particle of kinetic energy of 5×10^6 electron volts. The process which will give the greatest amount of energy available for radiation is the capture of the α-particle by the beryllium nucleus, Be^9, and its incorporation in the nuclear structure to form a carbon nucleus C^{13}. The mass defect of the C^{13} nucleus is known both from data supplied by measurements of the artificial disintegration of boron B^{10} and from observations of the band spectrum of carbon; it is about 10×10^6 electron volts. The mass defect of Be^9 is not known, but the assumption that it is zero will give a maximum value for the possible change of energy in the reaction $Be^9 + \alpha \rightarrow C^{13} +$ quantum. On this assumption it follows that the energy of the quantum emitted in such a reaction cannot be greater than about 14×10^6 electron volts. It must, of course, be admitted that this argument

* Curie and Joliot, 'C. R. Acad. Sci. Paris,' vol. 194, p. 273 (1932).

† Many of the arguments of the subsequent discussion apply equally to both radiations, and the term " beryllium radiation " may often be taken to include the boron radiation.

from mass defects is based on the hypothesis that the nuclei are made as far as possible of α-particles; that the Be^9 nucleus consists of 2 α-particles + 1 proton + 1 electron and the C^{13} nucleus of 3 α-particles + 1 proton + 1 electron. So far as the lighter nuclei are concerned, this assumption is supported by the evidence from experiments on artificial disintegration, but there is no general proof.

Accordingly, I made further experiments to examine the properties of the radiation excited in beryllium. It was found that the radiation ejects particles not only from hydrogen but from all other light elements which were examined. The experimental results were very difficult to explain on the hypothesis that the beryllium radiation was a quantum radiation, but followed immediately if it were supposed that the radiation consisted of particles of mass nearly equal to that of a proton and with no net charge, or neutrons. A short statement of some of these observations was published in 'Nature.'* This paper contains a fuller description of the experiments, which suggest the existence of neutrons and from which some of the properties of these particles can be inferred. In the succeeding paper Dr. Feather will give an account of some observations by means of the expansion chamber of the collisions between the beryllium radiation and nitrogen nuclei, and this is followed by an account by Mr. Dee of experiments to observe the collisions with electrons.

§ 2. *Observations of Recoil Atoms.*—The properties of the beryllium radiation were first examined by means of the valve counter used in the work† on the artificial disintegration by α-particles and described fully there. Briefly, it consists of a small ionisation chamber connected to a valve amplifier. The sudden production of ions in the chamber by the entry of an ionising particle is detected by means of an oscillograph connected in the output circuit of the amplifier. The deflections of the oscillograph were recorded photographically on a film of bromide paper.

The source of polonium was prepared from a solution of radium (D+E+F)‡ by deposition on a disc of silver. The disc had a diameter of 1 cm. and was placed close to a disc of pure beryllium of 2 cm. diameter, and both were enclosed in a small vessel which could be evacuated, fig. 1. The first ionisation chamber used had an opening of 13 mm. covered with aluminium foil of 4·5 cm. air equivalent, and a depth of 15 mm. This chamber had a very low natural effect, giving on the average only about 7 deflections per hour.

---

* 'Nature,' vol. 129, p. 312 (1932).

† Chadwick, Constable and Pollard, 'Proc. Roy. Soc.,' A, vol. 130, p. 463 (1931).

‡ The radium D was obtained from old radon tubes generously presented by Dr. C. F. Burnam and Dr. F. West, of the Kelly Hospital, Baltimore.

When the source vessel was placed in front of the ionisation chamber, the number of deflections immediately increased. For a distance of 3 cm. between the beryllium and the counter the number of deflections was nearly 4 per minute. Since the number of deflections remained sensibly the same when thick metal sheets, even as much as 2 cm. of lead, were interposed between the source vessel and the counter, it was clear that these deflections were due to a penetrating radiation emitted from the beryllium. It will be shown later that the deflections were due to atoms of nitrogen set in motion by the impact of the beryllium radiation.

When a sheet of paraffin wax about 2 mm. thick was interposed in the path of the radiation just in front of the counter, the number of deflections recorded by the oscillograph increased markedly. This increase was due to particles

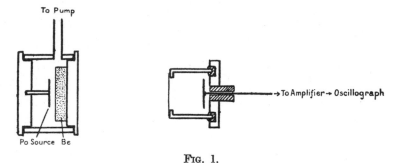

FIG. 1.

ejected from the paraffin wax so as to pass into the counter. By placing absorbing screens of aluminium between the wax and the counter the absorption curve shown in fig. 2, curve A, was obtained. From this curve it appears that the particles have a maximum range of just over 40 cm. of air, assuming that an Al foil of $1 \cdot 64$ mg. per square centimetre is equivalent to 1 cm. of air. By comparing the sizes of the deflections (proportional to the number of ions produced in the chamber) due to these particles with those due to protons of about the same range it was obvious that the particles were protons. From the range-velocity curve for protons we deduce therefore that the maximum velocity imparted to a proton by the beryllium radiation is about $3 \cdot 3 \times 10^9$ cm. per second, corresponding to an energy of about $5 \cdot 7 \times 10^6$ electron volts.

The effect of exposing other elements to the beryllium radiation was then investigated. An ionisation chamber was used with an opening covered with a gold foil of $0 \cdot 5$ mm. air equivalent. The element to be examined was fixed on a clean brass plate and placed very close to the counter opening. In this way lithium, beryllium, boron, carbon and nitrogen, as paracyanogen, were tested. In each case the number of deflections observed in the counter increased when the element was bombarded by the beryllium radiation. The ranges of the particles ejected from these elements were quite short, of the order of some millimetres in air. The deflections produced by them were of different sizes, but many of them were large compared with the deflection produced even by a slow proton. The particles therefore have a large ionising power and are probably in each case recoil atoms of the elements. Gases were investigated by filling the ionisation chamber with the required gas by circulation for several minutes. Hydrogen, helium, nitrogen, oxygen, and argon were examined in this way. Again, in each case deflections were observed which were attributed to the production of recoil atoms in the different gases. For a given position of the beryllium source relative to the counter, the number of recoil atoms was roughly the same for each gas. This point will be referred to later. It appears then that the beryllium radiation can impart energy to the atoms of matter through which it passes and that the chance of an energy transfer does not vary widely from one element to another.

It has been shown that protons are ejected from paraffin wax with energies up to a maximum of about $5 \cdot 7 \times 10^6$ electron volts. If the ejection be ascribed to a Compton recoil from a quantum of radiation, then the energy of the quantum must be about 55×10^6 electron volts, for the maximum energy which can be given to a mass m by a quantum $h\nu$ is $\dfrac{2}{2 + mc^2/h\nu} \cdot h\nu$.

The energies of the recoil atoms produced by this radiation by the same process in other elements can be readily calculated. For example, the nitrogen recoil atoms should have energies up to a maximum of 450,000 electron volts. Taking the energy necessary to form a pair of ions in air as 35 electron volts, the recoil atoms of nitrogen should produce not more than about 13,000 pairs of ions. Many of the deflections observed with nitrogen, however, corresponded to far more ions than this ; some of the recoil atoms produced from 30,000 to 40,000 ion pairs. In the case of the other elements a similar discrepancy was noted between the observed energies and ranges of the recoil atoms and the values calculated on the assumption that the atoms were set in motion by recoil from a quantum of 55×10^6 electron volts. The energies of the recoil atoms were estimated from the number of ions produced in the counter, as given by the size of the oscillograph deflections. A sufficiently good measurement of the ranges could be made either by varying the distance between the element and the counter or by interposing thin screens of gold between the element and the counter.

The nitrogen recoil atoms were also examined, in collaboration with Dr. N. Feather, by means of the expansion chamber. The source vessel was placed immediately above an expansion chamber of the Shimizu type, so that a large proportion of the beryllium radiation traversed the chamber. A large number of recoil tracks was observed in the course of a few hours. Their range, estimated by eye, was sometimes as much as 5 or 6 mm. in the chamber, or, correcting for the expansion, about 3 mm. in standard air. These visual estimates were confirmed by a preliminary series of experiments by Dr. Feather with a large automatic expansion chamber, in which photographs of the recoil tracks in nitrogen were obtained. Now the ranges of recoil atoms of nitrogen of different velocities have been measured by Blackett and Lees. Using their results we find that the nitrogen recoil atoms produced by the beryllium radiation may have a velocity of at least 4×10^8 cm. per second, corresponding to an energy of about $1 \cdot 2 \times 10^6$ electron volts. In order that the nitrogen nucleus should acquire such an energy in a collision with a quantum of radiation, it is necessary to assume that the energy of the quantum should be about 90×10^6 electron volts, if energy and momentum are conserved in the collision. It has been shown that a quantum of 55×10^6 electron volts is sufficient to explain the hydrogen collisions. In general, the experimental results show that if the recoil atoms are to be explained by collision with a quantum, we must assume a larger and larger energy for the quantum as the mass of the struck atom increases.

§ 3. *The Neutron Hypothesis.*—It is evident that we must either relinquish the application of the conservation of energy and momentum in these collisions or adopt another hypothesis about the nature of the radiation. If we suppose that the radiation is not a quantum radiation, but consists of particles of mass very nearly equal to that of the proton, all the difficulties connected with the collisions disappear, both with regard to their frequency and to the energy transfer to different masses. In order to explain the great penetrating power of the radiation we must further assume that the particle has no net charge. We may suppose it to consist of a proton and an electron in close combination, the " neutron " discussed by Rutherford* in his Bakerian Lecture of 1920.

When such neutrons pass through matter they suffer occasionally close

* Rutherford, ' Proc. Roy. Soc.,' A, vol. 97, p. 374 (1920). Experiments to detect the formation of neutrons in a hydrogen discharge tube were made by J. L. Glasson, ' Phil. Mag.,' vol. 42, p. 596 (1921), and by J. K. Roberts, ' Proc. Roy. Soc.,' A, vol. 102, p. 72 (1922). Since 1920 many experiments in search of these neutrons have been made in this laboratory.

collisions with the atomic nuclei and so give rise to the recoil atoms which are observed. Since the mass of the neutron is equal to that of the proton, the recoil atoms produced when the neutrons pass through matter containing hydrogen will have all velocities up to a maximum which is the same as the maximum velocity of the neutrons. The experiments showed that the maximum velocity of the protons ejected from paraffin wax was about $3\cdot3 \times 10^9$ cm. per second. This is therefore the maximum velocity of the neutrons emitted from beryllium bombarded by α-particles of polonium. From this we can now calculate the maximum energy which can be given by a colliding neutron to other atoms, and we find that the results are in fair agreement with the energies observed in the experiments. For example, a nitrogen atom will acquire in a head-on collision with the neutron of mass 1 and velocity $3\cdot3 \times 10^9$ cm. per second a velocity of $4\cdot4 \times 10^8$ cm. per second, corresponding to an energy of $1\cdot4 \times 10^6$ electron volts, a range of about $3\cdot3$ mm. in air, and a production of ions of about 40,000 pairs. Similarly, an argon atom may acquire an energy of $0\cdot54 \times 10^6$ electron volts, and produce about 15,000 ion pairs. Both these values are in good accord with experiment.*

It is possible to prove that the mass of the neutron is roughly equal to that of the proton, by combining the evidence from the hydrogen collisions with that from the nitrogen collisions. In the succeeding paper, Feather records experiments in which about 100 tracks of nitrogen recoil atoms have been photographed in the expansion chamber. The measurement of the tracks shows that the maximum range of the recoil atoms is $3\cdot5$ mm. in air at 15° C. and 760 mm. pressure, corresponding to a velocity of $4\cdot7 \times 10^8$ cm. per second according to Blackett and Lees. If M, V be the mass and velocity of the neutron then the maximum velocity given to a hydrogen atom is

$$u_p = \frac{2M}{M+1} \cdot V,$$

and the maximum velocity given to a nitrogen atom is

$$u_n = \frac{2M}{M+14} \cdot V,$$

whence

$$\frac{M+14}{M+1} = \frac{u_p}{u_n} = \frac{3\cdot3 \times 10^9}{4\cdot7 \times 10^8},$$

* It was noted that a few of the nitrogen recoil atoms produced about 50 to 60,000 ion pairs. These probably correspond to the cases of disintegration found by Feather and described in his paper.

and

$$M = 1 \cdot 15.$$

The total error in the estimation of the velocity of the nitrogen recoil atom may easily be about 10 per cent., and it is legitimate to conclude that the mass of the neutron is very nearly the same as the mass of the proton.

We have now to consider the production of the neutrons from beryllium by the bombardment of the α-particles. We must suppose that an α-particle is captured by a Be^9 nucleus with the formation of a carbon C^{12} nucleus and the emission of a neutron. The process is analogous to the well-known artificial disintegrations, but a neutron is emitted instead of a proton. The energy relations of this process cannot be exactly deduced, for the masses of the Be^9 nucleus and the neutron are not known accurately. It is, however, easy to show that such a process fits the experimental facts. We have

$$Be^9 + He^4 + \text{kinetic energy of } \alpha$$
$$= C^{12} + n^1 + \text{kinetic energy of } C^{12} + \text{kinetic energy of } n^1.$$

If we assume that the beryllium nucleus consists of two α-particles and a neutron, then its mass cannot be greater than the sum of the masses of these particles, for the binding energy corresponds to a defect of mass. The energy equation becomes

$$(8 \cdot 00212 + n^1) + 4 \cdot 00106 + \text{K.E. of } \alpha > 12 \cdot 0003 + n^1$$
$$+ \text{K.E. of } C^{12} + \text{K.E. of } n^1$$

or

$$\text{K.E. of } n^1 < \text{K.E. of } \alpha + 0 \cdot 003 - \text{K.E. of } C^{12}.$$

Since the kinetic energy of the α-particle of polonium is $5 \cdot 25 \times 10^6$ electron volts, it follows that the energy of emission of the neutron cannot be greater than about 8×10^6 electron volts. The velocity of the neutron must therefore be less than $3 \cdot 9 \times 10^9$ cm. per second. We have seen that the actual maximum velocity of the neutron is about $3 \cdot 3 \times 10^9$ cm. per second, so that the proposed disintegration process is compatible with observation.

A further test of the neutron hypothesis was obtained by examining the radiation emitted from beryllium in the opposite direction to the bombarding α-particles. The source vessel, fig. 1, was reversed so that a sheet of paraffin wax in front of the counter was exposed to the " backward " radiation from the beryllium. The maximum range of the protons ejected from the wax was determined as before, by counting the numbers of protons observed through different thicknesses of aluminium interposed between the wax and the counter.

The absorption curve obtained is shown in curve B, fig. 2. The maximum range of the protons was about 22 cm. in air, corresponding to a velocity of about $2\cdot74 \times 10^9$ cm. per second. Since the polonium source was only about 2 mm. away from the beryllium, this velocity should be compared with that of the neutrons emitted not at 180° but at an angle not much greater than 90°

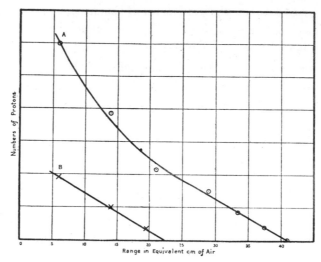

FIG. 2.

to the direction of the incident α-particles. A simple calculation shows that the velocity of the neutron emitted at 90° when an α-particle of full range is captured by a beryllium nucleus should be $2\cdot77 \times 10^9$ cm. per second, taking the velocity of the neutron emitted at 0° in the same process as $3\cdot3 \times 10^9$ cm. per second. The velocity found in the above experiment should be less than this, for the angle of emission is slightly greater than 90°. The agreement with calculation is as good as can be expected from such measurements.

§ 4. *The Nature of the Neutron.*—It has been shown that the origin of the radiation from beryllium bombarded by α-particles and the behaviour of the radiation, so far as its interaction with atomic nuclei is concerned, receive a simple explanation on the assumption that the radiation consists of particles of mass nearly equal to that of the proton which have no charge. The simplest hypothesis one can make about the nature of the particle is to suppose that it consists of a proton and an electron in close combination, giving a net charge 0 and a mass which should be slightly less than the mass of the hydrogen atom. This hypothesis is supported by an examination of the evidence which can be obtained about the mass of the neutron.

As we have seen, a rough estimate of the mass of the neutron was obtained from measurements of its collisions with hydrogen and nitrogen atoms, but such measurements cannot be made with sufficient accuracy for the present purpose. We must turn to a consideration of the energy relations in a process in which a neutron is liberated from an atomic nucleus ; if the masses of the atomic nuclei concerned in the process are accurately known, a good estimate of the mass of the neutron can be deduced. The mass of the beryllium nucleus has, however, not yet been measured, and, as was shown in § 3, only general conclusions can be drawn from this reaction. Fortunately, there remains the case of boron. It was stated in § 1 that boron bombarded by α-particles of polonium also emits a radiation which ejects protons from materials containing hydrogen. Further examination showed that this radiation behaves in all respects like that from beryllium, and it must therefore be assumed to consist of neutrons. It is probable that the neutrons are emitted from the isotope B^{11}, for we know that the isotope B^{10} disintegrates with the emission of a proton.* The process of disintegration will then be

$$B^{11} + He^4 \rightarrow N^{14} + n^1.$$

The masses of B^{11} and N^{14} are known from Aston's measurements, and the further data required for the deduction of the mass of the neutron can be obtained by experiment.

In the source vessel of fig. 1 the beryllium was replaced by a target of powdered boron, deposited on a graphite plate. The range of the protons ejected by the boron radiation was measured in the same way as with the beryllium radiation. The effects observed were much smaller than with beryllium, and it was difficult to measure the range of the protons accurately. The maximum range was about 16 cm. in air, corresponding to a velocity of $2 \cdot 5 \times 10^9$ cm. per second. This then is the maximum velocity of the neutron liberated from boron by an α-particle of polonium of velocity $1 \cdot 59 \times 10^9$ cm. per second. Assuming that momentum is conserved in the collision, the velocity of the recoiling N^{14} nucleus can be calculated, and we then know the kinetic energies of all the particles concerned in the disintegration process. The energy equation of the process is

Mass of B^{11} + mass of He^4 + K.E. of He^4

$\quad$ = mass of N^{14} + mass of n^1 + K.E. of N^{14} + K.E. of n^1.

---

* Chadwick, Constable and Pollard, *loc. cit.*

The masses are $B^{11} = 11 \cdot 00825 \pm 0 \cdot 0016$; $He^4 = 4 \cdot 00106 \pm 0 \cdot 0006$; $N^{14} = 14 \cdot 0042 \pm 0 \cdot 0028$. The kinetic energies in mass units are α-particle $= 0 \cdot 00565$; neutron $= 0 \cdot 0035$; and nitrogen nucleus $= 0 \cdot 00061$. We find therefore that the mass of the neutron is $1 \cdot 0067$. The errors quoted for the mass measurements are those given by Aston. They are the maximum errors which can be allowed in his measurements, and the probable error may be taken as about one-quarter of these.* Allowing for the errors in the mass measurements it appears that the mass of the neutron cannot be less than $1 \cdot 003$, and that it probably lies between $1 \cdot 005$ and $1 \cdot 008$.

Such a value for the mass of the neutron is to be expected if the neutron consists of a proton and an electron, and it lends strong support to this view. Since the sum of the masses of the proton and electron is $1 \cdot 0078$, the binding energy, or mass defect, of the neutron is about 1 to 2 million electron volts. This is quite a reasonable value. We may suppose that the proton and electron form a small dipole, or we may take the more attractive picture of a proton embedded in an electron. On either view, we may expect the " radius " of the neutron to be a few times 10^{-13} cm.

§ 5. *The Passage of the Neutron through Matter.*—The electrical field of a neutron of this kind will clearly be extremely small except at very small distances of the order of 10^{-12} cm. In its passage through matter the neutron will not be deflected unless it suffers an intimate collision with a nucleus. The potential of a neutron in the field of a nucleus may be represented roughly by fig. 3. The radius of the collision area for sensible deflection of the neutron

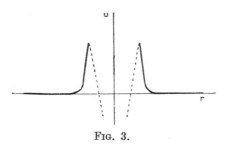

Fig. 3.

will be little greater than the radius of the nucleus. Further, the neutron should be able to penetrate the nucleus easily, and it may be that the scattering of the neutrons will be largely due to the internal field of the nucleus, or, in other words, that the scattered neutrons are mainly those which have penetrated

* The mass of B^{11} relative to B^{10} has been checked by optical methods by Jenkins and McKellar ('Phys. Rev.,' vol. 39, p. 549 (1932)). Their value agrees with Aston's to 1 part in 10^5. This suggests that great confidence may be put in Aston's measurements.

the potential barrier. On these views we should expect the collisions of a neutron with a nucleus to occur very seldom, and that the scattering will be roughly equal in all directions, at least as compared with the Coulomb scattering of a charged particle.

These conclusions were confirmed in the following way. The source vessel, with Be target, was placed rather more than 1 inch from the face of a closed counter filled with air, fig. 1. The number of deflections, or the number of nitrogen recoil atoms produced in the chamber, was observed for a certain time. The number observed was 190 per hour, after allowing for the natural effect. A block of lead 1 inch thick was then introduced between the source vessel and the counter. The number of deflections fell to 166 per hour. Since the number of recoil atoms produced must be proportional to the number of neutrons passing through the counter, these observations show that 13 per cent. of the neutrons had been absorbed or scattered in passing through 1 inch of lead.

Suppose that a neutron which passes within a distance p from the centre of the lead nucleus is scattered and removed from the beam. Then the fraction removed from the beam in passing through a thickness t of lead will be $\pi p^2 nt$, where n is the number of lead atoms per unit volume. Hence $\pi p^2 nt = 0 \cdot 13$, and $p = 7 \times 10^{-13}$ cm. This value for the collision radius with lead seems perhaps rather small, but it is not unreasonable. We may compare it with the radii of the radioactive nuclei calculated from the disintegration constants by Gamow and Houtermans,[*] viz., about 7×10^{-13} cm.

Similar experiments were made in which the neutron radiation was passed through blocks of brass and carbon. The values of p deduced in the same way were 6×10^{-13} cm. and $3 \cdot 5 \times 10^{-13}$ cm. respectively.

The target areas for collision for some light elements were compared by another method. The second ionisation chamber was used, which could be filled with different gases by circulation. The position of the source vessel was kept fixed relative to the counter, and the number of deflections was observed when the counter was filled in turn with hydrogen, nitrogen, oxygen, and argon. Since the number of neutrons passing through the counter was the same in each case, the number of deflections should be proportional to the target area for collision, neglecting the effect of the material of the counter, and allowing for the fact that argon is monatomic. It was found that nitrogen, oxygen, and argon gave about the same number of deflections; the target areas of nitrogen and oxygen are thus roughly equal, and the target area of argon is

[*] ' Z. Physik,' vol. 52, p. 453 (1928).

nearly twice that of these. With hydrogen the measurements were very difficult, for many of the deflections were very small owing to the low ionising power of the proton and the low density of the gas. It seems probable from the results that the target area of hydrogen is about two-thirds that of nitrogen or oxygen, but it may be rather greater than this.

There is as yet little information about the angular distribution of the scattered neutrons. In some experiments kindly made for me by Dr. Gray and Mr. Lea, the scattering by lead was compared in the backward and forward directions, using the ionisation in a high pressure chamber to measure the neutrons. They found that the amount of scattering was about that to be expected from the measurements quoted above, and that the intensity per unit solid angle was about the same between 30° to 90° in the forward direction as between 90° to 150° in the backward direction. The scattering by lead is therefore not markedly anisotropic.

Two types of collision may prove to be of peculiar interest, the collision of a neutron with a proton and the collision with an electron. A detailed study of these collisions with an elementary particle is of special interest, for it should provide information about the structure and field of the neutron, whereas the other collisions will depend mainly on the structure of the atomic nuclei. Some preliminary experiments by Mr. Lea, using the pressure chamber to measure the scattering of neutrons by paraffin wax and by liquid hydrogen, suggest that the collision with a proton is more frequent than with other light atoms. This is not in accord with the experiments described above, but the results are at present indecisive. These collisions can be more directly investigated by means of the expansion chamber or by counting methods, and it is hoped to do so shortly.

The collision of a neutron with an electron has been examined in two ways, by the expansion chamber and by the counter. An account of the expansion chamber experiments is given by Mr. Dee in the third paper of this series. Mr. Dee has looked for the general ionisation produced by a large number of neutrons in passing through the expansion chamber, and also for the short electron tracks which should be the result of a very close collision between a neutron and an electron. His results show that collisions with electrons are extremely rare compared even with those with nitrogen nuclei, and he estimates that a neutron can produce on the average not more than 1 ion pair in passing through 3 metres of air.

In the counter experiments a beam of neutrons was passed through a block of brass, 1 inch thick, and the maximum range of the protons ejected from paraffin wax by the emergent beam was measured. From this range the maximum velocity of the neutrons after travelling through the brass is obtained and it can be compared with the maximum velocity in the incident beam. No change in the velocity of the neutrons due to their passage through the brass could be detected. The accuracy of the experiment is not high, for the estimation of the end of the range of the protons was rather difficult. The results show that the loss of energy of a neutron in passing through 1 inch of brass is not more than about $0 \cdot 4 \times 10^6$ electron volts. A path of 1 inch in brass corresponds as regards electron collisions to a path of nearly 2×10^4 cm. of air, so that this result would suggest that a neutron loses less than 20 volts per centimetre path in air in electron collisions. This experiment thus lends general support to those with the expansion chamber, though it is of far inferior accuracy. We conclude that the transfer of energy from the neutron to electrons is of very rare occurrence. This is not unexpected Bohr* has shown on quite general ideas that collisions of a neutron with an electron should be very few compared with nuclear collisions. Massey,† on plausible assumptions about the field of the neutron, has made a detailed calculation of the loss of energy to electrons, and finds also that it should be small, not more than 1 ion pair per metre in air.

General Remarks.

It is of interest to examine whether other elements, besides beryllium and boron, emit neutrons when bombarded by α-particles. So far as experiments have been made, no case comparable with these two has been found. Some evidence was obtained of the emission of neutrons from fluorine and magnesium, but the effects were very small, rather less than 1 per cent. of the effect obtained from beryllium under the same conditions. There is also the possibility that some elements may emit neutrons spontaneously, *e.g.*, potassium, which is known to emit a nuclear β-radiation accompanied by a more penetrating radiation. Again no evidence was found of the presence of neutrons, and it seems fairly certain that the penetrating type is, as has been assumed, a γ-radiation.

Although there is certain evidence for the emission of neutrons only in two cases of nuclear transformations, we must nevertheless suppose that the neutron is a common constituent of atomic nuclei. We may then proceed to build up nuclei out of α-particles, neutrons and protons, and we are able to

---

* Bohr, Copenhagen discussions, unpublished.
† Massey, 'Nature,' vol. 129, p. 469, corrected p. 691 (1932).

avoid the presence of uncombined electrons in a nucleus. This has certain advantages for, as is well known, the electrons in a nucleus have lost some of the properties which they have outside, *e.g.*, their spin and magnetic moment. If the α-particle, the neutron, and the proton are the only units of nuclear structure, we can proceed to calculate the mass defect or binding energy of a nucleus as the difference between the mass of the nucleus and the sum of the masses of the constituent particles. It is, however, by no means certain that the α-particle and the neutron are the only complex particles in the nuclear structure, and therefore the mass defects calculated in this way may not be the true binding energies of the nuclei. In this connection it may be noted that the examples of disintegration discussed by Dr. Feather in the next paper are not all of one type, and he suggests that in some cases a particle of mass 2 and charge 1, the hydrogen isotope recently reported by Urey, Brickwedde and Murphy, may be emitted. It is indeed possible that this particle also occurs as a unit of nuclear structure.

It has so far been assumed that the neutron is a complex particle consisting of a proton and an electron. This is the simplest assumption and it is supported by the evidence that the mass of the neutron is about $1 \cdot 006$, just a little less than the sum of the masses of a proton and an electron. Such a neutron would appear to be the first step in the combination of the elementary particles towards the formation of a nucleus. It is obvious that this neutron may help us to visualise the building up of more complex structures, but the discussion of these matters will not be pursued further for such speculations, though not idle, are not at the moment very fruitful. It is, of course, possible to suppose that the neutron may be an elementary particle. This view has little to recommend it at present, except the possibility of explaining the statistics of such nuclei as N^{14}.

There remains to discuss the transformations which take place when an α-particle is captured by a beryllium nucleus, Be^9. The evidence given here indicates that the main type of transformation is the formation of a C^{12} nucleus and the emission of a neutron. The experiments of Curie-Joliot and Joliot,[*] of Auger,[†] and of Dee show quite definitely that there is some radiation emitted by beryllium which is able to eject fast electrons in passing through matter. I have made experiments using the Geiger point counter to investigate this radiation and the results suggest that the electrons are produced by a

[*] 'C. R. Acad. Sci. Paris,' vol. 194, p. 708 and p. 876 (1932).
[†] 'C. R. Acad. Sci. Paris,' vol. 194, p. 877 (1932).

γ-radiation.   There are two distinct processes which may give rise to such a radiation.   In the first place, we may suppose that the transformation of Be^9 to C^{12} takes place sometimes with the formation of an excited C^{12} nucleus which goes to the ground state with the emission of γ-radiation.   This is similar to the transformations which are supposed to occur in some cases of disintegration with proton emission, *e.g.*, B^{10}, F^{19}, Al^{27} ; the majority of transformations occur with the formation of an excited nucleus, only in about one-quarter is the final state of the residual nucleus reached in one step.   We should then have two groups of neutrons of different energies and a γ-radiation of quantum energy equal to the difference in energy of the neutron groups. The quantum energy of this radiation must be less than the maximum energy of the neutrons emitted, about $5 \cdot 7 \times 10^6$ electron volts.   In the second place, we may suppose that occasionally the beryllium nucleus changes to a C^{13} nucleus and that all the surplus energy is emitted as radiation.   In this case the quantum energy of the radiation may be about 10×10^6 electron volts.

It is of interest to note that Webster has observed a soft radiation from beryllium bombarded by polonium α-particles, of energy about 5×10^5 electron volts.   This radiation may well be ascribed to the first of the two processes just discussed, and its intensity is of the right order.   On the other hand, some of the electrons observed by Curie-Joliot and Joliot had energies of the order of 2 to 10×10^6 volts, and Auger recorded one example of an electron of energy about $6 \cdot 5 \times 10^6$ volts.   These electrons may be due to a hard γ-radiation produced by the second type of transformation.*

It may be remarked that no electrons of greater energy than the above appear to be present.   This is confirmed by an experiment† made in this laboratory by Dr. Occhialini.   Two tube counters were placed in a horizontal plane and the number of coincidences recorded by them was observed by means of the method devised by Rossi.   The beryllium source was then brought up in the plane of the counters so that the radiation passed through both counters in turn.   No increase in the number of coincidences could be detected.   It follows that there are few, if any, β-rays produced with energies sufficient to pass through the walls of both counters, a total of 4 mm. brass ; that is, with energies greater than about 6×10^6 volts.   This experiment further shows that the neutrons very rarely produce coincidences in tube counters under the usual conditions of experiment.

* Although the presence of fast electrons can be easily explained in this way, the possibility that some may be due to secondary effects of the neutrons must not be lost sight of.

† *Cf.* also Rasetti, ' Naturwiss.,' vol. 20, p. 252 (1932).

2 z 2

In conclusion, I may restate briefly the case for supposing that the radiation the effects of which have been examined in this paper consists of neutral particles rather than of radiation quanta. Firstly, there is no evidence from electron collisions of the presence of a radiation of such a quantum energy as is necessary to account for the nuclear collisions. Secondly, the quantum hypothesis can be sustained only by relinquishing the conservation of energy and momentum. On the other hand, the neutron hypothesis gives an immediate and simple explanation of the experimental facts; it is consistent in itself and it throws new light on the problem of nuclear structure.

Summary.

The properties of the penetrating radiation emitted from beryllium (and boron) when bombarded by the α-particles of polonium have been examined. It is concluded that the radiation consists, not of quanta as hitherto supposed, but of neutrons, particles of mass 1, and charge 0. Evidence is given to show that the mass of the neutron is probably between 1·005 and 1·008. This suggests that the neutron consists of a proton and an electron in close combination, the binding energy being about 1 to 2×10^6 electron volts. From experiments on the passage of the neutrons through matter the frequency of their collisions with atomic nuclei and with electrons is discussed.

I wish to express my thanks to Mr. H. Nutt for his help in carrying out the experiments.

FURTHER DEVELOPMENTS

The chief theoretical interest of this group lies in the paper by Richardson and Compton on 'The Photo-electric Effect'. In 1905 Einstein had deduced an equation showing how the maximum kinetic energy of an electron ejected from a photo-sensitive surface varied with the frequency of the incident radiation.

$\frac{1}{2}mv_m^2 = h\nu - p$ where v_m is the maximum velocity

h—Planck'cs onstant

ν—Frequency of incident light

p—Work necessary to remove the electron from the metal

The experiments of Richardson and Compton were intended to give experimental support to this equation and although they made allowance for errors previously uncorrected, e.g. contact potentials, their work was open to a number of objections. For example, Millikan[1] pointed out that even in the best available vacuum the surface of an alkali metal like sodium changes in the course of an experiment and the photo-potential and contact potential must consequently be measured simultaneously.

Millikan then examined the whole question again in a series of very precise and exhaustive experiments and showed beyond doubt that Einstein's photo-electric relation was correct.[2]

The photo-electric effect began as a chance observation by Hertz (1887), who noticed that the passage of ultra-violet light through the spark gap of his tuned detector circuit enabled the sparks to pass more easily and ended as one of the really serious pieces of evidence against the electromagnetic wave nature of light. On the wave theory the maximum energy of the emitted photo-electrons should increase with intensity, but it was shown to remain the same for incident light of a given frequency, even when the intensity dropped to a very small value. The photo-electrons were expelled from the surface very nearly instantaneously and there could be no question of energy storage. The maximum energy varied linearly with frequency and was not independent of it as demanded by classical theory.

The classical rules governing the interaction of light with matter had, therefore, to be discarded and it was necessary to postulate that, in this respect, light behaves as a stream of energy quanta (photons). Each photon may yield all its energy to an atom or retain it all; half-measures are excluded.

Cockcroft and Walton ushered in the era of modern nuclear physics when they succeeded in splitting a lithium nucleus in half with an artificially accelerated proton. ($_3Li^7(p,\alpha)_2He^4$). Previously Rutherford and his school had relied on the extremely energetic and stable α particle emitted during some radioactive changes to produce individual nuclear events and, since it required particles with energies of several million volts to transform even light nuclei, the task of giving, artificially, an ion an energy of this magnitude seemed beyond the resources of any laboratory at that time. However, Gamow suggested on theoretical grounds that there was a reasonable probability of success with particles of much lower energy and, accordingly, the attempt was made.

Two results of this work may be mentioned. Einstein's mass energy relation was shown to be true to within very fine limits and the success of the experiment opened the way to further development of man-made sources of high energy particles. These have the advantage of producing very large numbers of particles with controlled energies.

Compton and Doan made the first determination of X-ray wavelengths, using a ruled reflection grating. Stenstrom had shown in 1919 that the refractive index of some substances for X-radiation was less than one and, therefore, when the angle of incidence is large enough, total reflection takes place. The wavelength can then be determined in a manner exactly analogous to that used for the visible region of the spectrum.

[1] R. A. Millikan, 'Photo-electric Determination of Planck's 'h' ', *The Physical Review*, 1916, **7**.
[2] R. A. Millikan, *ibid*.

LIII. *The Photoelectric Effect.* *By* O. W. RICHARDSON *and* KARL T. COMPTON, *Princeton University* *.

[Plate XIII.]

PROBABLY there is no line of investigation more likely to lead to a correct understanding of the phenomena of photoelectric action than a careful determination of the relations between the nature of the metal, the frequency of the light, and the kinetic energy of the liberated electrons. A large amount of work has been done in the attempt to determine these relations, but the results have been very contradictory. For instance, von Baeyer and Gehrts †, and Klages ‡ found, in the case of several metals, that the maximum initial velocity of the electrons was independent of the metal used. Ladenburg § and other physicists have decided that the electronegative metals give off electrons with the greatest velocities; whilst Millikan and Winchester ‖ concluded that the initial velocity bears no relation to the Volta series. Most physicists who have investigated the subject believe that the maximum initial kinetic energy is a linear function of the frequency of the light; but some ¶ have obtained results supporting the view that the maximum velocity varies as the first power of the frequency.

The results of the present investigation show that there is a much greater unity in the relations between different metals and wave-lengths than has hitherto been supposed. In fact, it will be shown that the important features of the photoelectric behaviour of any metal are determined by a single parameter characteristic of the metal. The parameter has the dimensions of a frequency, and its significance will be explained later.

The first part of the paper is a discussion of the experimental data. These data may be of value in testing any theory of photoelectric action. In the latter part of the paper the results are applied to test the theories of these effects which have been developed by Einstein ** and by one of the authors ††.

* Communicated by the Authors.
† Ber. der Deutsch Physik. Ges. xxi. p. 870 (1910).
‡ Ann. der Physik, vol. xxxi. p. 343 (1909).
§ Verh. der Deutsch Physik. Ges. ix. p. 504, ibid. p. 165 (1907); Phys. Zeits. vol. viii. p. 592 (1907).
‖ Phil. Mag. vol. xiv. p. 185 (1907).
¶ Kunz, Phys. Rev. vol. xxxi. p. 536 (1910), vol. xxxiii. p. 208 (1911).
** Ann. der Physik, vol. xvii. p. 146 (1905).
†† Phys. Rev. vol. xxxiv. p. 146 (1912); Phil. Mag. vol. xxiii. p. 615 (1912); Science, vol. xxxvi. p. 57 (1912).

The main points wherein the present investigation differs from the earlier work on this subject are as follows :— (1) The contact difference of potential between the emitting and receiving electrodes is allowed for *. (2) The photo-electric cell is placed in position in an arm of a new type of monochromatic ultra-violet illuminator, made by Adam Hilger Ltd., of London, which is a distinct advance as a method of producing accurate and powerful illumination by monochromatic ultra-violet light. (3) The peculiar form of the photoelectric cell practically eliminates electron reflexion without the use of a screen and an auxiliary field, and at the same time it enables the distribution of total kinetic energy to be measured instead of simply the distribution of the velocity component normal to the emitting electrode.

The apparatus used is shown in fig. 1. The emitting electrode consists of a strip S of metal foil about 1 mm. wide and 5 mm. long placed at the centre of a glass bulb D of

Fig. 1.

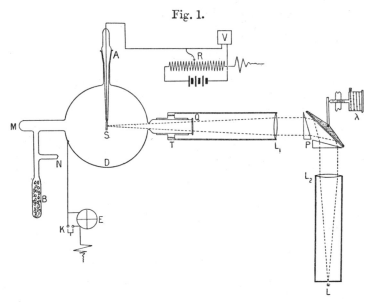

7·5 cm. diameter. This bulb is silvered on its inner surface. It is connected with an electrometer having a sensibility of 936 divisions per volt, and acts as the receiving electrode. The strip S is held in position by a thin platinum wire sealed in a small glass tube, and is introduced through the ground-

* See K. T. Compton, Phil. Mag. vol. xxiii. p. 579 (1912).

glass joint A. The neck of this bulb is closed by a quartz window Q. It is waxed firmly in a brass collar which screws into the telescope tube of the monochromatic illuminator at T, in such a position that the slit L is just focussed on the strip S so that the image of the slit for any particular wave-length of light may be made to coincide with the position of the strip. The final adjustment is made by using visible light as the source and looking through M. The strip S is shifted a little until it just shuts out the image. By turning the screw-head λ any desired wave-length may be thrown on S and its magnitude read off on the graduated scale. In the figure the illuminator is shown rotated through a right angle from its true position, about the axis of the telescope. The collimator should project out perpendicular to the plane of the paper. A quartz mercury lamp at L was used as the source of light. The apparatus was evacuated by a Gaede pump connected at N, and usually the tube B of coconut charcoal was used to obtain a still better vacuum.

The velocities of the liberated electrons were determined by varying the field between S and D by adjusting the sliding contact R, and the applied field was read directly from the voltmeter V. The distribution of velocity curves were obtained in the ordinary way.

The peculiarities of this apparatus are that the field between S and D is approximately radial, and that the area of the emitting electrode is very small compared with the area of the receiving electrode. In the first place, this arrangement makes it possible to measure the distributions of velocity of all the electrons irrespective of their angles of emission from S, and thus it gives the distribution of total energy of the electrons. In the second place, it makes the effect of electron reflexion practically negligible. A certain percentage of the electrons reaching D are reflected, this reflexion being diffuse. But none of these reflected electrons will return to S, except a very small proportion which start almost straight towards S. All the others will traverse comet-like paths past S and again strike D.

The metal strip to be tested was carefully scraped with a clean knife-blade. It was then placed quickly in position and the vacuum-pump started. The readings were taken as soon as the requisite vacuum was obtained.

The Distribution of Velocities.

The general character of the distribution of velocity curves is the same for all the metals, so that it will be sufficient to consider in detail the case of platinum only. With this metal readings were taken for wave-lengths 25, 23, and 21. The unit of wave-length is 10^{-6} cm. The readings are shown in Table I. V is the externally applied potential difference, R is the deflexion in scale-divisions per minute, and C is this deflexion reduced to a scale of 100 for the maximum deflexion. These readings may be taken as typical of all the distribution of velocity curves that we have obtained.

It is necessary to correct these readings for contact difference of potential. The method of determining this correction will be described later. After being thus corrected the numbers in Table I. are plotted thus:—o in fig. 2 (Pl. XIII.). The significance of these curves may be explained as follows:—Take, for instance, the curve for 23 λ. The ordinate at −0·5 volt is 44. This means that 44 per cent. of the electrons are liberated with velocities equal to or greater than that velocity which gives them sufficient energy to overcome an opposing difference of potential of 0·5 volt.

TABLE I.

V.	λ = 25.		λ = 23.		λ = 21.	
	R.	C.	R.	C.	R.	C.
+ 2	41	98	78	100	31	100
1	42	100	78	100	31	100
0·5	41	98	78	100	31	100
0·2	42	100	78	100	31	100
0·1	42	100	78	100	31	100
0·05	42	100				
0·0	40	95	76	97	30·5	98·5
− 0·1	27	64	68	87	29	93
0·2	9	22	54	69	26	84
0·3	3	7	44	56·5		
0·4	0	0	30·5	39	21	68
0·5	...	...	19	24		
0·6	...	...	8	10	15	48
0·7	...	...	1·5	2		
0·8	...	...	0	0	8·5	27
0·9	...	...	...	...	6·5	19
1·0	...	...	...	...	3	10

To obtain the relative number which are emitted with any given energy, we must differentiate these curves with respect to V. The result of this differentiation is shown in fig. 3. For wave-length 25 the number emitted with an energy corresponding to 0·2 volt is to the number corresponding to 0·1 volt as the ordinate in fig. 3 at 0·2 volt is to the ordinate at 0·1 volt, or as 90 is to 65, and so on.

An examination of these curves leads to a number of interesting conclusions.

(1) The maximum energy, expressed in volts, is a linear function of the frequency of the exciting light, within the limits within which the results of the experiments are consistent.

(2) The curves appear to be almost symmetrical with respect to their maximum ordinates. This shows that if the maximum energy is a linear function of the frequency, the average energy, which is equal within the limits of experimental error to the most probable energy, also bears a linear relation to the frequency.

(3) The curves intersect the voltage axis at finite angles, both at the end which corresponds to zero energy and at the end which corresponds to the maximum energy.

(4) If the wave-length is increased to a certain value, which is in the neighbourhood of $\lambda = 27$ in the case of platinum, the distribution of velocity curve will degenerate into a straight line coincident with the current axis. The photoelectric currents in this region were too small to permit of such a curve being obtained, but the experiments show that this limiting wave-length, which we may call λ_0, has a particular meaning. It is the longest wave-length that will produce any photoelectric effect from the metal under investigation, and the electrons emitted by this light are emitted with zero velocity. This wave-length λ_0, or the equivalent frequency ν_0, is that constant which has already been alluded to which determines the photoelectric properties of the metal.

Analysis of the Distribution of Velocity Curves.

Since the curves in fig. 3 show that the mean velocity of the emitted electrons is very close to the most probable velocity, it might be thought that the mean velocity should be the characteristic velocity received by the electrons under the primary influence of the light. The deviations from the mean would then be due to collisions with other electrons in the matter traversed, some of the emitted electrons losing and others gaining energy in this way. The results can, however, be equally well interpreted on the view that all the collisions in the interior of the matter result in a diminution of the energy of the emitted electrons. We shall limit the discussion to the case of a beam of light incident normally to the emitting surface.

Let each electron which is set free from its parent atom or equivalent system in the interior under the influence of the monochromatic radiation have a constant amount of kinetic energy T_0. We shall assume that this energy diminishes to $T_0 F_2(r)$ when the electron has traversed a distance r inside the matter from its point of origin, and in addition that it has to do a definite amount of work P in order to escape from the surface. The energy T of the electrons which originate at a distance r from the point where they escape from the surface is then a function of r only. It is given by

$$T = T_0 F_2(r) - P. \quad . \quad . \quad . \quad . \quad . \quad (1)$$

Consider all the electrons which emerge from an element dS of the surface, and which originate at a distance between r and $r+dr$ from the point of emergence. Let θ be the angle between the radius r and the internal normal to dS. Let λ_1 be the coefficient of extinction of the light with distance. Then the number of electrons which originate in an element of volume $d\tau$ at a depth defined by r and θ will be $e^{-\lambda_1 r \cos\theta} A d\tau$, where A is a constant. In addition to losing energy the electrons will diminish in number with the distance traversed in the matter. Let the proportion which disappear in this way in a distance r be $1 - F_1(r)$. Then the total number which reach dS and which come from a distance between r and $r+dr$ is

$$dN = \int_{-\pi/2}^{\pi/2} e^{-\lambda_1 r \cos\theta} A \cdot 2\pi r^2 \sin\theta \, dr \, F_1(r) \frac{dS \cos\theta}{r^2} d\theta, \quad . \quad (2)$$

$$= 2\pi A F_1(r) dr \, dS \int_0^1 e^{-\lambda_1 r x} x \, dx$$

$$= \frac{2\pi A \, dS}{\lambda_1^2} \cdot \frac{F_1(r)}{r^2} dr \left[1 - (1 + \lambda_1 r) e^{-\lambda_1 r} \right]. \quad . \quad . \quad (3)$$

Also $\qquad\qquad dT = T_0 F_2'(r) dr. \quad . \quad . \quad . \quad . \quad . \quad (4)$

Thus $\quad \dfrac{\partial N}{\partial T} = \dfrac{2\pi A \, dS}{\lambda_1^2 T_0} \dfrac{1}{r^2} \dfrac{F_1(r)}{F_2'(r)} \left[1 - (1 + \lambda_1 r) e^{-\lambda_1 r} \right]. \quad . \quad (5)$

The values of T which make N a maximum are given by $\dfrac{\partial N}{\partial T} = 0$, or

$$e^{-\lambda_1 r} = (1 + \lambda_1 r)^{-1}. \quad . \quad . \quad . \quad . \quad (6)$$

On this view T is determined by r alone, and the corresponding values of T are given by solving (6) for r and substituting in (1). The maximum value of the kinetic energy of the emitted electrons is that which corresponds to $r=0$, so that when $r=0$

$$\left(\frac{\partial N}{\partial T} \right)_{r=0} = \frac{\pi A dS}{T_0 F_2'(0)}. \quad . \quad . \quad . \quad . \quad (7)$$

Thus when T has its maximum value, $\frac{\partial N}{\partial T}$ has a finite value which is negative, since $F_2'(0)$ is negative. The value of $\frac{\partial N}{\partial T}$ when T=0 may be obtained by solving the equation $F_2(r)=P/T_0$ for r and substituting in (5). This value of $\frac{\partial N}{\partial T}$ is readily seen to be positive and finite, so that it is clear that the type of theory which supposes the maximum energy of the emitted electrons to be determined by the energy they receive under the influence of the light less a constant amount of work necessary for them to escape from the material is in satisfactory general agreement with the experimental results.

We shall not consider the numerical analysis of curves like those in fig. 3 in the present paper, but shall now turn to the experimental data which have been given by the other metals investigated.

Experiments with Different Metals.

Curves similar to those in fig. 2 were obtained by the same method for strips S of copper, bismuth, tin, zinc, aluminium, and magnesium, as well as platinum, using various wavelengths of light. The curves for aluminium are represented by the full lines in fig. 2 (Pl. XIII.). The results with the other metals are shown in figs. 4, 5, 6, 7, and 8.

In each of these cases the curves for different wave-lengths reach saturation at a common point. The dotted ordinate in each figure represents the actual position of the current axis according to the reading of the voltmeter V, and the point where the dotted line meets the volt-axis is the experimental position of zero volts. But when this position of zero volts is shifted so as to correct for the contact difference of potential between the silver bulb and the metal strip used, the current-axis is shifted so as to pass exactly through the saturation-point where the curves coincide. For instance, the contact-difference of potential between silver and zinc is just 1 volt. When this is corrected for by shifting the position of zero volts to the right a distance corresponding to 1 volt, it is seen that this point, which really corresponds to zero field acting on the electrons, exactly coincides with the position where the curves reach their common maximum. This correspondence between the contact-difference of potential and the shift necessary to place the ordinate of zero volts at the saturation-point is exact, so far as we have been able to determine, in every case except that of magnesium, fig. 4. But doubtless even here the discrepancy is only apparent.

Phil. Mag. S. 6. Vol. 24. No. 142. *Oct.* 1912.   2 Q

The fact that the shift required for coincidence is only 1·15 volts instead of 1·4 volts, the true contact-difference of potential between silver and magnesium, is probably due to slight oxidation of the magnesium, whereby the actual contact difference was reduced to 1·15 volts. So here, too, the shift and the contact-difference of potential probably correspond.

This point is also significant because it disproves the emission of electrons with apparent negative velocities. Since the curves reach their maxima at the ordinate which corresponds to zero volts, all the electrons possess velocities greater than zero. The occurrence of electrons with apparent negative velocities, that is to say, of electrons which are only completely liberated when there is an external electric field to draw them away from the surface of the emitting metal, has usually been supposed, in order to account for the fact that the distribution of velocity curves have often been observed to cut the axis of zero volts before reaching their maxima. Such an intersection with the current-axis is probably due either to the neglect of the effect of the contact difference of potential on the position of zero volts, or to something which prevents some of the electrons from reaching the receiving electrode unaided. Such an effect might be due to a poor vacuum, to electron reflexion, to the obstruction offered by a wire screen used in the effort to prevent reflexion, or to some peculiarity in the shape of the apparatus. Fortunately the difficulty seems to have been avoided in the form of apparatus used in this investigation.

It is now easy to understand why the values of the kinetic energies of the emitted electrons which have been published differ so widely. If the uncorrected position (the dotted line) were to be taken for the origin, it is evident that the different metals would appear to emit electrons with practically equal maximum velocities for a given wave-length, although actually those emitted by the electropositive metals possess the highest velocities.

In the case of sodium we have not been able to obtain the complete curves showing the distribution of kinetic energy. On account of the rapid photoelectric fatigue exhibited by this substance, we have only been able to determine the value of the maximum kinetic energy corresponding to different frequencies. Different methods were tried to reduce or avoid photoelectric fatigue, but they were only very partially successful. In our first experiments we cut the sodium surface in an atmosphere of hydrogen, carefully dried and purified, in a separate vessel attached to the bulb D ; so that the sodium strip could be placed in position without coming into contact with the air. But with the best care, the surface of the sodium coated over so rapidly that it gave no photoelectric current whatever. The plan finally adopted was to place a little strip of sodium in position at S, heat the bulb so as to drive off layers of adhering gas, and keep it under the highest vacuum obtainable with the Gaede pump for about 24 hours. Then the pump connexion was sealed off, and the bulb was left with a tube of phosphorus pentoxide and one of cocoanut charcoal immersed in liquid air for several hours more. After this a rod turning in a ground-glass joint provided with a mercury trap was turned, thus winding up a wire which drew a piece of Gillette razor-blade along so as to leave a fresh surface exposed to the light.

Even with these precautions the photoelectric sensitiveness of the sodium fell off rapidly, decreasing from a deflexion of 3000 divisions per minute to about 50 per minute in the course of two hours and a half. If photoelectric fatigue is due, as seems most probable, to the chemical effects of the surrounding atmosphere, it is clear that very minute amounts of matter can produce very sensible effects of this kind. The vacuum was unquestionably quite good in these experiments. Before applying the liquid air the pressure recorded by the McLeod gauge varied from amounts which were too small to be estimated, up to about 0·00001 mm.

As has been stated, we were not able to take the observations sufficiently quickly to obtain the complete velocity distribution curves for sodium. However, the maximum reading of the voltmeter at which any deflexion could be detected was quite easy to find. Such points correspond to the feet of the curves in Pl. XIII. fig. 2. These points were obtained as soon as possible after the sodium had been shaved and while the photoelectric currents were large, so that they should be quite accurate. In this way the following values were obtained :—

Wave-length	43·6	36·6	31·3	25·4	21
Apparent energy in equivalent volts...	−1·9	−1·5	−1·0	−0·2	+0·5
True energy in equivalent volts	0·6	1·0	1·5	2·3	3·0

The true values of the kinetic energy were obtained by taking the contact difference of potential between silver and sodium to be 2·5 volts. This determines the position of the maximum point in the curves like those in Pl. XIII. fig. 3.

2 Q 2

Having thus obtained the two end points, an estimate of the mean energy can be obtained by assuming that the shape of the curves is the same as that of those given by other substances which terminate at the same points.   This method was tested in a number of other cases, where all the data were known, and found to give results for the mean energy which agreed with the direct determinations.   Moreover, in almost all of the very large number of cases tried the curves between the same terminal points were identical to within the limits of experimental error.   The curve which showed the worst agreement with this rule is the aluminium curve for $\lambda = 31 \cdot 3$, which runs across from the platinum curve at $\lambda = 23$ to that at $\lambda = 25$.   This is shown in Pl. XIII. fig. 2. It is to be remembered, however, that a wave-length $\lambda = 31 \cdot 3$ gives very small currents even with aluminium, so that the curves in this part of the diagram cannot be determined very accurately.   The more typical behaviour is shown by the curves for the wave-length 21 for Pt and 25·4 for Al, which are almost identical throughout their course (Pl. XIII. fig. 2).

The Maximum and Mean Energies.   Comparison with Theory.

The maximum and mean energies of the electrons emitted under the influence of light of a given frequency are readily obtained from curves like those shown in Pl. XIII. fig. 3.   The maximum energy T_m, expressed in equivalent volts, is clearly equal to the intercept on the voltage axis between the point of intersection of the curves with this axis and that of the true axis of zero volts.   The mean energy in the same units T_r is equal to the area which is bounded on the left by the curve, on the right by the true axis of zero volts, and below by the voltage axis, divided by the maximum current.   The values of the maximum energy in this way are collected together in the following table (p. 585).

Leaving out of account for the present certain possible sources of systematic error, which will be considered more fully below, and which are likely to affect both the determinations of the mean and of the maximum energy in almost equal proportions, we are inclined to place more reliance on the measurements of the mean than on those of the maximum values.   In some cases the current-voltage curves (Pl. XIII. figs. 2 & 4–8) appear to approach the voltage axis quite gradually, so that the determination of the exact point of intersection is a very difficult matter.   Our electrostatic arrangements were quite sensitive and worked very satisfactorily ; but the currents in this region are extremely

Metal λ_0.	λ.	T_m.	T_r.	λ/λ_0.	Metal λ_0.	λ.	T_m.	T_r.	λ/λ_0.
Na 57·7	43·6	0·60	0·30	0·755	Zn 35·7	26·5	0·92	0·52	0·740
	36·6	1·00	0·50	0·635		25·3	1·25	0·625	0·713
	31·3	1·50	0·75	0·542		23·0	1·70	0·862	0·644
	25·4	2·30	1·15	0·440		21·0	2·03	1·06	0·590
	21·0	3·00	1·50	0·365					
					Sn 33·7	26·5	0·80	0·432	0·785
Al 41·1	31·3	0·90	0·365	0·760		25·4	1·10	0·520	0·750
	27·5	1·30	0·60	0·670		23·8	1·33	0·660	0·705
	25·3	1·50	0·74	0·615		22·0	1·73	0·810	0·650
	23·0	1·90	0·965	0·560					
	20·0	2·30	1·21	0·485	Bi 33·7	25·4	0·60	0·315	0·750
						23·0	0·90	0·450	0·680
Mg 39·0	27·5	0·85	0·45	0·730		21·0	1·15	0·587	0·620
	26·4	1·02	0·585	0·705					
	25·4	1·35	0·638	0·675	Cu 30·9	26·0	0·35	0·175	0·840
	23·0	1·80	0·85	0·612		25·4	0·48	0·230	0·820
						23·0	0·73	0·335	0·745
Pt 29·1	25·0	0·51	0·266	0·870		21·0	1·02	0·475	0·680
	23·0	0·99	0·47	0·790		20·0	1·25	0·550	0·645
	21·0	1·45	0·713	0·720					

The unit for λ is $1 = 10^{-6}$ cm. T_m and T_r are expressed in equivalent volts.

small, and the maximum potential observed is necessarily that at which the photoelectric current is balanced by the minute back leakage which is unavoidable in an apparatus of this character, and which arises chiefly from the ionization of the air in the shielding tubes and the like. It is possible that our measurements of the maximum energy might have been improved by using a source of ultra-violet light of greater intensity, as the Heraeus quartz mercury lamp was chosen for its steadiness rather than on account of the intensity which it furnished. However, it is probable that the chief sources of error in experiments on photoelectric action arise from chemical effects at the surfaces investigated rather than from defects in the electrical and optical arrangements used.

When the foregoing values of T_m and T_r are plotted against the corresponding frequencies ν, the results for each metal exhibit a linear relation between the corresponding variables. Except in the case of copper and bismuth the lines are almost parallel to each other for all the metals. The frequencies ν_0, and the corresponding wave-lengths λ_0, which correspond to T_m and $T_r = 0$, are determined by the intersection of these lines with the frequency axis. Together with the constant k, which determines the slope of the individual curves, they are collected together in the following table :—

Metal.	Values from T_m.			Values from T_r.		
	ν_0.	λ_0.	k_m.	ν_0	λ_0.	k_r.
Na	51·5	58·3	5·2	52	57·7	2·6
Al	63	47·7	4·3	73	41·1	2·6
Mg	78·5	38·2	5·2	80	37·5	2·55
Zn	80	37·6	5·1	84	35·7	2·8
Sn	83	36·2	4·9	89	33·7	2·75
Bi	91	33	3·55	89	33·7	1·9
Cu	100	30	3·8	97	30·9	1·65
Pt	104	28·8	5·85	103	29·1	2·8

The unit for λ_0 is $1 = 10^{-6}$ cm. and for k_m and k_r $1 = 10^{-27}$ erg sec.

The values of λ_0 given by the mean energy T_r are practically identical with those given by the maximum energy T_m except in the case of aluminium. When the two differ we are inclined to attach more weight to the values from T_r for the reasons already stated.

Some years ago Einstein * showed that it followed from the unitary theory of light that the maximum energy T_m of the electrons emitted under the influence of light should satisfy the equation

$$T_m = h\nu - P, \quad \ldots \quad \ldots \quad (8)$$

where ν is the frequency of the light, h is Planck's constant, and P the work which the electrons have to do in order to escape from the material. One of the writers † has recently shown that T_m and T_r have to satisfy the equations:—

$$T_m = h\nu - w_0, \quad \ldots \quad \ldots \quad (9)$$

$$T_r = s(h\nu - w_0) \quad \ldots \quad \ldots \quad (10)$$

where w_0 is the latent heat of evaporation of the electrons, per electron, at the absolute zero of temperature, and s is a quantity which depends upon the reflexion of electrons at the surface of the material. The precise definition of s is as follows. Consider the surface in question to form part of an isolated system in thermal equilibrium. It will be continually

* *Ann. der Physik*, vol. xvii. p. 146 (1905).
† O. W. Richardson, Phys. Rev. vol. xxxiv. pp. 146, 384 (1912); Phil. Mag. vol. xxiii. p. 615 (1912); Science, vol. xxxvi. p. 57 (1912).

emitting and receiving electrons. Of the incident group some will be absorbed and others reflected. Let the proportion absorbed be α. Then the proportion reflected is $1-\alpha$. Some of the electrons in the group under consideration have greater speeds than others; so that as the proportion reflected out of any group having a given speed is a function of the speed, the proportion of the energy, in a mixed incident group, which is reflected, will be different from the proportion of the incident number which is reflected. Let β be the proportion of the energy of the group, incident in the state of thermal equilibrium, which is absorbed. Then $s=\beta/\alpha$. As the proportion of incident electrons absorbed is smaller the higher the speed, it follows that s is a positive quantity which is less than unity.

The deduction of formulæ (9) and (10) does not depend on the unitary theory of light except in so far as the unitary assumption may implicitly underlie Planck's radiation formula, or rather Wien's form

$$\mathrm{E}(\nu\theta)=\frac{8\pi}{c^3}h\nu^3\,e^{-\frac{h\nu}{\mathrm{R}\theta}},\quad\ldots\ldots\quad(11)$$

which is used instead, as a sufficient approximation.

If we put $w_0=h\nu_0$ we have instead of (9) and (10)

$$\mathrm{T}_m=h(\nu-\nu_0),\quad \mathrm{T}_r=sh(\nu-\nu_0)\ \ .\ \ .\ \ .\quad(12)$$

or, in wave-lengths, putting $c=\nu\lambda=\nu_0\lambda_0$

$$\lambda\mathrm{T}_m=ch\left(1-\frac{\lambda}{\lambda_0}\right),\quad \lambda\mathrm{T}_r=sch\left(1-\frac{\lambda}{\lambda_0}\right).\quad.\ \ (13)$$

A more comprehensive test of these formulæ is afforded by Pl. XIII. fig. 9, which contains all the observations which we have made. The points corresponding to the different metals are indicated thus:—

Na•, Alo, Mg*, Zn▲, Sn+, Bi⅄, Cu×, and Pt⅃.

The values of λ_0 which have been used in constructing the figure are those given by plotting T_r, the mean energy, against ν. The points near the lines OB and OC represent values of T_m and those near OD and OE values of T_r. OA is the theoretical line for $\mathrm{T}_m=h(\nu-\nu_0)$ using the value of h given by radiation measurements, viz. $h=6\cdot55\times10^{-27}$ erg cm. Except in the case of copper and bismuth, all the values of T_m lie very near the line OB and all those of T very near the line OD. The slope of the line OB corresponds to $k_m=5\cdot4\times10^{-27}$ erg sec. instead of $6\cdot55\times10^{-27}$ erg sec.

It is thus about 20 per cent. less than the theoretical value. The slope of OD is almost exactly half of that of OB. The slope of OC is only about two thirds of that of OB, but the same relation holds between OE and OC as between OD and OB. It thus appears that s is very close to one half for all the metals investigated, even including copper and bismuth, for which the discrepancy between k_m and h is much greater than in the case of the other six metals.

The relation $T_r = sh(\nu - \nu_0)$ has only been shown theoretically to hold for the case of isotropic radiation, that is for incident radiation which is propagated with equal intensity in all directions, whereas all the values given are for light at approximately normal incidence. However, we made special experiments with platinum and aluminium to see whether rotating the strip S so as to change the angle of incidence of the light would make any alteration in the curves giving the distribution of kinetic energy. We were unable to detect any certain changes in the energy in this way, although the number of electrons emitted varied considerably. It would appear, therefore, that the difference in the distribution of energy among the electrons emitted by isotropic radiation and those emitted by radiation incident at a particular angle, is inappreciable or, at least, its determination is not a practical matter when the degree of precision which is at present attainable in experiments of this kind is taken into consideration.

The fact that all of the measured values of λT_m fall to the left of the line OA is perhaps not very surprising. Practically every source of experimental error tends to make the measured values of T_m too small. This would be the case, for example, if the surface of the strip were covered with a layer of photoelectrically inactive material such as the oxide of the metal or a layer of condensed gas or moisture; the effect of any slight leakage in the electrostatic system is also in the same direction. We are unable at present to urge any satisfactory reason why the metals copper and bismuth should appear to be in a class by themselves.

It is worth while remarking that the difference between the experimental and the theoretical relation of T_m to ν is what one would expect if there were a layer of photoelectrically inactive material at the surface of the strips which reduced the speed of the escaping electrons, provided the law of diminution of kinetic energy T with thickness x of material traversed were of the form

$$\delta T = -T f(x) \delta x. \quad . \quad . \quad . \quad . \quad (14)$$

This makes the energy lost proportional to the initial energy for different wave-lengths, and the relation between the observed T_m and ν a linear one. The slope, measured by k_m, of the experimental line would then be less than that (h) of the theoretical line. The two lines would intersect at $T_m=0$. This is in accordance with the experimental results if the experimental values of ν_0 are really identical with the least frequencies which would cause any electrons to be emitted from a perfectly clean surface. It might be, however, that the true values of ν_0 would be less than those observed, on account of the slowest electrons being completely stopped by such a layer. In that case the relation between T and x would have to be of the form

$$T = T_0 f(x) - g(x), \quad \ldots \ldots (15)$$

when T_0 is the maximum initial energy.

There is at present, so far as we are aware, no experimental evidence bearing on the law of loss of energy with matter traversed for these slowly moving electrons, but Sir J. J. Thomson * has deduced a formula of type (14) with $f(x) =$ constant, on theoretical grounds. The application of this formula can hardly be regarded as having much cogency in the present instance, but it is of some interest to see what it leads to, in the way of an estimate of the thickness of inactive matter required to produce the observed differences between theory and experiment. In the least favourable case, that of bismuth, assuming the inactive matter to be Bi_2O_3, we find $x = 2 \cdot 5 \times 10^{-4}$ cm. In the other cases the thickness would vary down to about one-tenth of this. Thicknesses of inactive matter of this magnitude should produce distinct optical effects. The only case in which we observed visible changes of this kind was that of copper, the surface of which became darker during the experiments. The existence of photoelectric fatigue shows that the surfaces of the metals do become covered with a layer of inactive matter. Tests which we have carried out show that the change in the maximum energy and in the distribution of energy of the emitted electrons due to photoelectric fatigue is uncertain, but is certainly inappreciable in comparison with the change in the number of electrons emitted. However, a layer of inactive matter might easily have the effect of reducing the *number* of escaping electrons very considerably without causing any comparable change in the distribution of velocity among those which got through, particularly as the mode of distribution is fairly irregular to start with. It is significant

* ‘Conduction of Electricity through Gases,’ 2nd edition, p. 379.

that the metals for which the values of k_m show the nearest approach to the theoretical value are platinum and sodium. The former is notoriously averse to oxidation and the surfaces of the latter were cut *in situ* in the best attainable vacuum.

The Values of ν_0 and λ_0.

According to the theory which underlies formulæ (9) to (13)

$$w_0 = h\nu_0, \quad \dots \dots \quad (16)$$

where w_0 is the latent heat of evaporation of electrons out of the material at the absolute zero of temperature. The value of w_0 can be obtained from thermoelectric data combined with the temperature variation of the rate of emission of electrons from the material when heated. The metal which has received the most extended study in this respect is platinum, and it is probable that a fairly reliable estimate of w_0 can be obtained for this material. If σ is the specific heat of electricity, one of the writers * has shown that

$$\sigma = \frac{1}{e} \left\{ \frac{R}{\gamma - 1} - \frac{\partial w}{\partial \theta} \right\}, \quad \dots \quad (17)$$

when e is the charge on an electron, R is the gas constant for one molecule, γ is the ratio of the two specific heats for the electrons, and w is their latent heat of evaporation, per electron, at temperature θ. According to Berg † the Thomson coefficient for platinum is practically constant between $-50°$ C. and $+100°$ C. and equal to $-9\cdot2 \times 10^2$ erg per E.M.U. per ° C. Thus from (17) w is a linear function of θ. If n is the total number of electrons emitted thermionically at θ, when the coefficient of reflexion of the electrons is neglected

$$n = A_1 \theta^{\frac{1}{2}} e^{\int \frac{w}{R\theta^2} d\theta}, \quad \dots \dots \quad (18)$$

where A_1 is independent of θ. Substituting the experimental numbers given by the Thomson effect, this becomes

$$n = A_2 \theta^{2\cdot11} e^{-w_0/R\theta}, \quad \dots \dots \quad (19)$$

where A_2 is independent of θ and w_0 is the value of w when $\theta = 0$.

We have applied the formula to determine w_0 from the experimental measurements of the saturation electronic

---

* O. W. Richardson, Phil. Mag. vol. xxiii. p. 605 (1912).

† *Cf.* Baedeker, *Elektrische Erscheinungen in Metallischen Leitern,* p. 76.

currents from platinum at different temperatures, which have been made by F. Deininger[*], H. A. Wilson[†], and O. W. Richardson[‡]. These are probably the most reliable determinations which have been made, and although they are not in perfect agreement there is no reason why any one of them should be rejected. The values of w_0 in equivalent volts calculated in this way are :—Deininger, 5·03; Wilson, 5·39; Richardson, 5·61. The mean is 5·34 volts or $8·32 \times 10^{-12}$ erg using $e = 4·67 \times 10^{-10}$ E.S.U. The value of ν_0 for platinum in the table on p. 586 is $1·03 \times 10^{15}$ sec.$^{-1}$ whence

$$h = w_0/\nu_0 = 8·07 \times 10^{-27} \text{ erg sec.} \quad . \quad . \quad . \quad (20)$$

It will be observed that this estimate of h depends only on thermionic, thermoelectric, and photoelectric measurements, and is quite independent of the estimate $k_m = 5·85 \times 10^{-27}$ erg sec. Nevertheless it is very close to the radiation value $h = 6·55 \times 10^{-27}$ erg sec. The value (20) is, in fact, just about as much in excess of the radiation value as the other is below it.

The discrepancy between the value of h from w_0/ν_0 and from the radiation formula might be due either to w_0 being too large or ν_0 being too small. It is possible that the values of ν_0 estimated from the linear relation between T and ν are too small for some unknown reason; but it is not possible that they are sufficiently in error to account for the whole of the discrepancy. This is shown by the fact that in the case of platinum the photoelectric emission was definitely measurable at $\lambda = 27$ as compared with the value $\lambda = 29·1$ deduced from the measurement of T_r. There is therefore only a possibility of an extension of λ_0 of about 2 units in this direction, and this would only account at most for about half the observed difference. As a matter of fact the tabulated values of λ_0 on p. 586, although rather higher than the wave-lengths at which photoelectric emission was observed to start, were never very far from them. Although we have made experiments in this direction with most of the substances investigated, we have not been able to satisfy ourselves that there is any certain difference between the tabulated values of λ_0 and the greatest wave-length at which photoelectric emission commences. The tests made, however, are not as delicate or reliable as might be desired, on account of the photoelectric insensitiveness of the materials in this

[*] *Ann. der Physik*, vol. xxv. p. 296 (1908).
[†] Phil. Trans. A, vol. ccii. p. 243 (1903).
[‡] Phil. Trans. A, vol. ccvii. p. xxiii. (1906).

region and of the fact that our source of light gave a line spectrum.

It seems, therefore, fairly certain that part of the increased value of h deduced from (20) must be due to w_0 being too large.   We think it improbable that w_0 is appreciably larger than what it pretends to be, namely, the part of the latent heat of evaporation of the thermionically emitted electrons which is independent of θ.   It may be, however, that w_0 is slightly smaller for the electrons emitted photoelectrically by the complete radiation, than it is for the electrons which are emitted thermionically.   If this could be established it would be important as showing that thermionic emission is something different from the photoelectric emission arising from the complete radiation characteristic of the temperature of the hot body [*].

The values of ν_0 for different substances are closely related to the contact differences of potential.   This is shown by the numbers in the following table, which represent the contact differences of potential between platinum and the different metals investigated :—

Metal. I.	Contact P.D. with Platinum. (Volts.)		
	Calculated. II.	Observed. III.	Calculated. IV.
Cu	·37	·13	·30
Bi	·77	·35	·64
Sn	·77	·62	·64
Zn	1·04	·90	·85
Mg	1·17	1·05	1·00
Al	1·62	1·2	1·31
Na	2·69	2·4	2·2

The observed values in column III. are the usual values, except in the case of Mg, where the observed value was ·25 volt less than that given in the standard tables.   The calculated values in columns II. and IV. are derived from the corresponding values of w_0 in different ways.   The differences of w_0 are taken to be equal to the differences of eV, where V is the corresponding intrinsic potential.   This is in accordance with the formula

$$w_m - w_p = e\left(V_m - V_p - \theta\frac{\partial}{\partial\theta}(V_m - V_p)\right), \quad . \quad . \quad (21)$$

[*] *Cf.* O. W. Richardson, Phil. Mag. vol. xxiii. p. 620 (1912).

since the term involving θ, which depends on the thermo-electric power of the metals, may be disregarded in the cases considered on account of its smallness. For similar reasons the differences of w may be taken to be the same thing as the differences of w_0.

The values in column II. were obtained by assuming that the value of w_0 for platinum was equal to that given by the thermionic measurements, viz. 5·34, in equivalent volts. A factor A was then determined so that $h\nu_0 = A \times 5\cdot34$ where $h = 6\cdot55 \times 10^{-27}$ erg sec. and $\nu_0 = 1\cdot03 \times 10^{15}$ sec.$^{-1}$ the value of ν_0 for platinum given by the experiments. This value of A was then used as a reduction factor to determine the value of w_0 from that of $h\nu_0$ for each of the other metals. This method is equivalent to assuming that the value of w_0 is the same for the photoelectric as for the thermionic emission, and that the large value of h given by (20) is due to some unknown error in $h\nu_0$ which affects the different metals proportionately.

The values in column IV. are simply the differences of $h\nu_0$ reduced to volts per unit charge. This method of calculation is equivalent to assuming either that w_0 is in error or that it is not the same thing for photoelectric as for thermionic emission. All things considered, both II. and IV. give a fair agreement with III., although the last column agrees better than the second. On the whole, the view which puts the error in (20) on w_0 has, so far, the best of the argument.

The Frequency of Characteristic Röntgen Rays.

If the formula $T_m = \nu h - w_0$ continues to apply no matter how high the frequency ν becomes, the frequency of characteristic Röntgen rays can be written down from known data. There is nothing in any derivation of the formula which would tend to confine its application to any limited range of frequency. On the other hand, its validity is closely connected with that of Planck's radiation formula, which has only been tested in the neighbourhood of the visible spectrum. The extension to the case of Röntgen rays can therefore only be regarded as speculative ; as a speculation however, it has some merit, since it is the only line of attack which seems open to us at present.

The researches of Sadler * and Beattie † have shown that when characteristic Röntgen rays fall on different substances, the energy of the emitted electrons is independent of the substance emitting them, being determined entirely by the

* Phil. Mag. vol. xix. p. 337 (1910).
† Phil. Mag. vol. xx. p. 320 (1910).

character of the X rays. Whiddington * has shown that the maximum energy of the emitted electrons is equal to that of the slowest cathode rays which will excite the characteristic Röntgen rays. He has measured this quantity in equivalent volts in a number of cases and has shown that, in general, for Barkla's K series of X rays the energy is proportional to the square of the atomic weight of the metal of which they are characteristic. These results are consistent with the formula $T_m = h\nu_0 - w_0$ for the energy of the emitted electrons provided ν_0, the frequency of the characteristic Röntgen rays, is given by

$$\nu_0 = 6\cdot55 \times M^2 \times 10^{14}, \quad . \quad . \quad . \quad . \quad (22)$$

where M is the atomic weight of the metal of which they are characteristic. This holds only for the rays which constitute Barkla's K series. The values for the L series should be given by substituting $\left(\dfrac{M}{2} - 25\right)$ for M in (22), to accord with Whiddington's conclusions. Thus the frequency of the Röntgen rays characteristic of copper would be, since they belong to the K series,

$$\nu_0 = 2\cdot64 \times 10^{18} \text{ sec.}^{-1}.$$

In the case of all these rays w_0 is negligible in comparison with $h\nu_0$. This accounts for the energy being independent of the metal of origin, as found by Sadler.

Palmer Physical Laboratory,
    Princeton, N. J.

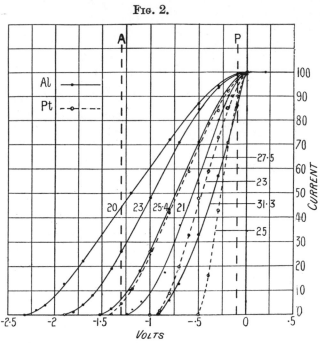

FIG. 2.

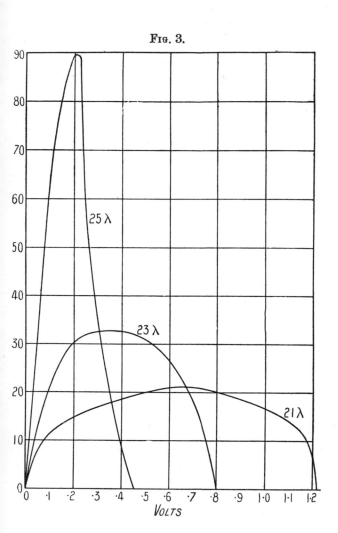

FIG. 3.

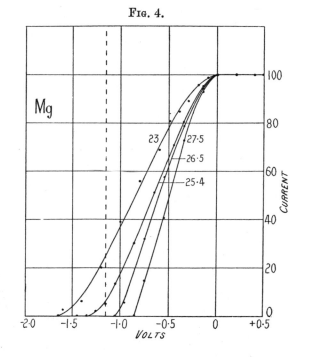

FIG. 4.

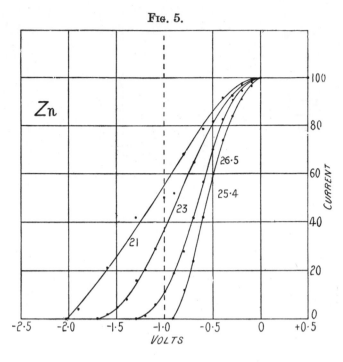

Fig. 5.

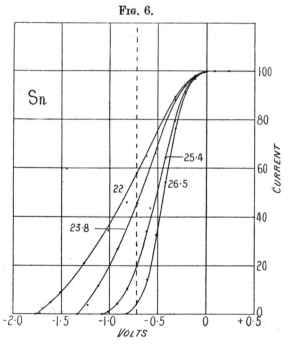

Fig. 6.

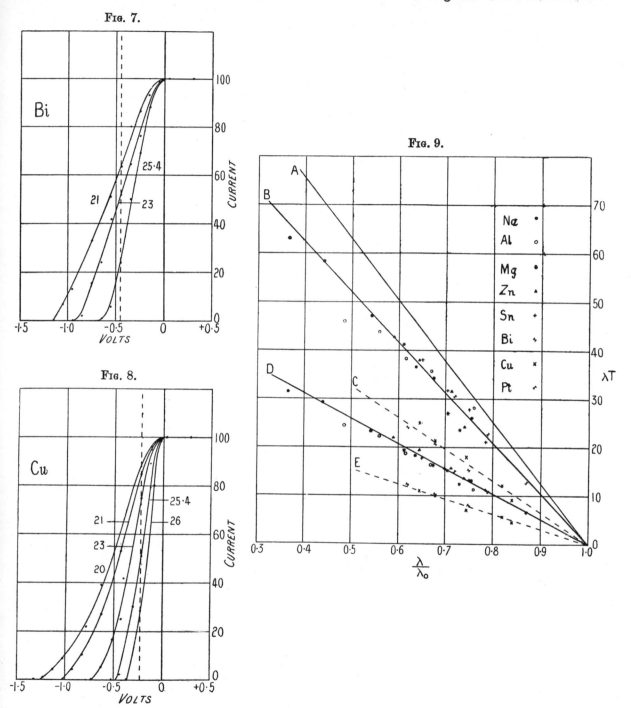

FIG. 7.

FIG. 8.

FIG. 9.

Experiments with High Velocity Positive Ions. II.—*The Disintegration of Elements by High Velocity Protons.*

By J. D. Cockcroft, Ph.D., Fellow of St. John's College, Cambridge, and E. T. S. Walton, Ph.D.

(Communicated by Lord Rutherford, O.M., F.R.S.—Received June 15, 1932.)

[Plate 12.]

1. *Introduction.*

In a previous paper* we have described a method of producing high velocity positive ions having energies up to 700,000 electron volts. We first used this method to determine the range of high-speed protons in air and hydrogen and the results obtained will be described in a subsequent paper. In the present communication we describe experiments which show that protons having energies above 150,000 volts are capable of disintegrating a considerable number of elements.

Experiments in artificial disintegration have in the past been carried out with streams of α-particles as the bombarding particles; the resulting transmutations have in general been accompanied by the emission of a proton and in some cases γ-radiation.† The present experiments show that under the bombardment of protons, α-particles are emitted from many elements; the disintegration process is thus in a sense the reverse process to the α-particle transformation.

---

* 'Proc. Roy. Soc.,' A, vol. 136, p. 619 (1932) denoted as (I) hereafter.

† Rutherford, Chadwick and Ellis, " Radioactive Substances."

2. *The Experimental Method.*

Positive ions of hydrogen obtained from a hydrogen canal ray tube are accelerated by voltages up to 600 kilovolts in the experimental tube described in (I) and emerge through a 3-inch diameter brass tube into a chamber well shielded by lead and screened from electrostatic fields. To this brass tube is attached by a flat joint and plasticene seal the apparatus shown in fig. 1. A target, A, of the metal to be investigated is placed at an angle of 45 degrees to the direction of the proton stream. Opposite the centre of the target is a side tube across which is sealed at B either a zinc sulphide screen or a mica window.

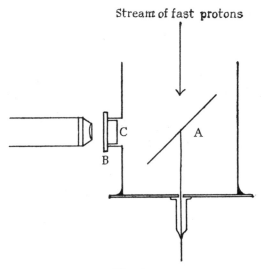

Fig. 1.

In our first experiments we used a round target of lithium 5 cm. in diameter and sealed the side tube with a zinc sulphide screen, the sensitive surface being towards the target. The distance from the centre of the target to the screen was 5 cm. A sheet of mica, C, of stopping power 1·4 cm. was placed between the screen and target and was more than adequate to prevent any scattered protons reaching the screen, since our range determinations* and the experiments of Blackett† have shown that the maximum range of protons accelerated by 600 kilovolts is of the order of 10 mm. in air. The screen is observed with a microscope having a numerical aperture of 0·6, the area of screen covered being 12 sq. mm. This arrangement with the fluorescent surface inside the vacuum is generally used in the preliminary investigations

* In course of publication.
† 'Proc. Roy. Soc.' A, vol. 134, p. 658 (1931).

of elements and when it is necessary to detect the presence of particles of short range.

The current to the target is measured by a galvanometer and controlled by varying the speed of the motor used for driving the alternator exciting the discharge tube (see Paper I). Currents of up to 5 microamperes can be obtained. Since metals bombarded by high-speed positive ions emit large numbers of secondary electrons for each incident ion, it is necessary to prevent the emission of these electrons if an accurate determination of the number of incident ions is required. This has been effected by applying a magnetic field of the order of 700 gauss to the target. Since it is well known that the majority of the secondary electrons have energies below 20 volts, such a field should be adequate to prevent secondary electron emission being a serious source of error.

An accurate determination of the exact composition of the beam of ions has not yet been made, but deflection experiments with a magnetic field in a subsidiary apparatus have shown that approximately half the current is carried by protons and half by H_2^+ ions. The number of neutral atoms appears to be small.

The accelerating voltage used in the experiments is controlled by varying the field of the alternator exciting the main high tension transformer. The secondary voltage of this transformer is measured by the method described in an earlier paper,* which rectifies the current passing through a condenser. A microammeter on the control table allows a continuous reading of this voltage to be obtained. The value of the steady potential produced by the rectifier system varies between 3 and 3·5 times the maximum of the transformer voltage according to the brightness of the rectifier filaments. The actual value of the voltage is determined by using a sphere gap consisting of two 75-cm. diameter aluminium spheres, one of which is earthed. In each experiment the multiplication factor of the rectifier system is determined for several voltages and intermediate points obtained by interpolation. The accuracy of the determination of the voltage by the sphere gaps has been checked by measuring the deflection of the protons in a magnetic field. It has been found that corrections of the order of 15 per cent. may be required as a result of the proximity of neighbouring objects or unfavourable arrangements of the connecting leads. The voltages given in this paper have all been corrected by reference to the magnetic deflection experiments.

* 'Proc. Roy. Soc.' A, vol. 129, p. 477 (1930).

3. *The Disintegration of Lithium.*

When the current passing to the target was of the order of 1 microampere and the accelerating potential was increased to 125 kilovolts, a number of bright scintillations were observed on the screen, the numbers being proportional to the current collected and of the order of 5 per minute per microampere at 125 kilovolts.

No scintillations were observed when the proton current was cut off by shutting off the discharge tube excitation or by interposing a brass flap between the beam and the target. Since the scintillations were very similar in appearance and brightness to α-particle scintillations, the apparatus was now changed to allow a determination of their range to be made. For this purpose a mica window having a stopping power of 2 cm. was sealed to the side tube in place of the fluorescent screen, which was now placed outside the window. It was then possible to insert mica screens of known stopping power between the window and the screen. In this way it became apparent that the scintillations were produced by particles having a well-defined range of about 8 cm. Variations of voltage between 250 and 500 kilovolts did not appear to alter the range appreciably.

In order to check this conclusion, the particles were now passed into a Shimizu expansion chamber, through a mica window in the side of the chamber having a stopping power of $3 \cdot 6$ cm. When the accelerating voltage was applied to the tube a number of discrete tracks were at once observed in the chamber whose lengths agreed closely with the first range determinations. From the appearance of the tracks and the brightness of the scintillations it seemed now fairly clear that we were observing α-particles ejected from the lithium nuclei under the proton bombardment, and that the lithium isotope of mass 7 was breaking up into two α-particles.

In order to obtain a further proof of the nature of the particles the experiments were repeated with an ionisation chamber, amplifier and oscillograph of the type described by Wynn Williams and Ward.* The mica window on the side tube was reduced to a thickness corresponding to a stopping power of $1 \cdot 2$ mm. with an area of about 1 sq. cm., the mica being supported on a grid structure. The lithium target was at the same time reduced in size to a circle of 1 cm. diameter in order to reduce the angular spread of the particles entering the counter. The ionisation chamber was of the parallel plane type having a total depth of 3 mm. and was sealed by an aluminium window having a stopping

* 'Proc. Roy. Soc.,' A, vol. 132, p. 391 (1931).

power of 5 mm. The degree of resolution of the amplifier and oscillograph was such that it was possible to record accurately up to 2000 particles per minute. With the full potential applied to the apparatus but with no proton current, the number of spurious deflections in the oscillograph was of the order of 2 per minute, whilst with an accelerating potential of 500 kilovolts and a current of 0·3 microamperes the number of particles entering the ionisation chamber per minute was of the order of 700.

In figs. 8, 9, 10 and 11, Plate 12, are shown the oscillograph records obtained as additional mica absorbers are inserted. It will be seen that the size of the deflections increases as additional mica is inserted, whilst the numbers fall off rapidly when the total absorber thickness is increased beyond 7 cm. In fig. 2 is plotted the number of particles entering the chamber per minute per micro-ampere for increasing absorber thickness and for accelerating potentials of 270 kilovolts and 450 kilovolts. The stopping power of the mica screens of windows has been checked and the final range determination made by a comparison with the α-particles from thorium C. We find that the range is 8·4 cm. Preliminary observations showed that between the lowest and highest voltages used, the range remained approximately constant. It is, however, of great interest to test whether the whole of the energy of the proton is communicated to the α-particles, and it is intended at a later date to examine this point more carefully. The general shape of the range curve, together with the evidence from the size of the oscillograph deflections, suggests that the great majority of the particles have initially a uniform velocity, but further investigation will be required with lower total absorption to exclude the possibility of the existence of particles of short range.

As is well known, the size of the oscillograph kicks are a measure of the ionisation produced by the particles. At the beginning of the range the size of the kicks observed was very uniform, whilst the average size varied with the range of the particle corresponding to the ionisation given by the Bragg curve. Fig. 3 shows the variation of the ionisation of the most numerous particles with range.

The sizes of the deflections were now compared with the deflections produced in the same ionisation chamber by α-particles from a polonium source, these deflections being recorded in fig. 12, Plate 12, for comparison. It has been shown in this way that the maximum deflection for the two types of particle is the same. This result, together with the uniformity of the ionisation produced by the particles, is sufficient to exclude the possibility of some of the particles being protons, since the maximum ionisation produced by a

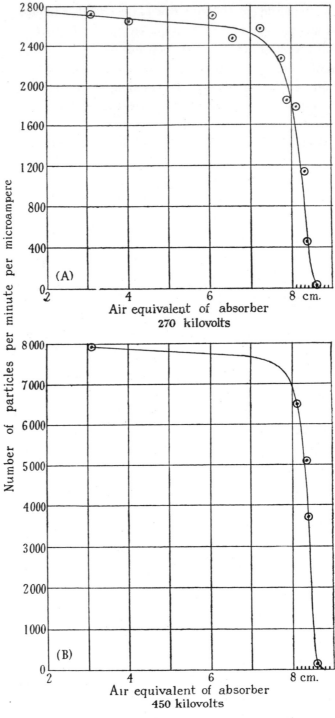

FIG. 2.

proton is less than 40 per cent. of the maximum ionisation produced by an α-particle.

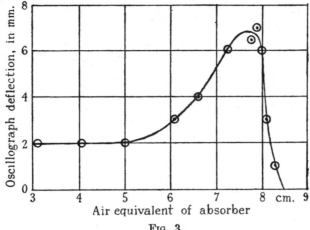

Fig. 3.

The variation of the numbers of particles with accelerating voltage was determined from the oscillograph records between 200 kilovolts and 500 kilovolts, the change in numbers being clear from the records, figs. 13, 14, 15, Plate 12. For voltages between 70 kilovolts and 250 kilovolts, the numbers of particles entering the ionisation chamber were counted by a single stage thyratron counter of the type described by Wynn Williams and Ward.* The results are plotted in fig. 4. The numbers increase roughly exponentially with the voltage at the lower voltages and linearly with voltage above 300 kilovolts.†

It is of great interest to estimate the number of particles produced by the bombardment of a thick layer of lithium by a fixed number of protons. In making this estimate we have assumed that the particles are emitted uniformly in all directions and that the molecular ions produce no effect. With these assumptions the number of disintegrations for a voltage of 250 kilovolts is 1 per 10^9 protons, and for a voltage of 500 kilovolts is 10 per 10^9 protons.

In considering the variation in numbers of particles with voltage it has, of course, to be borne in mind that with a thick target the effects are due to

---

* 'Proc. Roy. Soc.,' A, vol. 131, p. 191 (1931).

† All the measurements in a single run, in which more than 2000 particles were counted, are included in the figure. The spread of the points in the centre part of the curve is probably due to variations in the vacuum and therefore in the voltage applied during the experiment. In other runs no evidence was obtained for such a variation.

protons of all energies from the maximum to zero energy. It will be very important to determine the probability of disintegration for protons of one definite energy, and for this purpose it will be necessary to use thin targets. Preliminary experiments using evaporated films of lithium show that the probability or " excitation " function does not increase so rapidly with voltage as for the thick target, but owing to the small numbers of particles obtainable these experiments have not yet been completed.

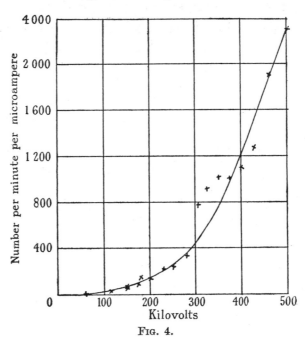

Fig. 4.

4. *The Interpretation of Results.*

We have already stated that the obvious interpretation of our results is to assume that the lithium isotope of mass 7 captures a proton and that the resulting nucleus of mass 8 breaks up into two α-particles. If momentum is conserved in the process, then each of the α-particles must take up equal amounts of energy, and from the observed range of the α-particles we conclude that an energy of $17 \cdot 2$ million volts would be liberated in this disintegration process. The mass of the $\mathrm{Li_7}$ nucleus from Costa's determination is $7 \cdot 0104$ with a probable error of $0 \cdot 003$. The decrease of mass in the disintegration process is therefore $7 \cdot 0104 + 1 \cdot 0072 - 8 \cdot 0022 = 0 \cdot 0154 \pm 0 \cdot 003$. This is equivalent to an energy liberation of $(14 \cdot 3 \pm 2 \cdot 7) \times 10^6$ volts. We conclude, therefore, that the observed energies of the α-particles are consistent with our hypothesis. An additional test can, however, be applied. If momentum is conserved in the disintegration, the two α-particles must be ejected in practically opposite directions and, therefore, if we arrange two zinc sulphide screens opposite to a small target of lithium as shown in the arrangement of fig. 5, we should observe a large proportion of coincidences in the time of appearance of the scintillations on the two screens. The lithium used in the experiments was evaporated on to a thin film of mica having an area of 1 sq. mm. and a stopping power of 1·1 cm., so that α-particles ejected from the lithium would pass easily through the mica and reach the screen on the opposite side of the lithium layer.

The two screens were observed through microscopes each covering an area of 7 sq. mm. and a tape recording machine was used to record the scintillations,

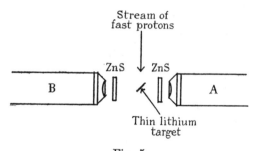

Fig. 5.

a buzzer being installed in the observation chamber to prevent the noise of the recording keys being audible to the observers. Five hundred and sixty-five scintillations were observed in microscope A and 288 scintillations in microscope B, the former being nearer the target. Analysis of the records showed that the results are consistent with the assumption that about 25 per cent. of the scintillations recorded in B have a corresponding scintillation in A. If we calculate the chance of a scintillation being recorded by B within x seconds of the record of a scintillation in A, assuming a perfectly random distribution of scintillations, and compare this with the observed record, the curve shown in fig. 6 is obtained. It will be seen that as the interval x is made less, the ratio of the observed to the random coincidences increases. We also plot for comparison the theoretical curve (shown by broken line) which would be obtained if there were 25 per cent. of coincidences. It will be seen that the two curves are in good accord. The number of coincidences observed is about that to be expected on our theory of the disintegration process, when we take into account the geometry of the experimental arrangement and the efficiency of the zinc sulphide screens. It is clear that there is strong evidence supporting the hypothesis that the α-particles are emitted in pairs. A more complete investigation will be made later, using larger areas for the counting device, when it is to be expected that the fraction of coincidences should increase.

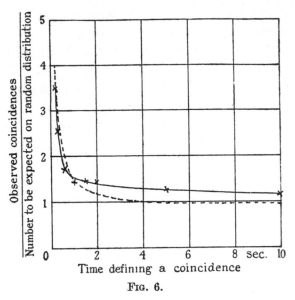

FIG. 6.

5. *Comparison with the Gamow Theory.*

In a paper which was largely responsible for stimulating the present investigation, Gamow† has calculated the probability $W_1{}^*$ of a particle of charge Ze, mass m and energy E, entering a nucleus of charge $Z'e$. Gamow's formula is

$$W_1{}^* = e^{\frac{-4\pi \sqrt{(2m)}}{h} \cdot \frac{ZZ'e^2}{\sqrt{(E)}} \cdot J_k},$$

where J_k is a function varying slowly with E and Z. Using this formula, we have calculated $W_1{}^*$, the probability of a proton entering a lithium nucleus, for 600, 300 and 100 kilovolts, and find the values $0 \cdot 187$, $2 \cdot 75 \times 10^{-2}$ and $1 \cdot 78 \times 10^{-4}$. Using these figures, our observed variation of proton range with velocity for a thick target, and assuming a target area of 10^{-25} cm.², the number of protons N required to produce one disintegration may be calculated. For 600 kilovolts we find N to be of the order of 10^6, and for 300 kilovolts of the order of 2×10^7.

The order of magnitude of the numbers observed is thus smaller than the

† ' Z. Physik,' vol. 52, p. 510 (1928).

number predicted by the Gamow theory, but a closer comparison must be deferred until the results for a thin target are available.

6. *The Disintegration of other Elements.*

Preliminary investigations have been made to determine whether any evidence of disintegration under proton bombardment could be obtained for the following elements : Be, B, C, O, F, Na, Al, K, Ca, Fe, Co, Ni, Cu, Ag, Pb, U. Using the fluorescent screen as a detector we have observed some bright scintillations from all these elements, the numbers varying markedly from element to element, the relative orders of magnitude being indicated by fig. 7 for 300 kilovolts. The results of the scintillation method have been confirmed by the electrical counter for Ca, K, Ni, Fe and Co, and the size of the oscillograph kicks suggests that the majority of the particles ejected are α-particles.

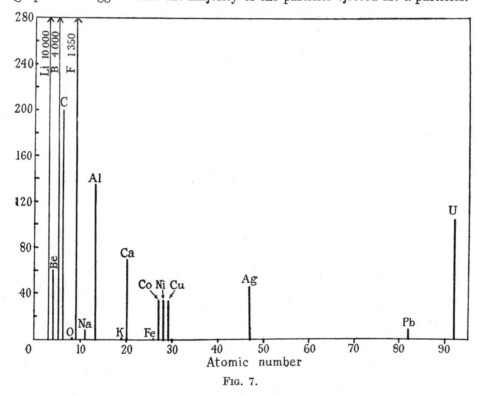

Fig. 7.

The numbers of particles counted have up to the present not been sufficient to enable these figures to be taken as anything other than an order of magnitude. In particular, the possibility must be borne in mind that some of the particles observed may be due to impurities. It may, however, be of some interest to describe briefly the general character of the effects observed in some of the more interesting cases.

Beryllium.—Two types of scintillation were observed with beryllium, a few bright scintillations having the appearance of α-particle scintillations together with a much greater number of faint scintillations appearing at about 500 kilovolts, the numbers increasing rapidly with voltage. We were not able to observe the faint scintillations outside the vacuum chamber, so that they are presumably due to particles of short range.

Boron.—Next to lithium, boron gave the greatest number of scintillations, most of the particles having a range of about 3·5 cm. Scintillations were first observed at voltages of the order of 115 kilovolts, the numbers increasing by more than 100 between this voltage and 375 kilovolts. The interesting problem as to whether the boron splits up into three α-particles or into Be_8 plus an α-particle must await an answer until more detailed investigation is made.

Fluorine.—Fluorine was investigated in the form of a layer of powdered calcium fluoride. A few scintillations were first observed at a voltage of 200 kilovolts, the numbers increasing by a factor of about 100 between this and 450 kilovolts. The range of the particles was found to be about 2·8 cm. On the assumption that they are α-particles, the energy would be $4·15 \times 10^6$ electron volts. If now we assume that the reaction is

$$F_{19} + H_1 = O_{16} + He_4$$

it is of particular interest to compare the observed energy with the energy to be expected from the mass changes, since all the masses involved are known, from the work of Aston, with fairly good precision.

Using Aston's data, the energy liberated should be $5·2 \times 10^6$ electron volts. Allowing for the energy taken by the recoil of the oxygen nucleus and the energy of the bombarding proton, the energy of the α-particle should be about 4·3 million volts, giving a range of 2·95 cm. in air, in good accord with the observed ranges.

Sodium.—A small number of bright scintillations were observed beginning at 300 kilovolts, the particles having ranges between 2 and 3·5 cm. In addition to the bright scintillations, a number of faint scintillations were observed similar to those seen in the case of beryllium. The faint scintillations are again presumably due to particles of short range since they could not be observed outside the tube. The probable α-particle transition would be

$$Na_{23} + H_1 = Ne_{20} + He_4.$$

Potassium.—Potassium is of special interest on account of its radioactivity. The very small effects observed may easily be due to an impurity. The most likely reaction to occur

$$K_{39} + H_1 = A_{36} + He_4,$$

would probably have a negative energy balance.

Iron, Nickel, Cobalt, Copper.—These elements follow each other in the periodic table, so that the small result obtained for iron compared with that for the following three elements is of special interest. The effect for iron is of the same order as that for potassium, and again may be due to impurity. For these elements most of the particles had a range of about 2·5 cm., but a few particles were present having a slightly longer range.

Uranium.—Using potentials of up to 600 kilovolts and strong proton currents, the number of scintillations observed was about four times the natural radio-active effect, and the artificially produced particles appeared to have a longer range than the natural ones. The numbers obtained did not appear to vary markedly with voltage.

We hope in the near future to investigate the above and other elements in much greater detail and in particular to determine whether any of the effects described are due to impurities. There seems to be little doubt, however, that most of the effects are due to transformations giving rise to an α-particle emission. In view of the very small probability of a proton of 500 kilovolts energy penetrating the potential barrier of the heavier nuclei by any process other than a resonance process, it would appear most likely that such processes are responsible for the effects observed with the heavier elements.

We have seen that the three elements, lithium, boron and fluorine give the largest emission of particles, the emission varying similarly with rise of voltage. These elements are all of the $4n + 3$ type, and presumably the nuclei are made up of α-particles with the addition of three protons and two electrons. It is natural to suppose that the addition of a captured proton leads to the formation of a new α-particle inside the nucleus. In the case of lithium, it seems probable that the capture of the proton, the formation of the α-particle and the dis-integration of the resulting nucleus into two α-particles must at this stage be regarded as a single process, the excess energy appearing in the form of kinetic energy of the expelled α-particles.* Until further and more accurate data are available it is not desirable to discuss at this stage the possible bearing of

---

* Such a view does not preclude the possibility that sometimes part of the energy may appear in another form, for example, as γ-radiation.

these new observations on the problems of astrophysics and on the question of the abundance of the elements.

In conclusion, we wish to express our thanks to Lord Rutherford for his constant encouragement and advice.   We are indebted to Dr. Wynn Williams for considerable assistance with the electrical recording apparatus, and to members of the research staff of Metropolitan-Vickers Electrical Company for their assistance in supplying much of the apparatus used in this work.   One of us (E.T.S.W.) has been in receipt of a senior research award from the Department of Scientific and Industrial Research.

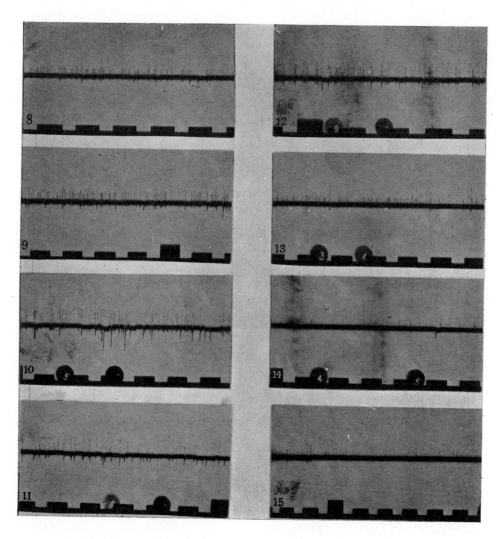

FIG. 8.—270 Kv. 4·0 cm. absorber.

FIG. 9.—270 Kv. 5·0 cm. absorber.

FIG. 10.—270 Kv. 6·6 cm. absorber.

FIG. 11.—270 Kv. 7·9 cm. absorber.

FIG. 12.—Polonium α-particles 2 cm. absorber.

FIG. 13.—250 Kv. 3·1 cm. absorber.

FIG. 14.—210 Kv. 3·1 cm. absorber.

FIG. 15.—175 Kv. 3·1 cm. absorber.

(Facing p. 240.)

X-RAY SPECTRA FROM A RULED REFLECTION GRATING

By A. H. Compton and R. L. Doan

Ryerson Physical Laboratory, University of Chicago

Communicated September 5, 1925

We have recently obtained spectra of ordinary X-rays by reflection at very small glancing angles from a grating ruled on speculum metal. Typical spectra thus obtained are shown in the accompanying figures. From some of these spectra it is possible to measure X-ray wave-lengths with considerable precision.

In order to reflect any considerable X-ray energy from a speculum surface it is necessary to work at small glancing angles, within the critical angle for total reflection. (See A. H. Compton, *Phil. Mag.*, **45**, 1121 (1923).) Within this critical angle, which in our experiments, using wave-lengths less than 1.6 angstroms, was less than 25 minutes of arc, the diffraction grating may be used in the same manner as in optical work. The wave-length is given by the usual formula,

$$n\lambda = D (\sin \phi + \sin i)$$

where i is the angle of incidence and ϕ is the angle of diffraction for the nth order. For small glancing angles this may be more conveniently written as

$$n\lambda = D \{\cos \theta - \cos(\theta + \alpha)\} \ldots \ldots \ldots \ldots (1)$$

in which θ is the glancing angle and α is the angle between the zero order and the nth order. For the small angles employed this may be written to a very close approximation as

$$\lambda = \frac{D}{n} \left(\alpha\theta + \frac{1}{2} \alpha^2 \right) \ldots \ldots \ldots \ldots \ldots (2)$$

In order that several orders of the spectrum should appear inside the critical angle, we had a grating ruled with a comparatively large grating space, $D = 2.000 \times 10^{-3}$ cm. Special pains were taken to obtain a well polished surface, and the ruling was rather light, so as to obtain good reflection from the space between the lines. The reflected beam thus obtained was just as sharply defined as the direct beam.

In our first trials the X-rays direct from the target of a water-cooled Coolidge tube were collimated by fine slits 0.1 mm. broad and about 30 cm. apart. There was some difficulty at first in determining the zero position of the grating but this was solved in the following manner. The primary X-ray beam was first allowed to fall directly upon the film. Then after a brief exposure the speculum grating was brought into the path of the beam by means of a slow motion screw and a longer exposure sufficed to record the reflected image of the zero order, together with the associated first and higher orders.   We were able, from the lines thus obtained on the film, to measure both θ and α.   Photographs of this type are shown in figure 2 for a copper tube and in figure 3 for a molybdenum tube.

We were not able, with the grating used, to separate sharply the different X-ray spectrum lines.   Therefore in order to get a precise measurement of one particular line we reflected the $K\alpha_1$ line of molybdenum from a calcite crystal and studied this beam with the ruled grating.   The experimental arrangement is shown diagrammatically in figure 1.   Typical diffraction patterns are shown in figures 4 and 5 for two different angles of incidence

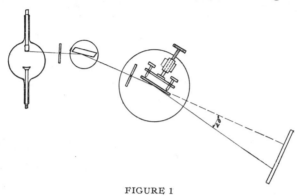

FIGURE 1

of the X-rays on the grating.   It was found that the intensity of the spectrum obtained increased with the glancing angle, θ.   Thus in figure 4, where $\theta = 0.00095$ radians, only the first order spectrum appears; whereas in figure 5, where $\theta = 0.00308$, there appear the first inside order and three outside orders.   The exposure was in each case about 9 hours.

By solving equation 2 for α it will be seen that the inside order cannot appear unless θ is greater than a certain limiting angle.   For precise wavelength measurements, however, it is important to have both inside and outside orders because an accurate setting is impossible on the broad zero order line.   The image due to the direct beam can of course be made of any desired intensity by controlling the length of its exposure.   If β_{-1} is the angle from the image of the direct beam to the first inside order, and β_{+1} that to the first outside order, the glancing angle θ is given by

$$\theta = \frac{\beta^2_{-1} + \beta^2_{+1}}{2(\beta_{-1} + \beta_{+1})}. \tag{3}$$

Using this value of θ, the wave-length can be calculated from equation 2. Following are some examples of measurements and calculations.   From the film shown in figure 5 we measured $\beta_{-1} = 0.004815$, $\beta_{+1} = 0.00725$.

Thus from equation 3, $\theta = 0.003140$, and $\alpha_{-1} = -0.001462$ and $\alpha_{+1} = 0.000972$. Substituting these values in equation 2, we get $\lambda = 0.704A$.

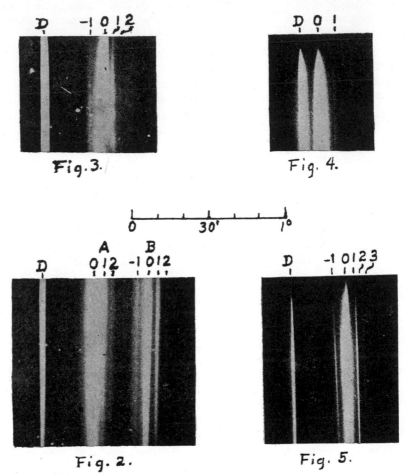

Figure 2. Spectrum of X-rays from copper target, excited at 20 kv. D = image of direct beam; for group A, glancing angle $\theta = 9'$, for B $\theta = 20'$. Numbers −1, 0, 1, 2 indicate the order of the spectrum. The absence of order −1 in group A is predicted by equation 2.

Figure 3. Spectrum of X-rays from molybdenum target, excited at about 35 kv.

Figures 4 and 5. Spectra obtained using the $K\alpha_1$ line of molybdenum.

The weighted mean value of our measurements on five films showing from 1 to 4 orders of the spectrum of the molybdenum $K\alpha_1$ line is

$$\lambda = 0.707 \pm 0.003A.$$

From crystal measurements this wave-length is determined as

$$\lambda = 0.7078 \pm 0.0002\text{A}.$$

The agreement is well within the probable error of our experiments. Our measurements of the spectra, obtained using a copper target, give in a similar manner wave-lengths intermediate between the α and β lines of copper, i.e., about 1.4 to 1.5A.

We see no reason why measurements of the present type may not be made fully as precise as the absolute measurements by reflection from a crystal, in which the probable error is due chiefly to the uncertainty of the crystalline grating space.

SOME TOOLS
OF THE TRADE

The last group of papers contains descriptions of two of the most important tools used by early workers in nuclear physics.

Wilson Cloud Chamber

C. T. R. Wilson started research on the production of clouds and from it developed the two particular uses with which we are concerned. Firstly, it enabled Thomson to measure the charge of an atom ionised by X-rays and, secondly, it led to the development of the Wilson Cloud Chamber. The cloud chamber has been of inestimable value and in Wilson's second paper he shows the power and flexibility of the tool he invented. Typically, it was used to demonstrate the existence of recoil electrons arising from the interaction of an X-ray photon with matter[1] (Compton effect), to examine the connection between the range and velocity of recoil atoms and the validity of the laws of conservation of energy and momentum[2] and to show that an α particle sometimes makes collisions in which momentum is conserved but energy is not[3]. The α particle was absorbed into the nucleus which became unstable and ejected a proton. The reaction may be written $N^{14}(\alpha, p)_8 O^{17}$. The photographs obtained were the first to be taken of the artificial transmutation of an element and were supplementary to the discussion of this same problem by Rutherford in his 1920 Bakerian lecture.

Aston's Mass Spectrograph

This arose from the parabola method of analysing gaseous ions developed by J. J. Thomson. Ions were allowed to pass through a very fine duct and then through a region in which existed parallel electrostatic and magnetic fields. All ions with the same value of e/m came to a focus on the limb of a particular parabola. The ions of other elements were focused on to a separate line. Thomson observed that the presence of neon always resulted in two curved lines on the photographic plate and in doing so detected the first isotope (Ne^{22}. Ne^{21}. was insufficiently abundant to be recorded).

Aston hoped to verify this result in an experiment more precise than Thomson's. He persevered until the First World War and, continuing this work after it, finally constructed the mass spectrograph. Not only did he succeed in separating the three stable isotopes of neon, but demonstrated the existence of the isotopes of many other elements. A further result of importance was that hydrogen had a mass definitely greater than 1, if $O=16$, the reason being that in oxygen part of the mass appears as binding energy. Aston's results permitted a large number of mass defects to be calculated from which, in turn, the energy released during fission could be calculated.

After this work no further doubt could remain as to the equality of the masses of atoms of a given isotope—a conclusion which had always been probable after Thomson's parabolae were found to be relatively sharp.

Note the neat method by which Aston constructed the collimating slits. This is just a small indication of Aston's extremely careful and meticulous ways as an experimenter.

[1] C. T. R. Wilson, *Proc. Roy. Soc.*, 1923, **104**.
[2] P. M. S. Blackett, 'The Study of forked α-ray Tracks', *Proc. Roy. Soc.*, 1923, **103**.
[3] P. M. S. Blackett, 'Ejections of Protons from Nitrogen Nuclei', *Proc. Roy. Soc.*, 1925, **107**.

XI. *Condensation of Water Vapour in the Presence of Dust-free Air and other Gases.*

By C. T. R. WILSON, *B.Sc.* (*Vict.*), *M.A.* (*Cantab.*), *of Sidney Sussex College, Clerk-Maxwell Student in the University of Cambridge.*

Communicated by Professor J. J. THOMSON, *F.R.S.*

Received March 15,—Read April 8, 1897.

THE behaviour of air saturated with aqueous vapour and allowed to expand suddenly, has been investigated by COULIER,[*] AITKEN,[†] KIESSLING,[‡] and R. v. HELMHOLTZ.[§] As is well known, if the moist air has been previously freed from "dust," no condensation takes place except on the walls of the vessel, even if the expansion be sufficient to produce considerable supersaturation. For convenience, the term "dust" is here used to include all nuclei which can be removed either by filtering or by repeatedly forming a cloud by expansion and allowing it to settle.

What is the limit, if such exists, to the degree of supersaturation which can be attained without condensation taking place throughout the moist air, is a question of considerable meteorological as well as purely physical interest. It was primarily with the object of finding an answer to this question that the experiments to be described were undertaken, such experimental evidence as already existed on the subject being of a very incomplete and contradictory character.

AITKEN[||] observed condensation when a large quantity of steam was passed into a receiver containing air which had been filtered through cotton wool. KIESSLING[¶] also produced a rainlike condensation in the same way. The latter observer also states that if saturated filtered air be even slightly expanded, scattered drops are formed visible only in direct sunlight. Again, AITKEN[**] mentions that in his dust-counting experiments, in which sudden expansion of the saturated air was produced by means of an air-pump, a very quick stroke of the pump was found to produce a

---

[*] 'Journal de Pharmacie et de Chimie," vol. 22, pp. 165 and 254, 1875.

[†] 'Trans. Roy. Soc.,' Edin., vol. 30, p. 337, 1880–81, and vol. 35, p. 1, 1890; 'Proc. Roy. Soc.,' Lond., vol. 51, p. 408, 1892.

[‡] 'Hamburger Abhandl. der Naturwissenschaften,' vol. 8, 1884; 'Götting. Nachr.,' p. 122, 1884, and p. 226, 1884.

[§] 'Wied. Ann.,' vol. 27, p. 509, 1886.

[||] 'Trans. Roy. Soc.,' Edin., vol. 30, p. 337.

[¶] 'Götting. Nachr.,' p. 226, 1884.

[**] 'Trans. Roy. Soc.,' Edin., vol. 35, p. 1, 1890.

shower of drops even in filtered air, while a slow steady one had no such effect. The increase of volume was always the same, and amounted to one-third of the initial volume. He attributes the difference to the shock which results from a rapid stroke of the pump.

R. v. HELMHOLTZ,* on the other hand, was unable to observe any trace of condensation in saturated filtered air, even with a fall of pressure of half an atmosphere. Whether, however, the pressure was reduced from one atmosphere to one-half, or from one-and-a-half atmospheres to one, is not clear; from his description of the method one would naturally take the latter interpretation. He deduces, however, a theoretical lowering of 50° C., and a ten-fold supersaturation which correspond to the former alternative.

BARUS,† who made an extensive series of observations on the colour phenomena of a steam jet under varying conditions as to boiler-pressure and the temperature and dust contents of the surrounding air, concluded that with sufficient supersaturation, condensation takes place independently of dust. He does not appear, however, to have been able to deduce from his measurements the degree of supersaturation which is required to bring about this condensation.

None of the experiments referred to above are entirely free from objection.

When steam is blown into filtered air, as was done by AITKEN and KIESSLING, it is likely to carry over with it small drops of spray from the boiler. Even if these drops be made to evaporate by superheating the steam, each will leave behind a nucleus consisting of the solid matter which it contained in solution or suspension.

The condensation noticed by KIESSLING with very slight expansion may have been due to a similar cause, for he appears to have brought the air in his apparatus into a saturated state by allowing it to bubble through water after it had been filtered. That such treatment does actually introduce nuclei requiring only a slight expansion of the saturated air to cause condensation upon them is proved by certain experiments described below. AITKEN‡ noticed, too, that if the water in his dust-counting apparatus was allowed to splash about, such nuclei were produced.

In none of the experiments mentioned above was the expansion very rapid, the apparatus in no case having been specially designed for the purpose of investigating this particular question. HELMHOLTZ's failure to obtain condensation may easily be explained by the expansion not being sufficiently rapid to produce anything like the theoretical lowering of temperature as, indeed, he himself admits.

The interpretation of steam-jet experiments, such as those of BARUS, is very difficult, especially as the phenomena depend largely on the roughness or smoothness of the bore of the nozzle from which the steam escapes. They cannot be taken as

---

* HELMHOLTZ, *loc. cit.*

† "Report on the Condensation of Atmospheric Moisture;" U.S. Department of Agriculture, Weather Bureau, 1895; also 'Phil. Mag.,' vol. 38, p. 19, 1894.

‡ 'Edin. Trans.,' vol. 35, p. 17, 1890.

proving beyond doubt that condensation may be made to take place by increasing the supersaturation alone, as so many of the conditions besides the degree of supersaturation must vary as the initial pressure of the steam, and consequently the velocity with which it escapes from the nozzle are increased.

Conditions to be satisfied by the Expansion Apparatus.

To obtain unequivocal proof of the production of condensation in moist air, free from all extraneous nuclei, it is necessary that we should not be dependent upon any process of filtering, for it might always be objected that the filtering apparatus only removed those particles which exceeded a certain size.

If, however, we expand repeatedly the same sample of moist air, while protecting it from all chance of contamination, we are able to test whether all nuclei of a permanent kind have been removed. For by making an expansion rather greater than is sufficient to cause condensation, and allowing the drops formed to settle, we remove in this way a certain proportion at least, and if the drops be few and large, almost the whole of the nuclei which are able to cause condensation with this degree of supersaturation.

If this process can be repeated indefinitely without any diminution in the number of drops formed, we are justified in concluding that the nuclei are being replaced by others as fast as they are removed, and are thus an essential part of the structure of the moist gas.

It is desirable also that the expansion should admit of accurate measurement and be exceedingly rapid, so that the lowest temperature and maximum supersaturation reached may be calculated with as small an error as possible due to the influx of heat during the expansion.

In a note* read before the Cambridge Philosophical Society, I gave an account of some preliminary results obtained with a form of apparatus which I believed to satisfy these conditions. It was there stated that condensation results from the sudden expansion of saturated dust-free air when v_2/v_1 exceeds a value not differing much from 1·258, where v_1, v_2 are the volumes of the air before and after expansion.

No description of the apparatus was published, as it was then in quite a rudimentary condition.

The first series of experiments to be described here was carried out with an improved apparatus of the same type.

Apparatus used in the first series of Experiments.

This is represented in vertical section in fig. 1.

The air to be expanded is contained in the inverted cylindrical glass vessel A,

---

* 'Proc. Camb. Phil. Soc.,' vol. 8, p. 306, 1895.

fixed like a diving-bell below the surface of the water, which nearly fills the outer vessel B.

The latter is a bell-jar of the form shown in the figure, resting on a ground-glass plate, to which it is wired down, and having a wide neck, closed by an indiarubber cork through which pass two glass tubes, the one, C, serving to regulate the quantity of water in B, and provided with a pinch-cock; through the other, D, the air occupying the upper part of B can be suddenly removed by opening communication with a large exhausted stoneware bottle F.

The water is prevented from following the air by means of the valve E.

Fig. 1.

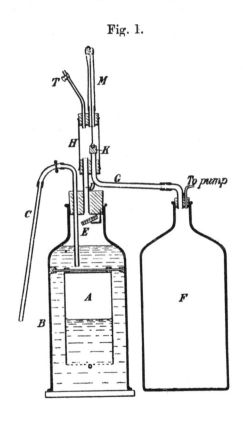

The result is a sudden expansion of the air in A. The increase in volume is equal to the volume of the space in the upper part of B occupied by air before the expansion, and can therefore be made more or less by running a little water out, or drawing some more in through the tube C.

By opening the tap T, which communicates with the atmosphere, air is admitted through the tube D, and the air in A contracts to its original volume.

To bring about very sudden communication with the exhausted vessel F, the arrangement shown in the upper part of the figure was used. A short glass tube, H, is closed at both ends by indiarubber corks, each bored to receive two glass tubes. Of these, D and T have already been referred to. The tube G, which leads to the vacuum vessel F, has its upper end ground smooth, and upon this rests the flat surface of an indiarubber cork K. This closes the opening of the tube in a perfectly air-tight manner, when the air above it is at atmospheric pressure, and the pressure in F is a small fraction of this, as it always was maintained during a series of experiments.

K can be pulled up by means of the vertical wire shown in the diagram, thus rapidly making free communication between D and G and causing the expansion. The tap T must of course previously be closed. In order that one may be able to work the arrangement from the outside without admitting air, the wire passes up through a thin-walled indiarubber tube, M, closed at its upper end by a cork in which the end of the wire is fixed. A cord attached to this cork and passing over a smooth peg fixed vertically above it, enables the observer to make the expansion, while watching the behaviour of the air in the cloud chamber A.

The tubes D and G had an internal diameter of about 8 millims., so that the fall of pressure in the air-space in the upper part of B must be very rapid. The valve E, which prevented the water in the bell-jar B from following the air into the tube D, was made by cutting a thin slice from the end of an indiarubber cork and supporting it with the smooth surface uppermost on a piece of cork just thick enough to float it. It was fixed by means of a wire hinge to the lower surface of the indiarubber cork of the bell-jar, in such a position that when raised by the water reaching it, it covered the hole bored for the tube D. The latter did not quite reach the lower surface of the indiarubber cork, so that when the valve closed the contact was between two indiarubber surfaces.

This valve was found to work perfectly when the excess of pressure below was sufficient, and smooth indiarubber surfaces were used.

The bell-jar had a diameter of about 14 centims. and was about 30 centims. high. The inner vessel had a diameter of about 9 centims. A vertical glass scale, divided into millimetres, fixed by means of sealing-wax to the outside of the inner vessel, enables the observer to note with the aid of a telescope the level of the water before and after expansion. From a subsequent calibration the initial and final volumes are obtained.

To make visible any condensation in the form of fog or rain, the light from a luminous gas-flame is brought by means of a convex lens to a focus at the centre of the cloud chamber A. Any condensation which may result is most distinctly seen when the eye is placed just out of reach of the directly transmitted light. This method of illumination was used both by AITKEN and R. v. HELMHOLTZ. The experiments were performed in a dark room. When an expansion was made the only source of light was that mentioned above. After the result had been noted, light was admitted by raising a shutter in order that the readings of volume might be made.

The inside of the inner vessel, A, was cleaned before use, first with caustic potash and then with nitric acid, and well washed with distilled water. After this treatment the water forms a uniform film over the surface of the glass, instead of collecting into drops and preventing a satisfactory view of the interior.

This apparatus appeared to fulfil very well the purpose for which it was designed. Nothing can gain access to the air imprisoned in the inner vessel except by solution in and diffusion through the surrounding water.

The water surface which forms the lower boundary to the space occupied by the air under observation, drops suddenly to a new position, where it comes to a sudden stop, without any splashing, and remains stationary as long as may be desired. The whole movement is certainly over in a small fraction of a second, as the expansion appears to the eye to be instantaneous. That it should be rapid is what one would expect, as the initial driving pressure is nearly one atmosphere, and the distance travelled rarely amounted to more than two centimetres.

There is this further advantage in such a method of expanding the air, that the rate of expansion is most rapid just before it is completed, because the driving pressure still remains considerable, and the water is therefore moving with constantly increasing velocity until it brings itself to a sudden stop by closing the valve E.

Thus the final stage of the expansion, when the temperature is lowest, and therefore the influx of heat most rapid, is that which is most quickly passed through.

The motion of the water cannot, of course, be stopped instantaneously ; in practice it was always found that some small air bubbles were left imprisoned around the valve E. These, being compressed by the impact, probably served to diminish considerably the strain on the apparatus.

With a thin float the volume of these bubbles was quite a negligible fraction of that of the air which escaped before the valve closed. If any considerable fraction of the air were left behind when the valve closed, an error would be introduced by its momentary compression, the actual maximum value reached being really greater than what is afterwards measured by an amount equal to the momentary diminution in the total volume of the air bubble.

Method of Conducting the Experiments.

To charge the apparatus with air reasonably free from laboratory gases, the bell-jar, with the inner vessel fixed inside it, was removed from the ground-glass plate on which it rested, and allowed to remain at an open window for some time. It was then placed on the glass plate, and bound tightly down with wire.

Distilled water, which had been boiled for some time to remove the greater part of the dissolved gases, was then poured in till it nearly filled the bell-jar. By inclining the whole, air was allowed to escape from the inner vessel till only a convenient volume remained. The bell-jar was then again nearly filled up with water, and the apparatus then connected up as already described and shown in fig. 1.

The glass-plate was levelled by means of levelling screws supporting the tripod on which the plate was fixed. The reading telescope was then fixed some distance off, on a level with the surface of the water in the inner vessel.

Some water was now allowed to escape through the tube C, and the level of the water read on the glass scale by means of the telescope. The tap T was then closed, expansion made by pulling the cord which opens communication with the vacuum vessel F, and the effect on the contents of the expansion chamber A noted. The new level of the water in the inner vessel was again read by the telescope, and the air made to contract to its former volume by opening the tap T. The same expansion could be repeated as often as was wished, or the air could be expanded to a greater extent by first running out a little water through C. If it was desired to try the effect of a smaller expansion the tap T was only slightly opened, and was closed before the water in B had quite returned to its original level. Then the pinch-cock on the tube C was opened for a moment while the end of the tube was dipped into a beaker of water.

To find the volumes corresponding to the various readings, the bell-jar, with its inner vessel, was removed from the glass plate after every series of observations, and fixed in an inverted position so that the water could be poured into the inner vessel. The whole arrangement was then adjusted so that the ground surface of the rim of the bell-jar was level. The weight of water which had to be poured in to fill the inner vessel up to the various readings on the scale was then determined, the telescope being fixed in exactly the same relative position as in the expansion experiments.

General Account of the Phenomena Observed.

The air was generally admitted into the apparatus in the way already described, and, therefore, without any attempt to remove dust by filtering. Repeated expansion of saturated air, as AITKEN has shown, removes all " dust " particles, and this method was generally employed in these experiments.

The first expansion made, whether large or small in amount, unless the air had been allowed to stand for many hours in the apparatus, always produced a fog. This was allowed to settle as completely as possible before allowing the air to contract to its original volume. In this way a considerable proportion of the dust was removed, the particles being carried down by the drops which condensed upon them into the water below.

When this process was several times repeated, the resulting fog became by degrees coarser-grained, the drops being both fewer and larger, and therefore, falling more quickly. The fog passed at length into a fine rain. When this stage was reached one more expansion was generally sufficient to remove the remainder of the dust particles, and any further expansion, unless it exceeded the limit spoken of below, was without visible effect.

AITKEN* was able to remove all the dust particles from saturated air by repeatedly increasing its volume by $\frac{1}{50}$ of its initial amount.   An even smaller expansion was found in these experiments to be sufficient for that purpose, but the time taken for the removal of the dust was naturally much shorter when larger expansions were used, on account of the larger size and more rapid fall of the drops in the latter case.

If, after the dust has been removed in this way the successive expansions be made greater and greater, no visible effect is produced till v_2/v_1, the ratio of the final to the initial volume, is equal to about 1·252.   When v_2/v_1 exceeds this value a shower of drops is invariably produced.   The drops are not very numerous, even with considerably greater expansions, yet, however often we expand the air, no diminution in the number of the drops can be detected.

Now, when, owing to the presence of dust particles, a shower of similar density is produced with a smaller expansion, all the dust particles appear to be carried down with the water drops, and the next expansion produces no condensation.

Thus, the nuclei which enables condensation to take place when the expansion exceeds the limit mentioned, are only present in small numbers at any given time, but as fast as they are removed they are replaced by others of the same kind.

Expansion required to produce Rain-like Condensation in Dust-free Saturated Air.

A large number of observations must generally be made in order to obtain within narrow limits a single determination of the ratio of v_2 to v_1 when condensation just takes place.

When expansions of comparatively small amount had ceased to cause condensation, each increase in volume was made considerably greater than the preceding, till a shower of drops was observed.   Then an observation was made with the apparatus adjusted to give a rather smaller final volume (the initial volume remaining practically constant), and perhaps no condensation seen.   By making in this way a series of alternately greater and smaller expansions of gradually diminishing difference, a stage was at length reached when the smallest measurable difference in the final volume was sufficient to determine whether condensation should result or not.

A large number of experiments were made during the summer of 1895.   Only the results of the last series of measurements then made are given in the table which follows.   The apparatus has been improved from time to time and the later experiments were carried out exactly as described above.

The mean of the results previously obtained for the critical value of v_2/v_1, however, is practically identical with that given below, and all the determinations of this ratio have results lying between 1·24 and 1·26.

* 'Edin. Trans.,' 35, p. 1.

In the following table, v_1 is the initial volume and v_2 the final volume when the expansion is just sufficient to cause rain-like condensation.

	Date.	$t°$ C.	v_1	v_2	v_2/v_1
1.	September 4	22·0	292·9	367·3	1·254
2.	,, 4	22·4	293·4	367·8	1·253
3.	,, 5	28·8	313·1	392·5	1·253
4.	,, 5	27·2	308·5	385·8	1·250
5.	,, 6	27·8	312·5	390·8	1·250
6.	,, 6	26·0	309·8	386·7	1·248
7.	,, 7	24·5	302·0	378·3	1·252
				Mean	1·252

The same air was used on September 7 as on the previous day; otherwise the experiments were made on a different sample of air each day.

It will be noted that the expansion required is sensibly the same at all temperatures between 22° and 28° C. Accurate measurements of the initial temperature are therefore unnecessary in these experiments.

The results given in the table show no greater variation than are to be expected from the degree of accuracy of the volume measurements. The level of the water could be read by means of the telescope to the nearest tenth of a millimetre, corresponding to an error of half a cubic centimetre in the volume measurements. There may be an error of this amount in the measurement of both v_1 and v_2, and hence an error of 4 units in the fourth figure in the ratio, when the initial volume amounts to about 300 cub. centims.

Other Experiments made with the same Apparatus.

1. When sunlight was used to illuminate the drops, exactly the same expansion was required to bring about visible condensation.

The result, therefore, does not depend on the kind of illumination used.

2. Experiments were made to see if the nuclei which cause the rain-like condensation could be removed by repeated filtering. For this purpose a hole was bored through the glass plate on which the apparatus rested. A glass tube reaching to the roof of the inner vessel was passed through a cork which closed this hole. Through it the air could be drawn out into an inverted WOLFF's bottle, arranged to act as an aspirator, and could be driven from the one vessel to the other as often as was desired.

A tightly-packed cotton-wool filter was inserted between the expansion apparatus and the WOLFF's bottle. Passing the air repeatedly backwards and forwards through the filter was found to be without effect upon the appearance of the rain-like condensation, or the expansion required to produce it.

3. When no cotton-wool filter was present the air could be passed from the one vessel to the other and back without any effect, so long as it was not allowed to bubble through the distilled water in either vessel. If, however, the air had to bubble through water on being driven back, quite a small expansion was sufficient to cause a shower even some minutes later.

4. As already stated, the air may be allowed to expand considerably more than is necessary to produce condensation without the drops becoming very numerous.

With very great expansions, however, if, for example, the increase in volume be made twice as great as is necessary for condensation to result, a dense fog showing colours and settling slowly is produced.

Second Form of Apparatus.

The apparatus already described was not suitable for experiments upon pure gases, on account of the large volume of water present.

To remove all the dissolved gases from so large a quantity of water would have been very difficult.

Another reason for changing the form of the apparatus was that I wished to investigate in what way the number of drops produced depended upon the degree of supersaturation reached. It appeared, from the experiments already made, that the drops remained comparatively few with expansions considerably greater than that required to cause condensation to begin, and over a considerable range there was no appreciable increase in the number with increasing expansion. Yet, with very large expansions, the number was very great, and the drops sufficiently small to produce a coloured fog which settled very slowly.

The first apparatus was not convenient for making measurements with very large expansions, so no attempt was made to investigate with it whether there was a sudden transition from the one form of condensation to the other. It was thought that another form of apparatus would be more suitable for the purpose.

A very rapid expansion is evidently required for this investigation. For, let us consider one cubic centimetre of saturated air which is expanded rapidly. If we suppose the effect of the walls to be negligible, the ordinary equation for the cooling of a gas by adiabatic expansion may be applied to find the lowering of temperature and the resulting supersaturation till the volume amounts to $1 \cdot 252$ centims. At this stage, as we have seen, condensation begins upon a comparatively small number of scattered nuclei. There must at once result from the initial condensation a simultaneous loss of vapour and rise of temperature in the region immediately surrounding each incipient drop. The subsequent growth of the drop must be more or less gradual, being the result of the comparatively slow processes of diffusion and heat conduction.

If the expansion be slow, the supersaturation can nowhere greatly exceed that required for the formation of the first drops.

With very sudden expansions, however, even if they be much greater than that required to produce rain-like condensation, the drops which are the first to begin to form will not have time to grow sensibly before the expansion is completed, and their influence on the temperature and vapour contents of the air will be confined to a very small region round each. In that case the lowest temperature and maximum supersaturation reached throughout the greater part of the moist air will be the same as that calculated on the assumption that no condensation takes place.

The more numerous the drops, the shorter must the time taken in expansion be made, in order that there should be no sensible error due to the formation of the drops commencing before the expansion is completed.

Now the time of expansion can be made shorter in a small machine. The new expansion apparatus was therefore made upon quite a small scale, the effect of the reduced dimensions in increasing the error due to the walls being counterbalanced by the great reduction in the time of expansion.

The expansion ought evidently to be made most rapid just before it is completed, since it is just in the later stages of the expansion that drops are being formed, and we wish to reduce, as far as possible, their chance of growing appreciably before the expansion is completed. This end was kept in view in designing the apparatus.

The expansion apparatus (fig. 2), is made wholly of glass, to reduce the risk of contamination of the gas under investigation. This is contained in the space A under a pressure of from 20 to 40 centims. of mercury above that of the atmosphere. This expansion chamber A, is bounded below by the hollow-glass piston P, which is ground down so that it just slides freely in the outer tube.

There is, as indicated in the figure, an annular constriction on the latter. Into this the lower end of the piston has been ground with fine emery, so that, with no other lubricant than water, it prevents the gas in A escaping, even when the excess of pressure above is half an atmosphere or more.

The lower end of the tube is conical, with a circular aperture about 1 centim. in diameter, closed by a glass plug G. The grinding here, too, has to be sufficiently thorough to enable a pressure of two atmospheres to be maintained above it for several minutes without leakage, with only one or two drops of water to serve as lubricant.

The upper end of the tube is drawn out and joined to a narrow-bore tube provided with a stopcock T_1, serving for the introduction of the gas and water.

When the apparatus is in use, the inner surface of A is covered with a film of water, which also fills the narrow space left between the piston and the walls of the tube.

By pumping air by means of the mercury pump on the left, into the space C below the piston, we can drive up the latter and so compress the gas in A to any extent we please.   Then, on pushing up the plug G, we suddenly reduce the pressure in the small space C to that of the atmosphere, and the piston flies back to its original position, producing a sudden expansion of the gas in A.

After each expansion a small quantity of water is driven in through T_1.   This serves to keep the walls of A covered with a film of water and to lubricate the piston.   The greater part of it runs down and collects above the latter.   When the

Fig. 2.

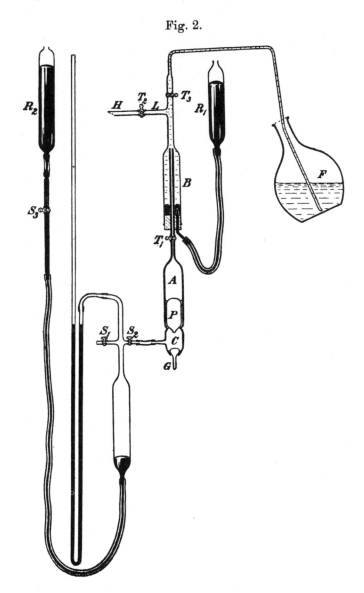

piston is driven up again so that it is suspended freely in the tube, it gradually floats up through this water till it comes to rest with the water scarcely reaching above the straight part of its sides.   In this way the water which lubricates the piston is continually being renewed, and the gradual contamination of the gas which would otherwise result by solution and diffusion of the air from below through the water is almost indefinitely retarded.

The machine used in nearly all the experiments described below was made from moderately thick-walled tubing, having an internal diameter of 2 centims. The expansion chamber A was between 4 and 5 centims. long, and had a capacity, when the piston was in its lowest position, of about 15 cub. centims. The cylindrical part of the piston was about 3 centims. in length.

The time required for the expansion to be completed must be very short. For the distance travelled by the piston was never so great as 2 centims., even with the greatest expansions used. To support the weight of the piston alone, required an excess of pressure below of 1 millim. of mercury. Now the driving pressure, even when the expansion was almost completed, was probably never less than 100 times as great as this. With the largest expansions used, when the piston had still to travel less than 2 centims., the initial driving pressure was more than an atmosphere, that is, about 760 times that required to balance the weight of the piston. This is on the assumption of an exceedingly rapid fall of pressure in the space below the piston when the plug G is driven up. If we make this assumption, the force driving the piston is always some hundreds of times its weight, and its initial acceleration some hundreds of time "g." Even an average acceleration of $100g$ would enable the 2 centims to be travelled in about $\frac{1}{150}$ of a second.

Although the time taken may actually be considerably greater than this, these considerations are sufficient to show that it is likely to be exceedingly short.

Further, the piston must be moving with constantly increasing velocity till brought to a sudden stop at the constriction into which it fits.

The fact that contact takes place simultaneously over a considerable area, probably saves the tube from being broken by the blow it receives from the piston. The film of water which covers both surfaces, doubtless helps to break the shock. On two occasions, a machine was made only slightly larger than the one whose dimensions are given above, but in each case it was shivered by the impact almost the first time the piston was allowed to fly. More than one machine was useless, owing to the piston being driven so tightly home when the expansion was made, that all efforts failed to release it. To avoid this latter defect, it was found necessary to make the constriction a very sudden one. Great care has also to be taken to make it perfectly symmetrical; otherwise there is almost certain to be a space left between the piston and some part of the wall of the tube just above the constriction. In this, air-bubbles are apt to be entangled when the piston flies into the constriction. These may work their way up into A, and in addition they cause a splashing of the water by their momentary compression and subsequent expansion.

A supply of water for the lubrication of the piston is stored in the vessel B. The space over the mercury is completely filled with water up to the stopcocks T_2 and T_3, which remain closed throughout any series of experiments. By fixing the mercury reservoir R_1 at a sufficient height, the water in B is kept at a pressure high enough to drive it into A when the tap T_1 is opened. In this way the water is preserved from contamination with air, and only comes in contact with glass and mercury. It has been obtained free from dissolved gases by boiling distilled water rapidly down to about one-sixth of its bulk in the flask shown on the right. While it is boiling down, R_1 is repeatedly raised and lowered, to wash out any imprisoned air or unboiled water from B and the tube leading to the flask.

While the water is still boiling, B is filled by lowering R_1, a depth of about 1 centim. of mercury being, however, always left in B to prevent the water from coming in contact with the indiarubber stopper which closes the lower end of the tube. The tap T_3 is then closed and R fixed high enough to give the requisite pressure.

Introduction of the Gas.

The apparatus used in the preparation of the various gases was, in all cases, made entirely of glass, all joints being made with the blow-pipe. It was fused on to the end of the tube H (fig. 2). The methods of preparing the various gases are described later. The whole gas generating apparatus must first be filled with the pure gas up to the tap T_2, which is now kept closed.

Before introducing the gas into the expansion apparatus, A and B must first be filled with air-free water. This is done in the following way.

The piston P is drawn up to the top of A by opening the tap T_1 and lowering the mercury reservoir R_1, the other taps being closed. The gas which has collected in B is then driven out through T_3 by raising R_1 after closing T_1. Water is then drawn from the flask F, which is kept boiling the whole time, into B, and T_3 is closed. Again, T_1 is opened and water is introduced into A, driving the piston before it. A now contains water with a bubble of air at the top; this is driven into B by lowering R_1. The tap T_1 is closed, while the greater part of the water still remains in A, from which it slowly escapes by the floating up of the piston.

The small quantity of water which remains above the piston has, of course, been contaminated by contact with the air or other gas which originally occupied A. To replace it by pure water, B is first filled with air-free water as described in the last section. A small quantity of this is then passed into A while still hot, so that it floats above the cold water already there. It is, therefore, mainly the latter which flows away as the piston gradually rises. More water is run in from B before the piston quite reaches the top of A. This process is repeated two or three times, and finally the piston is driven right down to the bottom of A, which is thus completely filled with water. The tap T_1 is left open and R_1 raised to a considerable height, and the piston thus pressed down into the constriction so that the water does not escape.

When the apparatus has cooled, the piston is drawn up by lowering R_1, but is not allowed to rise quite to the top of A.   There is very little risk of contamination by air at this stage, because the piston is slowly floating upwards, and the water filling the narrow space round the piston has therefore a comparatively great downward velocity.   Diffusion of the air upwards through this water is thus prevented.

Then T_1 is closed, and some of the gas to be investigated drawn into B by lowering R_1 and opening T_2.   It is then driven into A by opening T_1 and raising R_1, T_2 being closed.   This pumping process is repeated till the pressure in A is rather in excess of what is required.

The gas which remains in B is driven out through T_3, which is then closed, and T_1 opened for a moment, so that the narrow-bore tube and stop-cock are filled with water.   It is necessary, of course, for this purpose that R_1 should be raised high enough to overcome the pressure in A; it is, in fact, now kept permanently fixed at such a level throughout all subsequent operations.

The excess of water always remaining above the piston in A at this stage is now allowed to escape by applying sufficient pressure below to drive the piston up a little. The pressure is applied by pumping air into C, by means of the mercury compressing pump shown at the extreme left of the diagram.   The plug G is then pushed up and the piston thus allowed to fly back into the constriction.

To prevent contamination of the gas, the glass taps T_1 T_2 T_3 are lubricated with water only.   The only one which requires to be used after the above operations are completed is T_1.   Since this is filled with water under considerable pressure, there is no danger of air gaining access through it.

Method of producing expansion of any desired amount.

With this apparatus, direct volume measurements were not made, but the relative volume change was deduced from measurements of the initial pressure, and the pressure exerted by the saturated gas at the same temperature when occupying the increased volume.   The final volume v_2, being that of A when the piston is at the bottom, is always the same; and the corresponding pressure p_2 at the temperature of the room shows only comparatively small changes resulting from variations temperature, and from the solution of the gas by the small quantity of water which is run through the apparatus.

This final pressure p_2 was measured in the following way.   A mark was made in the wall of A approximately on a level with the top of the piston, when this was in its lowest position.

A telescope was then fixed in a clamp about one metre off, and its height adjusted till the mark appeared to coincide with the top of the piston.   By means of the compressing pump air was driven into C till the pressure was sufficient to drive up the piston a little.   Then S_2 being left open and S_1 closed, the tap S_3, regulating the flow of mercury in the pump, was closed and the reservoir R_2 lowered and fixed in such a position that S_3 could be worked by the observer while looking through the telescope.

S_3 was then opened very slightly so that the mercury flowed very slowly through it into R_2 thus lowering the pressure in C. The slow descent of the piston was watched and S_3 closed just as the piston reached its zero position. The pressure in C as indicated by the open mercury pressure gauge was then read to the nearest millimetre.

To obtain the actual pressure in A we have to add to the pressure indicated by the gauge the barometer reading and to subtract the pressure required to support the weight of the piston. This last term enters as a constant correction which was determined combined with any constant error of the manometer, by noticing the pressure required to support the piston, when there was free communication between the inside of A and the atmosphere. At the same time the freedom of the apparatus from errors in the pressure-readings due to friction between the piston and the walls of the tube was tested by taking readings first while the piston was being raised and then while it was allowed to sink slowly down. No difference was detected.

To obtain any desired initial pressure in A, S_3 is opened, while R_2 is in its lower position in order to draw in air through S_1 which is then closed and S_2 opened, R_2 is then hung on a support fixed as high as can be conveniently reached, and S_3 is closed just as the pressure, as indicated by the manometer, reaches the desired amount. To make the expansion S_2 is closed and the plug G suddenly pressed up. The manometer is again read after expansion.

In the case of the more insoluble gases, when the temperature was steady, the measurement of the final pressure did not require to be determined after each expansion. Several expansions could under such conditions be made without any sensible change in the pressure measured when the piston was at the bottom of the tube.

In order that the rain-like condensation might be visible, the experiments were done in a dark room, and the same method of illumination was employed as in the case of the larger apparatus.

The glass, too, was kept clear inside by periodically removing the expansion apparatus and washing the inside with caustic potash and nitric acid and rinsing well with distilled water.

Temperature was measured by a mercury thermometer hung beside the expansion apparatus. This method is sufficiently accurate for the purpose, as the result of an expansion of a given amount was sensibly constant throughout the ordinary range of room temperature. It is necessary, however, that the temperature should be known sufficiently accurately to enable the vapour pressure to be found within the nearest millimetre of mercury. An error of half a degree in the temperature reading does not make a difference of much more than half a millimetre in the vapour pressure.

Calculation of v_2/v_1 from the Observations of Pressure.

To obtain the ratio of the final to the initial volume we have, when the gas present obeys BOYLE's law,

$$v_2/v_1 = P_1/P_2,$$

where P_1 is the pressure exerted by the gas alone before expansion, and P_2 is its pressure after expansion, when the temperature has risen to its former value.

Now

$$P_1 = p_1 + B - \pi - w,$$

and

$$P_2 = p_2 + B - \pi - w,$$

where p_1, p_2 are the pressures measured by the mercury gauge, before and after expansion, as already described, B is the atmospheric pressure, π is the maximum vapour pressure at the temperature of experiment, and w is the pressure required to balance the weight of the piston.

Results obtained with Air in the small Apparatus.

The same phenomena are observed as in the larger apparatus, as well as others to be described later.

After the removal of "dust" by repeated expansion, no condensation takes place within the moist air, unless v_2/v_1 exceeds a certain limit. With greater expansions rain-like condensation results. As will be seen from the following table, measurements of this critical value of v_2/v_1 made with the two machines give identical results, although the larger one contained twenty times as great a volume of air as the smaller. The expansion, therefore, appears to be sufficiently rapid to prevent the walls having any sensible effect.

EXPANSION required for Rain-like Condensation in Air.

Pressures all given in millims. of mercury.   Correction for piston weight $w = 1$ millim.

	Date.	B.	t° C.	π.	p_1.	P_1.	p_2.	P_2.	$P_1/P_2 = v_2/v_1$.
1	February 13 . .	775	18·5	16	651	1409	372	1130	1·247
2	,, 14 . .	775	17·5	15	685	1444	386	1145	1·261
3	,, 17 . .	776	15·5	13	685	1447	392	1154	1·254
4	,, 22 . .	764	16·5	14	602	1351	330	1079	1·252
5	,, 22 . .	764	16·5	14	506	1255	254	1003	1·251
6	March 2 . . .	750	18·5	16	654	1387	377	1110	1·250
								Mean	1·252

The apparatus was charged with a fresh supply of air each day.

The results of all the measurements made with the small apparatus on the rain-like condensation are given in the table.

The expansion can be measured with quite as great accuracy as in the larger apparatus, but the whole number of drops when condensation first begins is inconveniently small in the small apparatus. This makes the measurements of the critical value of v_2/v_1 more troublesome.

Each determination of this requires a large number of observations to be made, p_1 being always made less or greater according as the previous expansion had brought down a shower or not. In this way it was possible, finally, to obtain the least value of p_1, necessary in order that a shower should result within about 2 millims.

It will again be noticed that the result obtained is with the limits of experimental error independent of the temperature between 15·5° and 18·5° C.

We may summarise the results of the measurements made with both machines upon the expansion required for rain-like condensation in the following statement.

When saturated air free from all extraneous nuclei is suddenly expanded, rain-like condensation takes place if the ratio of the final to the initial volume exceeds 1·252. This is true if the initial temperature is between 15° and 28° C.

It will be noticed that this expansion is less than that used by AITKEN in the experiments already referred to. The difference between the result of making the stroke of his pump slow or quick was therefore evidently due to the expansion not being quick enough to give the theoretical lowering of temperature.

Phenomena observed with Expansions greater than that required to produce Rain-like Condensation.

If a series of expansions be made of constantly increasing amount, the following phenomena are observed.

The drops are, if the expansion be only slightly greater than is sufficient to produce condensation, only few in number. More of them are seen if the expansion be somewhat greater, but even when v_2/v_1 is as great as 1·37, the condensation still takes the form of a shower of drops, which settle within a few seconds. To the eye there is no marked difference in the density of the shower over quite a wide range of expansions.

If, however, v_2/v_1 be increased from 1·37 to 1·38, the increase in the number of drops is so great that there is no longer any resemblance to a shower of rain, but a fog results, taking a minute or more to settle.*

* [*Note added July 22nd, 1897.*—When expansion results in a fog, it is of course necessary to get rid of all traces of it before proceeding to a fresh observation. This was done by repeated expansions of moderate amount, as in the removal of the original dust particles.]

With expansions greater than this, the density of the fog appears to go on increasing with great rapidity as the expansion is increased. It is now convenient to remove the condensing lens and examine the fog by looking directly through it at the gas-flame. Coloured diffraction rings make their appearance when v_2/v_1 is about 1·38 and they increase rapidly in brilliancy and size as the expansion is made greater and greater.

Before v_2/v_1 reaches 1·40, the region within the first ring, which is whitish with smaller expansions, becomes brightly coloured. With greater expansions, the rings rapidly become so large that the colour corresponding to the central part of the field fills the whole tube.

The colour phenomena beyond this stage are surprisingly definite. They are best observed by looking through the cloud chamber slighly to one side of the source of light, which ought now to be made as bright as possible, and have a black background.

If v_2/v_1 be between 1·41 and 1·42, brilliant greens and blue-greens are seen. At about 1·42 there is a very rapid change from blue to red through violet. The violet appears only for a very small range of expansion, a change of one or two millimetres in the initial pressure being sufficient to complete the change from blue to red.

As the expansion is further increased, the colour passes from red through yellow to white. With expansions greater than about 1·44, the fog is always white with a greenish or bluish tinge.

The whole of these colour phenomena, it will be seen, are confined to quite a narrow range of expansions. Below 1·38 the drops are too large and few; and above 1·44 they appear to be too small to produce the colours.

Colours of exactly the same kind were obtained by KIESSLING* and by AITKEN† by expanding ordinary moist unfiltered air; but in the reverse order, pale yellow being the first to appear, followed with increasing expansions by a reddish colour, then by blue, and then green.

The explanation of the difference plainly, is that in their experiments the number of the drops was determined by the number of "dust" particles present, and increased expansion caused a larger quantity of water to condense on each particle.

Increasing the expansion thus increased the size of the drops. Now in the experiments here described, the greater the expansion, the smaller appear to be the resulting drops, which indicates that as the supersaturation is increased, a larger number of nuclei come into play, so that each receives a smaller share of the water which condenses.

Similar phenomena are exhibited by light transmitted through a steam-jet under

* GÖTTING., 'Nachr.,' 1884, p. 226.
† 'Proc. Roy Soc.,' vol. 51, p. 422, 1892.

certain conditions. They have been investigated by R. V. HELMHOLTZ,[*] AITKEN[†] and, in a more elaborate way, by BARUS.[‡]

Measurements of the Expansion required to produce Cloud-like Condensation.

The transition from rain-like to cloud-like condensation is sudden enough to enable one to measure, with considerable accuracy, the value of the ratio v_2/v_1 when cloud-like condensation just begins. There is, in fact, a second condensation point, below which the drops are few, and the number shows only a slight increase with increasing expansion; while above it the number increases at an excessively rapid rate with increasing expansion.

EXPANSION required for Cloud-like Condensation in Saturated Air.

Date.	B.	$t°$ C.	π.	p_1.	P_1.	p_2.	P_2.	$P_1/P_2 = v_2/v_1$.	Result.
February 14. .	775	17·5	15	706	1465	308	1067	1·373	Rain
„ 14. .	775	17·5	15	712	1471	308	1067	1·378	Fog
„ 15. .	775	18·5	16	791	1549	369	1127	1·375	Rain
„ 15. .	775	18·5	16	795	1553	369	1127	1·378	Fog
„ 18. .	769	15·0	13	803	1558	381	1136	1·372	Rain
„ 18. .	769	15·0	13	813	1568	381	1136	1·380	Fog

The transition from rain to fog takes place when v_2/v_1 is between 1·37 and 1·38.

The above results were obtained using the same method of illumination as in the experiments on rain-like condensation. Observations were also made with the condensing lens removed.

FIRST Appearance of Diffraction Rings.

Date.	B.	$t°$ C.	π.	p_1.	P_1.	p_2.	P_2.	$P_1/P_2 = v_2/v_1$.
February 24	776	15	13	676	1438	279	1041	1·381
„ 25	772	13	11	667	1427	277	1037	1·376
March 2	750	18	15	807	1541	380	1114	1·383
„ 2	750	18·5	16	715	1448	318	1051	1·378
							Mean .	1·379

[*] 'Wied. Ann.,' 32, p. 1, 1887.

[†] 'Proc. Roy. Soc.,' vol. 51, p. 422, 1892.

[‡] BARUS, loc. cit., also 'Phil. Mag.,' vol 35, p. 315, 1893.

Observations were also made of the time taken by the drops to settle, as v_2/v_1 was gradually increased. This was of course very short when the condensation took the rain-like form. It showed a very sudden increase when the rain was replaced by fog.

For example, such measurements were made in connection with the last observation given in the preceding table.

$v_2/v_1.$
1·378   Colours scarcely visible, drops settled in a few seconds.
1·381   Rings faint, drops took about one minute to settle.
1·385   Rings brilliant, took several minutes to settle.

All these methods of making evident the change from rain to fog agree in showing that this takes place when v_2/v_1 lies between 1·37 and 1·38.

Colour Observations.

The colour phenomena change so rapidly as v_2/v_1 is increased from 1·38 to 1·40 that consistent measurements were not possible. In the tables which follow the observations therefore begin where the brilliant greens previously referred to first appear. The colours are those seen on looking through the tube, almost, but not quite in the direction of the source of light.

February 25. $t = 13°$ C.		March 3. $t = 18°$ to $19°$ C.	
$v_2/v_1.$	Colour.	$v_2/v_1.$	Colour.
1·408	Brilliant green	1·410	Green
1·408	„ „	1·410	„
1·412	„ „	1·413	„
1·414	„ „	1·416	Blue-green
1·414	„ „	1·418	Brilliant blue
1·419	Blue-green	1·419	Violet
1·419	Purple	1·420	„
1·422	„	1·420	Reddish-purple
1·424	Brilliant red	1·426	Red
1·426	Red	1·429	Reddish-yellow
1·428	„	1·436	Yellowish-white
1·429	„	1·448	White
1·434	Reddish	1·469	Greenish-white
1·437	Reddish-white		
1·453	Greenish-white		
1·458	„ „		

When the greenish-white fog appeared, the colour was the same from whatever point the tube was viewed, out of the direct line of the incident light. The particles are then evidently small enough to scatter the red light less than the blue.

Meteorological Applications.

The question of the degree of supersaturation reached in these experiments is postponed till the results obtained with other gases have been given. In considering the meteorological applications we are directly concerned with the expansion required to cause condensation in air originally saturated. For adiabatic expansion to result in condensation in saturated air free from all foreign nuclei, we have seen that the final volume must exceed 1·252 times the initial volume.

To obtain the corresponding ratio between the final and initial pressures we have

$$p_1 v_1{}^\gamma = p_2 v_2{}^\gamma,$$

or

$$\frac{p_2}{p_1} = \left(\frac{v_1}{v_2}\right)^\gamma.$$

where γ is the ratio of the specific heat of air at constant pressure to that at constant volume. The difference in γ for dry and moist air is small, and may here be neglected, γ being therefore taken as equal to 1·41.

Now

$$\frac{v_1}{v_2} = \frac{1}{1·252}, \quad \text{therefore} \quad \frac{p_2}{p_1} = \frac{1}{1·252^{1·141}} = ·728.$$

Condensation must therefore take place in air free from foreign nuclei when the pressure is reduced adiabatically to ·728 of the value which it has when the air is just saturated. The drops which are formed are, as we have seen, comparatively few. The fall of pressure required is sensibly the same for all values of the initial temperature between 28° and 15° C., and it is therefore probable that the result may be applied to considerably lower temperatures without any great error.

It is natural to suppose that when there is an upward current of moist air, the foreign nuclei will be left behind through becoming loaded with the water which condenses on them, and that the air which rises above the lower cloud layer thus formed will be dust-free and supersaturated.

It follows from the results of these experiments that condensation will again begin when the air reaches such a height that the pressure is reduced to about ·73 of that at the upper surface of the lower cloud.

It is not likely that the cloud-like condensation obtained with greater expansion has any meteorological significance. For it is unlikely that there can ever be such a sudden uprush of air as to enable any great degree of supersaturation to be maintained when drops have already begun to form.

Oxygen.

Preparation.—Potassium permanganate was heated in a small glass tube fused on to H (fig. 2). This was exhausted and then heated till the pressure considerably exceeded that of the atmosphere, and the process of alternate exhaustion and heating many times repeated.

The mercury reservoirs B, R_1 with the taps T_2, T_3 served as a pump.

Results.—Oxygen behaves exactly like air in these experiments. The expansion required to produce both rain-like and cloud-like condensation, is practically the same in both. The colour phenomena are also exactly alike.

EXPANSION required to produce Rain-like Condensation in Saturated Oxygen.

Pressures all given in millimetres of mercury.   Correction for piston weight,
$$w = 1 \text{ millim.}$$

Date.	B.	$t°$ C.	π.	p_1.	P_1.	p_2.	P_2.	$P_1/P_2 = v_2/v_1$.
May 8	769	17	14	594	1348	318	1072	1·258
„ 14	768	20	17	638	1388	357	1107	1·254
„ 15	768	21	18	579	1328	307	1056	1·258
							Mean	1·257

A fresh supply of oxygen was used each day.

EXPANSION required to produce Cloud-like Condensation in Oxygen.

	Date.	B.	$t°$ C.	π.	p_1.	P_1	p_2.	P_2.	$P_1/P_2 = v_2/v_1$.
	May 9	769	18·0	15	732	1485	318	1071	1·386
1	„ 14	767	20·5	18	659	1407	273	1021	1·378
2	„ 14	766	21·5	19	665	1411	273	1019	1·385
								Mean	1·383

Measurements were also made of the ratio v_2/v_1 when the colour produced by the expansion was the sensitive tint between the blue and red referred to in the account of the colour phenomena observed in the experiments with air.

EXPANSION required to produce the Sensitive Tint.

Date.	B.	$t°$ C.	π.	p_1.	P_1.	p_2.	P_2.	$P_1/P_2 = v_2/v_1$.	Colour.
March 6 . .	752	19·5	17	804	1538	347	1081	1·423	Violet
„ 7 . .	775	17·5	15	799	1558	341	1100	1·417	„
							Mean	1·420	

Carbonic Acid.

Preparation.—Potassium bicarbonate was heated in a glass tube, fused directly to H. This was repeatedly heated and pumped out.

Results.—Carbonic acid shows, like air and oxygen, the two kinds of condensation, each requiring a definite minimum expansion for its production.

The measurements could not be made with the same accuracy in this case on account of the solubility of the gas in water. This caused a continual falling off in the pressure, necessitating the reading of the final pressure p_2 after each expansion.

On account of the difference in γ, the results with CO_2 are not directly comparable with those obtained with air, the same expansion corresponding to a different fall of temperature.

The colour phenomena were not looked for.

In the table which follows, the pressure readings corresponding to the greatest expansion which was made without condensation, as well as those of the least expansion which resulted in condensation, are given. In the case of the more insoluble gases, the difference between these only amounted to 2 millims. ; here, as will be seen, it is considerably greater.

RAIN-LIKE Condensation in CO_2.

Date.	B.	$t°$ C.	π.	p_1.	P_1.	p_2.	P_2.	P_1/P_2.	Result.
May 23	764	19	16	710	1457	333	1080	1·349	0
„	764	19	16	700	1447	314	1061	1·364	Rain
May 25	775	17	14	605	1355	247	997	1·359	0
„	775	17	14	612	1362	245	995	1·369	Rain
May 25	775	17	14	599	1349	242	992	1·360	0
„	775	17	14	603	1353	240	990	1·367	Rain

Condensation begins when P_1/P_2 is between 1·36 and 1·37.

For pressure changes within these limits (between $1\frac{1}{2}$ and 2 atmospheres) BOYLE's law is sufficiently nearly obeyed to justify us in saying that condensation begins when v_2/v_1 lies between 1·35 and 1·37. REGNAULT found* that if the pressure of the CO_2 was changed from 1 atmosphere to 2, the ratio of the initial to the final volume was $2 \times 1·0076$. The difference between P_1/P_2 and v_2/v_1 is therefore well within 1 per cent.

CLOUD-LIKE Condensation in CO_2.

Date.	B.	$t°$ C.	π.	p_1.	P_1.	p_2.	P_2.	P_1/P_2	Result.
May 25	775	17·5	15	738	1487	223	972	1·530	Rain
,, ...	775	17·5	15	734	1503	230	979	1·535	Fog

All the above results were obtained with the same sample of CO_2. On absorbing the gas by KOH a bubble amounting to less than 1 part in 1000 of the whole remained. The gas had been in the expansion apparatus for three days and 50 expansions had been made. The contamination which takes place by air diffusing through the lubricating water round the piston is therefore certainly very slight. In the experiments with CO_2 the lubricating water was less frequently renewed, and a smaller quantity run in at a time than with the less soluble gases. There was, therefore, even less chance of contamination of the latter than of the CO_2.

Hydrogen.

This was prepared by passing steam over sodium. This method was used by SCOTT in his experiments on the composition of water.†

The apparatus for the preparation of the gas is shown in fig. 3.

The water was contained in the bulb A and the sodium in B, which was prolonged into a narrower tube C, fused directly to H in fig. 2. The vertical tube D served for the introduction of the water.

The sodium was previously heated in a tube, kept exhausted by the water pump. The tube was held for several minutes in a Bunsen flame, and the sodium then poured off into the clean part of the tube.

The water to be introduced into A was obtained free from dissolved gases by boiling rapidly down in a flask to about one-sixth of the original volume. This was drawn up through D without allowing it to cool, the end of D dipped under mercury and the apparatus immediately pumped out. The mercury rose in D, which now served as pressure-gauge and safety-tube.

The bulb A was now warmed till the pressure exceeded that of the atmosphere, and bubbles began to escape through the mercury in E.

The flame was then removed, and the apparatus again pumped out to as low a

---

* 'Comptes Rendus,' vol. 23, p. 794 (1846).

† 'Phil. Trans.,' 1893, p. 543.

pressure as possible. Hydrogen was thus generated and pumped out several times, and lastly a vigorous stream of hydrogen was allowed to escape through the water in the flask F (fig. 2) by opening the taps T_2 and T_3. The flame was then removed and T_2 closed, the gas which still continued to come off escaping through the safety-tube D. The hydrogen was then ready to be pumped into the expansion apparatus as required. Even in the cold, hydrogen is slowly formed by the water vapour reaching the sodium by diffusion, and escapes through the safety-tube. No further heating was therefore required when a fresh charge was wanted in the expansion apparatus.

Results.—The phenomena attending condensation in presence of hydrogen differed considerably from those observed with other gases.

As in air and oxygen, dense condensation begins when v_2/v_1 is between 1·37 and 1·38, and the number of particles rapidly increases with increasing expansion. With very slightly smaller expansions, however, the drops are excessively few, and if v_2/v_1 be less than 1·36, they are either absent altogether or at the most one or two

Fig. 3.

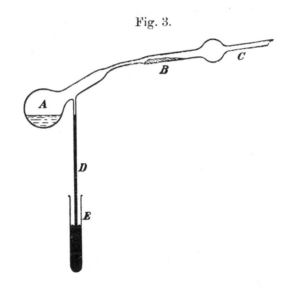

scattered drops are seen. It was found impossible to get any consistent measurements of the minimum expansion required to make these drops appear. In no case was any condensation at all observed when v_2/v_1 was less than 1·30, while in one series of observations no condensation resulted when v_2/v_1 was as great as 1·356.

It is likely that this irregular condensation is due to impurities in the gas. For the observations in which no condensation whatever was observed, even when v_2/v_1 was not much below 1·36, were all made when the hydrogen was comparatively fresh, before it had been allowed to expand more than a very few times. The slight contamination which may take place by diffusion of air through the water lubricating the piston may account for their subsequent appearance. The contamination which can take place in this way must, as has been shown, be very slight; but it is quite possible that an exceedingly small trace of air would be sufficient to cause the slight condensation which is observed. It must be remembered that even if only one drop separates out it will be seen. Colours like those observed in the other gases made their appearance when the expansion exceeded that required to produce the dense condensation. Measurements, however, were not made of the expansion required to produce a given colour.

EXPANSION required to produce Dense Condensation in Hydrogen.

Date.	B.	$t°$ C.	π.	p_1.	P_1.	p_2.	P_2.	$P_1/P_2 = v_2/v_1$.
Aug. 4	763	22·0	20	670	1412	283	1025	1·378
„ 6	767	20·5	18	661	1409	267	1015	1·388
„ 6	767	21·0	18	652	1400	269	1017	1·377
„ 6	767	21·0	18	653	1401	269	1017	1·378
							Mean	1·380

Chlorine.

This was prepared by heating hydrochloric acid with potassium bichromate.

The apparatus is shown in fig. 4. The U-tubes contained water. A supply of the gas was collected in the tube SP, by allowing a rapid stream to pass for about three-quarters of an hour, and then closing the stopcock, and sealing off at P with the blow-pipe.

Fig. 4.

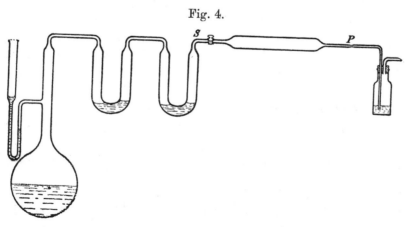

The tube was then cut at S. The part from S to P was then removed, and the open end joined to L (fig. 2) in place of the stopcock T_2. The chlorine was then pumped into the expansion apparatus when required, the reservoir B (fig. 2) with the tubes connected to it being of course first completely filled with well-boiled water. The tube SP was throughout protected from the light by a wrapping of black paper.

2 P 2

After use, the chlorine was absorbed by driving KOH into the expansion chamber. (This was done by expelling the water from B, and drawing in potash in its place, and then opening T_1, while R_1 was raised sufficiently high to overcome the pressure in A.) The bubble which remained was then drawn up into the capillary tube for measurement.

Out of the three samples of chlorine used, two were analysed in this way. In both cases the volume of gas unabsorbed amounted to between 1 and 2 parts in 1000 of the whole.

Results.—Chlorine shows both kinds of condensation, each requiring a definite minimum expansion. With expansions greater than was necessary to produce cloud-like condensation, colour phenomena were observed like those exhibited by air and oxygen.

The solubility of the chlorine introduced difficulties of the kind experienced with CO_2, interfering considerably with the exactness of the measurements. The final pressure p_2 had to be measured after each expansion, no water being run in till after this measurement was completed.

The drops when the condensation was of the rain-like form appeared to the eye to be much more numerous in chlorine than in the other gases.

EXPANSION required to produce Rain-like Condensation in Chlorine.

Date.	B.	t° C.	π.	p_1.	P_1.	p_2.	P_2.	P_1/P_2.	Result.
August 20 . .	761	21·5	19	443	1184	166	907	1·306	Rain.
„ 20 . .	761	21·5	19	420	1161	153	894	1·299	0
August 24 . .	760	20	17	560	1302	257	999	1·304	Rain.
„ 24 . .	760	20	17	549	1291	252	994	1·299	0

Rain-like condensation begins when P_1/P_2 is about 1·30.

EXPANSION required to produce Cloud-like Condensation in Chlorine.

Date.	B.	t° C.	π.	p_1.	P_1.	p_2.	P_2.	P_1/P_2.
August 28	768	18	15	741	1490	280	1029	1·448
„ 28	768	18	15	660	1409	223	972	1·449

Cloud-like condensation begins when P_1/P_2 is about 1·45. The second observation was made with the condensing lens removed, the readings given being those corresponding to the least expansion required to make coloured rings appear. With greater expansions the size and brilliancy of the rings rapidly increased.

We cannot suppose that chlorine at the pressures and temperatures used in these experiments obeys BOYLE's law even approximately. It is not allowable, therefore, to put $P_1/P_2 = v_2/v_1$.

Nitrogen.

This was prepared by adding ammonium chloride to a nearly saturated solution of sodium nitrite, till no more would dissolve, and warming gently. In the first series of experiments a concentrated solution of potassium bichromate was added. This was omitted in the later experiments. The gas was allowed to pass through two U-tubes containing strong caustic potash solution.

The apparatus for the preparation of the gas is shown in fig. 5.

Fig. 5.

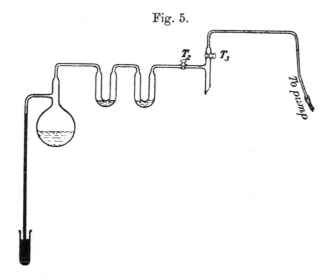

The liquid was drawn into the flask through the vertical tube. This was then made to dip below the surface of mercury contained in a small test-tube. The apparatus was then connected to the water-pump, and the liquid in the flask allowed to boil under very low pressure, by warming gently. This was allowed to continue for some time. The tap T_2 was then closed, and the heating continued till the pressure exceeded that of the atmosphere and the nitrogen began to escape through the safety-tube. T_2 was then again opened and the gas allowed to escape through T_2 and T_3. The temperature of the flask was never allowed to rise more than was sufficient to give a steady stream of the gas, which gradually ceased after the removal of the flame. Finally T_2 was closed and the heating discontinued. The nitrogen could then be pumped out when required.

Results.—The results are practically identical with those obtained with air and oxygen.

The experiments of October 6 were made with the same expansion apparatus as had been used with the other gases. This was unfortunately broken immediately afterwards and the apparatus made to replace it was much smaller, having a capacity of only 8 cub. centims., the length of the expansion chamber being 4 centims., and that of the piston 5 centims. The pressure required to balance the weight of the piston was about 2 millims. of mercury. The volume of the gas is, therefore, smaller, and the rate at which it expands slower than in the former machine.

EXPANSION Required to Produce Rain-like Condensation in Nitrogen.

Date.	B.	$t°$ C.	π.	p_1.	P_1.	p_2.	P_2.	$P_1/P_2 = v_2/v_1$.
October 6	754	13	11	681	1423	390	1132	1·257
November 19	765	17·5	15	562	1310	289	1037	1·263
„ 19	764	17	14	546	1294	276	1024	1·264
„ 19	764	17	14	540	1288	275	1023	1·259
November 30	772	11	10	610	1370	321	1081	1·267
							Mean	1·262

The number of drops appeared to be small in nitrogen.

EXPANSION Required to Produce Cloud-like Condensation in Nitrogen.

Date.	B.	$t°$ C	π.	p_1.	P_1.	p_2.	P_2.	$P_1/P_2 = v_2/v_1$.
October 6	754	13·5	12	765	1506	350	1091	1·380
November 21	775	15·0	13	713	1473	307	1067	1·380
„ 21	775	15·0	13	709	1469	304	1064	1·381
							Mean	1·38

The colour phenomena were exactly like those observed in air.

Measurements were made of the expansion required to produce the sensitive tint.

Date.	$t°$ C.	v_2/v_1.
October 6	13·5	1·417
November 28.	11·5	1·434
„ 28.	11·5	1·430
Mean		1·427

The observations of November 28 were made with the smaller machine, those of October 6 with that which had been used for the experiments on the other gases.

Supersaturation Resulting from a Given Expansion.

By the supersaturation is here meant the ratio of the actual density of the vapour when the expansion has just been completed, and the minimum temperature has therefore been reached to the density of vapour which is in equilibrium over a flat surface of water at that temperature.

It is assumed in what follows that the expansion is completed before any appreciable amount of water has had time to condense on the walls, or in drops throughout the moist gas.

To find the lowest temperature reached we have the well-known equation for the cooling of a gas by adiabatic expression,

$$\frac{\theta_2}{\theta_1} = \left(\frac{v_1}{v_2}\right)^{\gamma-1},$$

where θ_1, θ_2, are the initial and final absolute temperatures, and γ is the ratio of the specific heat at constant pressure to that at constant volume. This has been assumed below to be the same as in the dry gas, the effect on γ of the small quantity of vapour present being neglected. The error introduced in this way, as pointed out by R. v. HELMOLTZ,[*] is inappreciable at temperatures below 30° C.

Knowing θ_1 and v_2/v_1, the ratio measured in these experiments, we can, therefore, calculate θ_2.

Let π_1, π_2 be the pressure of saturated vapour over a flat surface of water at the temperature θ_1, θ_2 respectively. π_1 is then the initial pressure of the vapour before expansion. The volume of the vapour is suddenly changed from v_1 to v_2. We cannot, however, calculate the resulting change in its pressure, there being no reason to suppose that BOYLE's law is even approximately obeyed by the highly supersaturated vapour. There is no such uncertainty, however, as to the density of the vapour, which must change inversely as the volume. It is for this reason that the supersaturation is here defined as the ratio of the actual to the equilibrium density over a flat surface, and not in terms of the corresponding pressure.

The supersaturation, according to the above definition, is equal to

$$S = \rho'/\rho_2,$$

where ρ' is the final density of the vapour before condensation takes place, and ρ_2 is the density of the saturated vapour at the temperature θ_2.

But $\dfrac{\rho'}{\rho_1} = \dfrac{v_1}{v_2}$, therefore, $S = \dfrac{\rho_1}{\rho_2} \times \dfrac{v_1}{v_2}$.

Now the actual density of saturated water vapour in the presence of air at ordinary atmospheric temperatures, has been shown by SHAW[†] to agree very closely with the

---

[*] 'Wied. Ann.,' xxvii., p. 508 (1886).
[†] 'Phil. Trans.,' 1888, A, p. 83.

density calculated on the assumption that the vapour behaves like a perfect gas. We may, therefore, write

$$\frac{\rho_1}{\rho_2} = \frac{\pi_1}{\pi_2} \times \frac{\theta_2}{\theta_1}.$$

Therefore, $S = \frac{\pi_1}{\pi_2} \times \frac{\theta_2}{\theta_1} \times \frac{v_1}{v_2} = \frac{\pi_1}{\pi_2} \times \left(\frac{v_1}{v_2}\right)^{\gamma}.$

Supersaturation Required for Rain-like Condensation.

For convenience of comparison the calculations have been made for the case where the initial temperature t_1 is 20° C. As we have seen, the ratio v_2/v_1 when condensation just begins, is within the limits of experimental error, constant within the ordinary range of room temperature.

Chlorine is too far removed from the condition of a perfect gas for the fall of temperature to be calculated. The error from the same cause may also be considerable in the case of CO_2.

In the following table REGNAULT's numbers have been used for the vapour pressure at temperatures above the freezing point. The vapour pressures over water below the freezing point are from a paper by JUHLIN,[*] who has measured directly the pressure over water over a considerable range of temperature below the freezing point. t_1, t_2 are the initial and final temperatures Centigrade, $\theta_1 = t_1 + 273$, $\theta_2 = t_2 + 273$.

	θ_1.	π_1.	v_2/v_1.	γ.	θ_1/θ_2.	t_2.	π_2.	$S = \frac{\pi_1}{\pi_2}\left(\frac{v_1}{v_2}\right)^{\gamma}$
Air	293	17·39	1·252	1·41	1·097	− 5·8	3·02	4·2
Oxygen	293	17·39	1·257	1·41	1·098	− 6·2	2·93	4·3
Nitrogen	293	17·39	1·262	1·41	1·100	− 6·7	2·83	4·4
Carbonic Acid . .	293	17·39	1·365	1·31	1·101	− 6·9	2·78	4·2
(Chlorine . . .	293	17·39	1·30	1·32	1 087	− 3·5	3·58	3·4)

Hydrogen does not appear in this table, as no regular rain-like condensation was observed.

It will be noticed that the supersaturation required to cause condensation is practically the same in CO_2 as in the other gases, in spite of the great difference in v_2/v_1.

The supersaturation is in each case the greatest which can exist at the temperature t_2° C. without condensation resulting.

To find to what extent this depends upon the temperature, we may make use of the fact that v_2/v_1, when the resulting supersaturation is just sufficient to cause condensation, is in the case of air constant for temperatures between 15·5° C. and 28·8° C.

* 'Bihang till K. S. Vet. Akad. Handlingar,' Bd. 17.

SUPERSATURATION required to cause Condensation in air at different temperatures.

t_1.	θ_1.	π_1.	v_2/v_1.	γ.	θ_1/θ_2.	t_2.	π_2.	$S = \dfrac{\pi_1}{\pi_2}\left(\dfrac{v_1}{v_2}\right)^\gamma$.
15·5	285·5	13·12	1·252	1·41	1·097	− 10	2·197	4·35
20°	293	17·39	1·252	1·41	1·097	− 5·8	3·02	4·2
28·8	301·8	29·45	1·252	1·41	1·097	+ 2·2	5·377	4·0

Thus the maximum supersaturation is 4·35 at − 10° C. and 4·0 at + 2·2° C. It therefore diminishes with rising temperature at the rate of about ·03 per degree.

Supersaturation required to produce Cloud-like Condensation.

The calculations are again made for an initial temperature of 20° C.

The results for Air, Oxygen, Hydrogen, and Nitrogen are grouped together, the difference in the observed value of v_2/v_1 when the dense condensation begins being no greater than can be accounted for by experimental errors. In all these gases the least value of v_2/v_1 when the condensation first becomes cloud-like is about 1·38. In air, however, in which more exact measurements were attempted, the beginning of the change from the rain-like to the cloud-like form could be detected when v_2/v_1 only slightly exceeded 1·37.

The calculations have therefore been made taking $v_2/v_1 = 1·375$. $t_1 = 20°$ C.

	θ_1.	π_1.	v_2/v_1.	γ_1.	θ_1/θ_2.	t_2.	π_2.	$S = \dfrac{\pi_1}{\pi_2}\left(\dfrac{v_1}{v_2}\right)^\gamma$
Air, O, H, N . .	293	17·39	1·375	1·41	1·140	− 15·8	1·41	7·9
CO$_2$	293	17·39	1·53	1·31	1·141	− 16·2	1·37	7·3
(Chlorine . . .	293	17·39	1·44	1·32	1·124	− 12·3	1·83	5·9)

If then by sudden cooling a supersaturation exceeding 7·9 be produced at a temperature of about − 16° C., the condensation, instead of taking place on a small number of scattered nuclei, as with a smaller degree of supersaturation, takes place upon a very large number, the number of nuclei which come into play increasing at a very rapid rate with increasing expansion. It will be noticed that the supersaturation required to produce either kind of condensation is practically the same in all gases, the rain-like condensation, however, being absent in hydrogen.

Supersaturation required to produce the sensitive tint.

At first sight it might seem that when the expansion is so great that a very large number of drops begin to grow before it is completed, the maximum supersaturation must be much less than is obtained by calculation according to the above method. It is difficult, however, to understand the constancy of the results obtained in the observations of the colour phenomena unless the supersaturation resulting from expansion of a given amount is always the same in spite of the variations which there must be in the rate of expansion. If the maximum supersaturation be independent of variations in the rate of expansion, it must be because the maximum supersaturation reached does not differ much from what would result from an infinitely rapid expansion.

This is, perhaps, not very surprising if we consider how little time the drops have to grow before the expansion is completed. To produce the sensitive tint in air v_2/v_1 must be made equal to 1·420. It is only while v_2/v_1 is increasing from 1·38 to 1·42, that the number of drops in process of formation is at all considerable, that is, when the piston has already completed nine-tenths of its journey. Now the piston must be moving with constantly increasing velocity; the whole distance moved by the piston amounts to less than 1·5 centimetres; the time taken to travel the last tenth of this, that is, less than 1·5 millimetres, must therefore be very short. We have seen that the time taken to travel the whole distance is itself very short. The growth of the drops too, as has already been pointed out, cannot be very rapid. It is quite likely therefore that even when they are very numerous, the quantity of water which separates out upon them before the expansion is complete may be too small to diminish appreciably the final supersaturation reached.

The supersaturation required to produce the sensitive tint in air is calculated below.

t_1.	θ_1.	π_1.	v_2/v_1.	γ.	θ_1/θ_2.	t_2.	π_2.	$S = \dfrac{\pi_1}{\pi_2}\left(\dfrac{v_1}{v_2}\right)^{\gamma}$.
20°	293	17·39	1·420	1·41	1·155	− 19·2	1·07	9·9

On the number of the drops.

It is possible to obtain some information as to the number of the drops formed for a certain range of supersaturation from the colour phenomena. For from the colours we ought to be able to deduce the size of the full-grown drops, and the total quantity of water which condenses in consequence of the corresponding expansion may be calculated. With the exceedingly dense fogs with which we are now dealing there is no doubt that the water which condenses on the walls will be small in quantity compared with what condenses in the form of drops. From the quantity of water which separates, and the size of the drops, we may calculate the number, assuming the water to be equally divided among them.

It is assumed here that the cloud-particles are actually liquid drops and not ice-crystals, in spite of the fact that the condensation begins at temperatures much below the freezing point, and that the temperature when the particles are full grown is, as we shall see, also slightly below the freezing point.

Let us consider first the quantity of water which separates out in consequence of an expansion of a given amount. Let us suppose the expansion to be completed before the drops have grown to more than a very small fraction of their final size, so that the theoretical lowering of temperature results. Let t_1 be the temperature Centigrade before expansion, t_2 the lowest temperature reached.

In consequence of the condensation of the water, heat is set free, and the temperature of the moist air rises. A stationary state is reached at a temperature t_3, when just so much water has separated that the vapour remaining is in equilibrium in contact with the drops. The subsequent changes will be slow, being due to the inflow of heat and vapour from the walls. They appear to have little effect upon the size of the drops, for the colour changes very little, and only gradually fades away ; evidently through the drops becoming unequal in size. This is not difficult to understand, for the air which comes in contact with the walls of the tube, since these are covered with water, must remain saturated in spite of its rise in temperature.

If we consider 1 cub. centim. of the moist gas, we have the following equation connecting the temperature t reached at any moment with the quantity of water q which has condensed,

$$Lq = CM\,(t - t_2),$$

where M is the mass of unit volume of the gas and C its specific heat at constant volume. It will not introduce any serious error, for the present purpose, if we neglect the heat spent in raising the temperature of the small quantity of vapour present. L is the latent heat of vaporisation, which changes slightly as the temperature changes during the process, but may be considered with sufficient exactness as equal to 606, its value at 0° C.

Now,

$$q = \rho_1 - \rho,$$

where ρ_1 is the density of the vapour just before condensation begins, and ρ the mean density of the vapour remaining uncondensed at any moment.

Thus,

$$L\,(\rho_1 - \rho) = CM\,(t - t_2),$$

or

$$\rho = \rho_1 - \frac{CM}{L}\,(t - t_2).$$

2 Q 2

If we consider the experimental results obtained with air on March 3rd, we have, when the violet colour results, $v_2/v_1 = 1\cdot420$, the initial temperature being 19° C., and the pressure, when the volume $= v_2$ and the temperature $= 19°$ C., being equal to 1039 millims. of mercury. The density of air at standard temperature and pressure is $\cdot00129$ grm. per cubic centimetre.

Therefore,

$$M = \cdot00129 \times \frac{1039}{760} \times \frac{273}{292} = \cdot00165.$$

The lowest temperature calculated from the expansion is

$$t_2 = -20\cdot2.$$

Also,

$$\rho_1 = \rho_0 \times \frac{v_1}{v_2},$$

where $\rho_0 = $ density of saturated steam at the temperature t_1.

When $t_1 = 19°$ C.

$$\rho_0 = \cdot0000162,$$

therefore,

$$\rho_1 = \cdot0000162 \times \frac{1}{1\cdot42} = \cdot000114.$$

Now C, the specific heat of air at constant volume $= \cdot167$.

We, therefore, find for the density of the vapour, when the temperature has risen from t_2 to t,

$$\rho = \cdot000014 - \frac{\cdot167 \times \cdot00165 \,(t - t_2)}{606}$$

$$= \cdot000014 - 4\cdot55 \times 10^{-7} \,(t - t_2).$$

If we put $t = -4°$ C., we obtain for ρ the value $4\cdot0 \times 10^{-6}$. Now, the density of the saturated vapour at that temperature is $3\cdot7 \times 10^{-6}$. More vapour would, therefore, condense, and the temperature would rise further. If $t = -3°$ C., ρ calculated from the above equation $= 3\cdot6 \times 10^{-7}$; but the density of saturated vapour at $-3°$ C. is $4\cdot0 \times 10^{-7}$. Condensation will, therefore, not go so far as this, but only till the temperature rises to about $-3\cdot5°$ C., and the density of the vapour has fallen to about $3\cdot8 \times 10^{-6}$ grm. per cubic centimetre.

This gives us for the quantity of water which separates out from each cubic centi-metre

$$\rho_1 - \rho_2 = 11\cdot4 \times 10^{-6} - 3\cdot8 \times 10^{-6}$$

$$= 7\cdot6 \times 10^{-6} \text{ grm.}$$

In considering how far the condensation would go, the density of vapour in equi-librium when in contact with drops of the size of those actually present should have

been used, not that over a flat surface.   But for drops of 5×10^{-5} centim. in radius
the difference, as calculated by Lord KELVIN's formula, does not amount to more than
1 or 2 per cent., and is negligible for the present purpose.

The exact theory of the colour phenomena which are produced by clouds of small
water drops such as are formed in these expansion experiments, has not, as far as I
am aware, been worked out.   This is especially true of the colours filling the centre
of the field within the diffraction rings.   Since the whole of the colour phenomena
from the first appearance of small diffraction rings to the disappearance of all colour,
except the bluish or greenish-white, are confined within quite a narrow range of
expansions, the size of the drops evidently diminishes with great rapidity with
increasing expansion.

When all diffraction colours disappear, and the fog appears white from all points of
view, as it does when v_2/v_1 amounts to about 1·44, we cannot be far wrong in assuming
that the diameter of the drops does not exceed one wave-length in the brightest part
of the spectrum, that is, about 5×10^{-5} centim.   That the absence of colour is not
due to the inequality of the drops is evident from the fact that the colours are at
their brightest when v_2/v_1 is only slightly less than 1·44, and from the perfect regularity of the colour changes up to this point.

Taking the diameter of the drops as 5×10^{-5} cub. centim., we obtain for the
volume of each drop about 6×10^{-14} cub. centim., or its mass is 6×10^{-14} grm.

Now, we have seen that when the expansion is such as produces the sensitive tint
(when $v_2/v_1 = 1·42$), the quantity of water which separates out is about $7·6 \times 10^{-6}$ grm.
in each cubic centimetre.   With greater expansions rather more must separate out.
We, therefore, obtain as an inferior limit to the number of drops, when $v_2/v_1 = 1·44$,

$$\frac{7·6 \times 10^{-6}}{6 \times 10^{-14}} = 10^8$$

per cubic centimetre.

Effect of the Röntgen Rays on Condensation.

A statement of the results obtained when moist air is subjected to the action of the
Röntgen rays, and then allowed to expand, has already been published,* but the
experimental details were not given.   The experiments were made with the second
form of apparatus (fig. 2).   A bulb which was giving out the X-rays energetically, as
tested by a fluorescent screen, was fixed about 10 centims. from A.   It was found
that if expansion was made when the bulb was in action, or within a second or two
after switching off the current from the induction coil, the number of drops produced
was greatly increased if the expansion was such as would have caused rain-like condensation in the absence of the rays.   Instead of a shower settling in one or two

* 'Proc. Roy. Soc.,' vol. 59, p. 338, 1896.

seconds, a fog lasting for more than a minute was produced.   If, however, v_2/v_1 was below 1·25, no condensation resulted, whether the rays were acting or not.

The same results were obtained when the expansion vessel was completely wrapped up in tinfoil, which was only removed after the expansion had been made and the current had been switched off.   Direct electrical action was thus excluded.

The air inside A is probably sufficiently well shielded from electrical effects by the film of water which covers the inner surface of the walls.   For it was afterwards found that no effect was produced on the condensation when A was placed directly between the terminals of an induction coil while the expansion was made.

The nuclei introduced by the X-rays only persist a few seconds.   No effect is noticed if the expansion be made half a minute after the current has been turned off.

It will be noticed that in these experiments the rays had to pass through the glass walls of the tube, and must, therefore, have been very much reduced in intensity.

RICHARZ* has recently shown that the condensation of the steam-jet becomes dense under the action of the X-rays.   The intensity of the radiation was probably much greater in his experiments, for the rays had merely to pass through aluminium.

Hydrogen.—The action of the X-rays when hydrogen was substituted for air was afterwards investigated.   It was considered unnecessary in this case, for the reasons already mentioned, to take any precautions for shielding off direct electrical action. The arrangements were in other respects exactly as in the experiments with air. The hydrogen was obtained as already described.

In the first experiments the following results were obtained :—

v_2/v_1.		Result.
1·308 1·296	No X-rays X-rays	No condensation Fog

Several experiments were then made with the tube exposed to the rays, each expansion being made less than the preceding one.   The number of cloud-particles was observed to diminish with diminishing expansion, till, when v_2/v_1 was made equal to 1·260, only a few drops were formed, and none were seen when v_2/v_1 was equal to 1·255.

Further measurements were now made of the smallest expansion required to cause condensation when the moist hydrogen was under the influence of the X-rays.

* 'Wied. Ann.,' vol. 59, p. 592, 1896.

v_2/v_1.		Result.
1·326	No X-rays	No condensation
1·253	X-rays	Drops very few
1·309	X-rays	Fog
1·246	X-rays	No condensation
1·259	X-rays	Shower

With the X-rays on, condensation begins when v_2/v_1 lies between 1·246 and 1·253, the density of the condensation increasing rapidly with increasing expansion.

Fresh hydrogen was now prepared. The bulb was 30 centims. from the cloud chamber.

X-rays on in all Cases.

v_2/v_1.	Result.
1·251	No condensation
1·254	Very few drops
1·253	Very few drops
1·251	No condensation
1·258	Drops few
1·272	Dense shower
1·282	Fog

Thus it appears that condensation begins in hydrogen originally saturated when v_2/v_1 is between 1·251 and 1·253, if the gas be exposed to the action of the X-rays. Condensation therefore begins when the supersaturation reaches the same limit as is necessary for rain-like condensation in air, the supersaturation required to produce condensation under ordinary conditions being nearly twice as great.

As in the case of air the nuclei introduced by the RÖNTGEN rays only last a few seconds. Thus immediately after obtaining condensation when v_2/v_1 was as low as 1·253, if the expansion was made while the gas was exposed to the X-rays, an experiment was made in which the current was switched off half a minute before the expansion. Although v_2/v_1 was as great as 1·315, no condensation resulted. When, however, a similar expansion was made with only a few seconds' interval a slight fog resulted.

Since the X-rays make condensation begin in hydrogen, with a much smaller expansion than is necessary in their absence, it is much more easy to detect the effect of very weak radiation than in air, where only an increase in the number of the drops results from the action of the rays.

It was found that the effect of the rays was quite noticeable, even when the bulb producing them was at a considerable distance away. For example, quite a distinct shower was produced with the bulb 120 centims. off, when v_2/v_1 was equal to 1·326, while an expansion of the same amount made immediately afterwards with the current switched off from the coil caused no condensation.

When the bulb was as far away as this it was found necessary to make rather greater expansion to bring about condensation, than when stronger radiation fell on the expansion apparatus. With the bulb 120 centims. off condensation was first detected when v_2/v_1 was equal to 1·278, none being visible with smaller expansions.

Since every nucleus, capable of promoting condensation, in vapour supersaturated to the extent reached at the completion of the expansion, becomes visible by the growth of a drop around it, it is not surprising that even weak radiation should have a visible effect.

I have not yet made any experiments* to see if X-radiation, which has not been weakened by passing through glass, makes the condensation begin at a lower supersaturation or not. The experiments of RICHARZ, to which reference has already been made, do not give us any information on this point, as the extent of the supersaturation reached in a steam-jet is unknown.

Interpretation of the Results.

The view here taken as to the meaning of the phenomena described in this paper is briefly as follows :—

In aqueous vapour in the presence of air, oxygen, nitrogen, or carbonic acid, there always exists at any moment a small number of nuclei, capable of acting as centres of condensation when the density of the vapour reaches a certain value amounting at — 6° C. to about 4·2 times that of the vapour in equilibrium over a flat surface of water at the same temperature.

The nuclei capable of acting as centres of condensation when the supersaturation lies between this lower limit and another amounting at 16° to 7·9 are comparatively few, and their number depends on the nature of the gas, for they appear to be absent in moist hydrogen. No attempts have yet been made to count the drops produced when the supersaturation lies between these limits, but from the appearance of the resulting shower they almost certainly do not amount to nearly 100 in a cubic centimetre.

When the X-rays, or such components of the radiation as are able to pass through glass, act upon moist air or hydrogen, similar nuclei are produced in much greater numbers, those of them which are the most effective in helping condensation again requiring exactly the same minimum supersaturation in order that condensation may take place upon them.

The number of nuclei capable of acting as centres of condensation when the supersaturation, even slightly, exceeds the upper limit mentioned, is, whatever gas be present, very large, and the number which come into play increases with enormous

* See note at the end of the paper.

rapidity as the supersaturation is increased, reaching in air, oxygen, or nitrogen probably many millions per cubic centimetre under a tenfold supersaturation. In the other gases the observations in the colour phenomena necessary for this estimate were not made. There is no indication in these experiments of any limit to the number of drops which could be formed by sufficiently increasing the supersaturation.

It is possible to make an approximate calculation of the size of the smallest drops which would be able to grow in vapour supersaturated to any given extent.

The formula given by Lord KELVIN[*] for the effect of curvature of a surface upon the pressure of the saturated vapour in contact with it only applies, in its original form, to cases where the curvature is not sufficiently great to make the density of the vapour over the curved surface differ more than very slightly from that over a flat surface. Here we wish to calculate the curvature necessary to make the equilibrium density of the vapour from four to eight times that over a flat surface.

If we assume that the supersaturated vapour obeys BOYLE's law, and that the surface tension retains its ordinary value in the case of the very small drops with which we are dealing, there is no difficulty in seeing how the formula must be modified to allow of its being extended to such cases as the present. Both of these conditions are, unfortunately, likely to be far from being satisfied.

If we make these assumptions, the formula becomes, when the density of the vapour is as in the present case small compared with that of the liquid, identical with that obtained in a different way by R. v. HELMHOLTZ,[†]

$$\log_e \frac{p}{P} = \frac{2T}{Rs\theta r},$$

where p is the vapour pressure in contact with drops of radius r, P that over a flat surface at the same temperature θ; T is the surface-tension, s the density of the liquid, and R the constant in the equation $p/\rho = R\theta$. Since BOYLE's law is assumed to hold, p/P is equal to the ratio of the corresponding densities, that is, to what is here called the supersaturation S. We thus obtain for the radius of the drops just in equilibrium

$$r = \frac{2T}{R\theta \log_e S},$$

since s in the case of water is equal to unity. R for water vapour is equal to $4\cdot6 \times 10^6$.

The results of the application of this formula are here given.

* 'Proc. Roy. Soc.,' Edin., VII., p. 63 (1870).

† 'Wied. Ann.,' xxvii., p. 508 (1886).

Radius, in centims., of drops just large enough to grow in vapour supersaturated to the extent required to make rain-like condensation begin in the presence of Air.

$t°$ C.	θ.	T.	S.	r.
−10	263	77	4·35	$8·7 \times 10^{-8}$
− 6	267	76	4·2	$8·6 \times 10^{-8}$
+ 2	275	75	4·0	$8·6 \times 10^{-8}$

r thus appears to be constant over the range of temperature − 10° C. to + 2° C. The value obtained for r is not changed by as much as 3 per cent. when the air is replaced by nitrogen, oxygen, or CO_2, or by hydrogen under the action of the X-rays.

Radius, in centims., of drops just large enough to grow when supersaturation is sufficient to make the dense condensation begin in Air, Oxygen, Nitrogen, or Hydrogen.

$t°$ C.	θ.	T.	S.	r.
−16	257	78	7·9	$6·4 \times 10^{-8}$

If we consider the difference in the value found for S in CO_2 to be real, and not due merely to the error in the calculation of the cooling, due to deviation of CO_2 from the condition of a perfect gas, we find that r in CO_2 is about 3 per cent. greater than in these other gases.

Radius, in centims., of drops just large enough to grow when the supersaturation is such that the sensitive tint is produced in the presence of Air or Oxygen.

$t°$ C.	θ.	T.	S.	r.
−19	254	79	9·9	$5·9 \times 10^{-8}$

The difference when nitrogen is substituted for Air or Oxygen is exceedingly small.

It cannot be assumed that the surface tension retains its ordinary value in drops of such small radii, which are not great compared with molecular dimensions. We know, in fact, from the behaviour of thin films, that it does not. These numbers therefore can only be considered as giving a very rough approximation to the absolute size of the water drops which would actually be in equilibrium in vapour of the various degrees of supersaturation.

They furnish, however, a convenient means of expressing the relative efficiency of the nuclei in helping condensation. Thus, the nuclei producing rain-like condensation are equivalent in their effect on the condensation, to water drops of radii between $6·4 \times 10^{-8}$ and $8·7 \times 10^{-8}$ centim. There are, as we have seen, certainly not more than 100 of these in each cubic centimetre of moist air, and they are absent in hydrogen. The nuclei equivalent to water drops whose radii lie between the narrow limits $5·9 \times 10^{-8}$ and $6·4 \times 10^{-8}$ centim. amount to many millions per cubic centimetre.

It is difficult to account for the immense number of these latter nuclei, otherwise than on the view that they actually are simply small aggregates of water molecules, such as may come into existence momentarily through encounters of the molecules. On this view the dimensions of the molecules cannot be small compared with 6×10^{-8} centim. BARUS* states that if it were possible to measure the supersaturation required to make steam condense in the absence of dust, the dimensions of the molecules could be calculated with the aid of LORD KELVIN's formula. Probably he takes some such view as that here suggested.

The nuclei which bring about the rain-like condensation, and the greater number of which appear to be equivalent in their power of causing condensation to water drops of not much less than $8·7 \times 10^{-8}$ centim. are probably of a different character.

As, however, I am continuing these experiments, it would be premature at the present stage to discuss the various views that might be held as to their nature.

[*Note added July* 22, 1897.

Further Experiments on the Action of the X-rays.—I have lately repeated the experiments on air, using an expansion apparatus provided with a window of very thin aluminium, so arranged that the whole of the contents of the tube were exposed to the rays of a suitably placed Röntgen lamp.

This gave results identical with those already obtained, no condensation resulting when the air was expanded while exposed to the rays unless v_2/v_1 exceeded $1·25$, while with expansions even slightly exceeding this, a comparatively dense fog resulted; only a few scattered drops appearing with similar expansions in the absence of the rays.

As was to be expected, much denser fogs were obtained under the action of the rays with this apparatus than with that formerly used.

A glass plate of 7 millims. thick, placed over the window, appeared to cut off the effect of the rays completely.]

* 'Phil. Mag.,' vol. 38, p. 34 (1894); also "Report on the Condensation of Atmospheric Moisture." U. S. Department of Agriculture, Weather Bureau, 1895.

2 R 2

On an Expansion Apparatus for making Visible the Tracks of Ionising Particles in Gases and some Results obtained by its Use.

By C. T. R. WILSON, M.A., F.R.S.

(Received June 7,—Read June 13, 1912.)

[PLATES 6—9.]

In a recent communication* I described a method of making visible the tracks of ionising particles through a moist gas by condensing water upon the ions immediately after their liberation. At that time I had only succeeded in obtaining photographs of the clouds condensed on the ions produced along the tracks of α-particles and of the corpuscles set free by the passage of X-rays through the gas. The interpretation of the photographs was complicated to a certain extent by distortion arising from the position which the camera occupied.

The expansion apparatus and the method of illuminating the clouds have both been improved in detail, and it has now been found possible to photograph the tracks of even the fastest β-particles, the individual ions being rendered visible. In the photographs of the X-ray clouds the drops in many of the tracks are also individually visible; the clouds found in the α-ray tracks are generally too dense to be resolved into drops. The photographs are now free from distortion. The cloud chamber has been greatly increased in size; it is now wide enough to give ample room for the longest α-ray, and high enough to admit of a horizontal beam of X-rays being sent through it without any risk of complications due to the proximity of the roof and floor.

The Expansion Apparatus.

The essential features of the expansion apparatus are shown in fig. 1. The cylindrical cloud chamber A is 16·5 cm. in diameter and 3·4 cm. high; the roof, walls and floor are of glass, coated inside with gelatine, that on the floor being blackened by adding a little Indian ink. The plate glass floor is fixed on the top of a thin-walled brass cylinder (the "plunger"), 10 cm. high, open below, and sliding freely within an outer brass cylinder (the "expansion cylinder") of the same height and about 16 cm. in internal diameter. The expansion cylinder supports the walls of the cloud chamber and rests on a thin sheet of indiarubber lying on a thick brass disc, which forms the bottom of a shallow receptacle containing water to a depth of about 2 cm. The

* 'Roy. Soc. Proc.,' 1911, A, vol. 85, p. 285.

U

water separates completely the air in the cloud chamber from that below the plunger. The base plate rests on a wooden stand, not shown on the diagram.

The expansion is effected by opening the valve B and so putting the air space below the plunger in communication with the vacuum chamber C

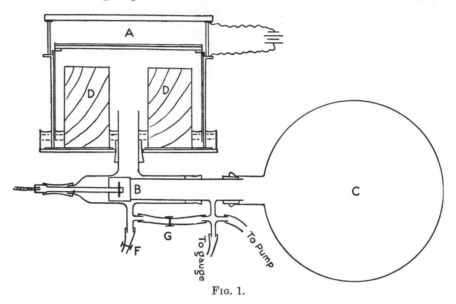

Fig. 1.

through wide glass connecting tubes of about 2 cm. in diameter. The floor of the cloud chamber, in consequence, drops suddenly until brought to a sudden stop, when the plunger strikes the indiarubber-covered base plate, against which it remains firmly fixed by the pressure of the air in the cloud chamber. To reduce the volume of air passing through the connecting tubes at each expansion the wooden cylinder D was inserted within the air space below the plunger.

The valve is opened by the fall of a weight W released by a trigger arrangement T (fig. 3). On closing the valve and opening communication with the atmosphere through the pinch-cock F, the plunger rises and so reduces the volume of the air in the cloud chamber. By means of the two pinch-cocks F and G (the latter on a tube communicating with the vacuum chamber), the plunger may be adjusted to give any desired initial volume v_1 between the upper limit v_2—the maximum volume of the cloud chamber— and the lower limit reached when the pressure below the plunger is that of the atmosphere.

The final volume v_2 is always the same (about 750 c.c.), the expansion ratio v_2/v_1 depending only on the initial volume. A scale attached to the side of the cloud chamber enables the position of the top of the plunger to be read, and hence the **initial** volume to be determined, the area of the cross-section of the plunger and **the** maximum volume v_2 of the cloud chamber being known.

In setting up the apparatus, the plunger is placed on the rubber-covered base plate, and the expansion cylinder slipped over it, a hole in the side of the cloud chamber being open at this stage to allow of the imprisoned air escaping. Then, by blowing in air through F, momentarily opened for the purpose, the plunger is driven up to a height sufficient to allow of the largest desired expansions being made. The aperture in the wall of the cloud chamber is then closed, and the mass of imprisoned air remains unchanged during subsequent operations.

The gelatine layer under the roof of the cloud chamber is connected, through a ring of tinfoil cemented between the cylindrical wall and the roof, with one terminal of a battery of cells of which the other terminal is connected, through the brass expansion cylinder and plunger, with the layer of blackened gelatine on the floor of the cloud chamber. An approximately uniform vertical electric field of any desired intensity may thus be maintained in the cloud chamber.

The gelatine lining of the roof and walls is formed by pouring into the cloud chamber, before attaching it to the expansion cylinder, a hot solution containing about 4 per cent. of gelatine and 0·1 per cent. of boracic acid and allowing the surplus to drain away by inverting the vessel. The thin coating of gelatine which remains is allowed to dry over calcium chloride. The cloud chamber is cemented to the expansion cylinder by means of gelatine.

A comparatively thick layer (about 1 mm.) of a solution containing 15 per cent. of gelatine, 2 per cent. of boracic acid, and 3 per cent. of Indian ink is poured on to the glass plate which forms the floor of the cloud chamber, the brass walls of the plunger being prolonged for about 1 mm. above the upper surface of the plate, thus forming a shallow receptacle for the gelatine and making an efficient electric contact with it. The blackened gelatine is not allowed to dry, but at once covered to prevent evaporation and to protect it from dust till ready for use. The gelatine is in all cases previously sterilised by heat.

Method of Illuminating and Photographing the Clouds.

As in the experiments described in my last paper, a Leyden jar discharge through mercury vapour at atmospheric pressure is used for the instantaneous illumination of the clouds resulting from the expansion. A horizontal silica tube (fig. 2) about 15 cm. long, and having an internal diameter of about 1 mm., is filled with mercury and enclosed, for the central 4 cm. of its length, by a close-fitting silver tube about 2 mm. thick, and having a slot about 1 mm. wide extending from end to end. The silver tube when heated by a small flame serves to keep the enclosed portion of the silica tube at a nearly uniform temperature high enough to vaporise the mercury, and thus

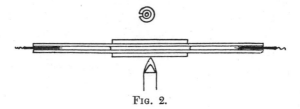

Fig. 2.

form a mercury-vapour spark-gap. Connection with the Leyden jars is made through platinum wires fused through the ends of glass tubes filled with mercury and inserted into the ends of the silica tube.

The silica tube is first filled with mercury, the end pieces inserted, and a small flame placed under the silver tube. When the mercury occupying the portion of the silica tube which is surrounded by the silver jacket has all been vaporised (the excess of mercury escaping from the ends of the tube) no further change takes place and the spark-gap is ready for use. The very considerable capillary forces set up when the mercury is forced into the narrow space between the glass end pieces and the surrounding silica tube effectually prevent the violent oscillatory motions which are apt to be the principal source of trouble in the use of a mercury spark-gap of this type.

For firing the spark the arrangement used is essentially that which has generally been employed in instantaneous photography by the Leyden jar discharge. The outer coatings of two sets of 4 or 5 "gallon" Leyden jars, standing on the floor of the room, are connected to the terminals of the illuminating spark. The inner coatings are connected to the terminals of a Wimshurst machine and to two brass balls separated by a space of about 5 cm. which forms the primary spark-gap. The jars having been charged almost to sparking potential, a metal ball is allowed to fall between the terminals of the primary spark-gap, causing a spark to pass at both gaps. The ball whose fall causes the spark is hung by a fine thread, just strong enough to carry it, from the weight W which works the valve of the expansion apparatus.

The arrangements for firing the spark at a definite interval after the expansion are shown diagrammatically in fig. 3. The weight W is carried by a cord which passes through an iron ring in a firm support, and thence nearly horizontally to the trigger T, to which it is attached by a loop. A second string, slack at this stage, connects a point on the first cord with the valve of the expansion apparatus. On pulling the trigger the cord attached to it is released and the weight falls until the second string is stretched tight, when it is brought to a sudden stop, the valve being simultaneously opened and the expansion thereby effected. The thread breaks at this moment and the steel

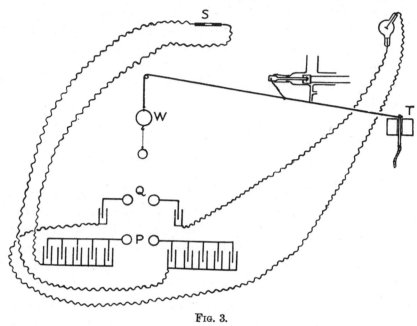

FIG. 3.

sphere continues to fall, finally passing through the primary spark-gap, P, and causing the illuminating spark to pass at S. The upper spark-gap, Q, shown in the figure, was only employed in the experiments with X-rays.

In the experiments described in this paper, the camera lens has always occupied one of the two positions indicated diagrammatically in fig. 4, (a) and (b). In (a) the small circle represents a transverse section of a narrow

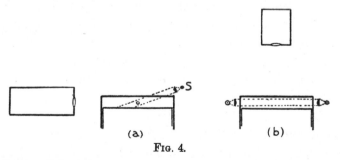

(a)   (b)

FIG. 4.

horizontal beam of ionising rays crossing a diameter of the cloud chamber. The camera looks in a horizontal direction normal to the ionising beam. The mercury spark-gap is at S, at the principal focus of a cylindrical lens about

20 cm. long and 2 cm. wide, and having a focal length of about 3 cm. With this arrangement the whole of the cloud produced by a considerable length of the ionising beam is illuminated, while the direction of the incident light makes a comparatively small angle (about 25°) with the axis of the camera.

Arrangement (b) has been used chiefly with the α-rays, which give clouds of sufficient density to scatter a large amount of light at right angles to the illuminating beam. The camera lens is vertically over the centre of the cloud chamber; and by means of two similar mercury spark-gaps (arranged in series), each at the principal focus of a cylindrical lens like that used in (a), a horizontal stratum of about 2 cm. in vertical thickness and extending across the whole area of the vessel, is illuminated.

The lens which I have used is a Beck "isostigmar," the full aperture, marked F 5·8, being utilised; Ilford "Monarch" plates were employed.

Ionisation by α-Rays.   (Plate 6, and fig. 1 of Plate 7.)

Fig. 1 (Plate 6) is a typical photograph of the cloud obtained on expansion when a minute quantity of radium is placed on the tip of a wire projecting into the cloud chamber. A potential difference of 40 volts was maintained between the roof and floor, the roof being at the higher potential. The camera was placed with its axis vertical, and a horizontal section of the cloud chamber, about 2 cm. in depth, was illuminated (arrangement (b) of fig. 4). The β-rays are not visible in the photographs obtained with this mode of illumination.

The narrow, sharply defined rays of these photographs are clouds condensed along the tracks of α-particles which have traversed the supersaturated air after the expansion, so that there has been very little time for the ions to diffuse before losing their mobility through condensation of water upon them. The diffuse rays are clouds condensed upon ions set free by α-particles which have traversed the air before its expansion, so that there has been time for diffusion of the ions before the formation of the cloud. The weaker the electric field, the greater is the maximum possible age, and consequent diffuseness, of the tracks which may be present; with a potential difference of only two or three volts, wide finger-like clouds are formed on expansion.

α-rays which pass after the expansion can only leave visible trails if the degree of supersaturation still remains sufficient to cause water to condense on the ions. In the immediate neighbourhood of the cloud already condensed on an older track, the supersaturation remaining may be insufficient to cause condensation, although elsewhere the α-particle may leave a visible trail. This is doubtless the explanation of the fact that most of the sharply defined trails only seem to begin at some considerable distance from the radium, the diffuse cloud trails formed at the moment of expansion being so closely packed near the source of the rays that there is little chance of an α-particle, ejected after the expansion, finding the supersaturation necessary for rendering its trail visible, until it has travelled for some distance.

Except in the case of photographs taken very soon after the insertion of the radium, the trails of α-particles from the emanation and later radio-active products also appear. Fig. 4 is a photograph of the cloud formed by expansion after the radium-tipped wire had been for some days in the cloud chamber and had then been removed; α-rays are seen running in all directions. A sharply defined trail may sometimes be observed crossing one or more diffuse ones, and is then frequently invisible for some little distance on either side of the diffuse ray, the necessary supersaturation not being attained owing to previous condensation on the ions of the older trail.

For some purposes (if, for example, the ranges of the α-particles were under investigation) it would be necessary to know definitely whether the α-particle giving rise to any given trail had passed before or after the expansion, the density of the air traversed being different in the two cases. The trails of α-particles passing previously to the expansion have their dimensions altered between the liberation of the ions and the deposition of water upon them; but, the displacement of the air being everywhere nearly in a vertical direction, the horizontal dimensions are almost unaffected. In the photographs it will be observed that the diffuse rays are shorter than the sharply defined rays in accordance with the greater density of the air at the moment of passage of the α-particle.

There is no difficulty in securing that the particles whose tracks are being photographed shall have passed either all before or all after the expansion. It is only necessary to attach to the plunger a vertical plate (glass 2 mm. thick was used) immediately in front of the source of the rays, and with a horizontal slot so placed that it shall be at the level of the radiant point either before or after the expansion. Fig. 2 is a photograph taken under the latter condition; the diffuse tracks are now absent. This method is, of course, inapplicable to the study of the rays from the emanation within the cloud chamber.

As will be seen from the photographs, the α-rays are generally straight over the greater part of their length, but they nearly all are bent, often abruptly, in the last 2 mm. of their course. Abrupt bends through considerable angles are seen much earlier in the course of some of the rays.

In fig. 3 of Plate 6 is shown an enlargement of a particularly interesting trail.   Here there are two absolutely abrupt bends—the first through about $10\frac{1}{2}°$, the second through about 43°.   There is a very well-marked spur at the second bend, which it is difficult to interpret otherwise than as being due to ionisation by the recoil of the atom, by collision with which the course of the α-particle has been abruptly changed.   (But for the spur this α-ray shows an astonishingly close resemblance to one in a diagram constructed by Prof. Bragg* to illustrate what he considered to be likely forms of α-ray paths.)

Apart from these sudden bends a certain amount of curvature is apparent in some of the tracks.   In some cases, where the curvature occurs close to the walls of the cloud chamber, it is certainly a spurious effect, due to displacement of the tracks by air motions or to optical distortion arising from a thickening of the gelatine round the circumference of the roof. Where, however, it appears at no great distance from the centre of the cloud chamber it is probably genuine, indicating deviation of the α-particle by repeated small deflections.   There is generally unmistakably genuine curvature in the last millimetre of the track.

The photographs thus furnish evidence of two distinct ways in which α-particles are "scattered" in passing through air, what Rutherford† has called "single" and "compound" scattering respectively.   And, as Rutherford has contended, the scattering of large amount is in the case of α-particles mainly due to the former process, that is to say, it is the result of single deflections through considerable angles and not a cumulative effect due to a very large number of minute deviations.

When the α-rays arise from the emanation it is possible to photograph the complete track of an α-particle, including the beginning and end.   The latter is at once recognisable by its characteristic bend or hook.   In figs. 4 and 5 (Plate 6) are shown the tracks of two α-particles, each of which has completed its course in the illuminated layer ; in both cases the beginning of the trail is seen to be marked by an enlarged head in which the cloud is of greater density than elsewhere.   This may represent ionisation by the recoil of the atom from which the α-particle has escaped.   The same characteristic head appears at what is presumably the beginning of other, obviously foreshortened, tracks whose ends lie outside the illuminated layer.

Of the two complete α-ray tracks from the emanation one has a length (when reduced to 760 mm. and 15° C.) of 4·3 cm., in good agreement with the usually accepted value of the range.   The other is apparently somewhat shorter, about 3·8 cm., the low value being probably due to foreshortening.

* 'Archives of the Röntgen Ray,' April, 1911.
† 'Phil. Mag.,' 1911, vol. 21, p. 669.

Some photographs of α-ray trails were obtained with the camera in the lateral position and with oblique illumination—arrangement (a) of fig. 4 (p. 281).   The radium tipped wire was surrounded by a glass tube about 1 mm. wide open at the end and projecting for about 1 cm. beyond the radium, the object being to confine the rays to a moderately narrow pencil with its axis in the plane for which the camera was focussed.

An example of one of the photographs obtained in this way is shown in Plate 7, fig. 1, which is an enlargement of the original negative.   The track of an α-particle is seen near the bottom of the picture.   Some of the ions appear to have retained their mobility in the supersaturated atmosphere long enough to enable them to travel some distance under the action of the electric field before growing into drops, thus giving rise to a vertical sheet or curtain of drops.   The effect is most marked above the main track, *i.e.* on the side to which the negative ions would travel.

I have not yet succeeded in obtaining photographs in which all the drops in a known length of the cloud trail left by an α-particle could be counted. It would obviously be of interest to determine by a direct method of this kind the number of ions produced by an α-particle.

Ionisation by β-Rays.   (Plate 7.)

When the camera is in the lateral position and oblique illumination is used the individual cloud particles, so long as they are not too close together for resolution, leave distinct images on the photographic plate.   It is possible, therefore, to photograph the track of any ionising particle, however small the number of ions produced per centimetre of its path may be.

Some photographs of β-ray trails were obtained along with those of the α-rays in the course of the experiments last described.   Figs. 1, 3, and 4 of Plate 7 were obtained in this way; fig. 2 shows the result of passing a narrow beam of γ-rays through the cloud chamber; the tracks in this case are doubtless those of β-particles starting in the walls of the vessel.

The almost straight trail of figs. 3 and 4 (the actual length of trail photographed amounts to about 4 cm.) is evidently that of a β-particle in the earlier stage of its free existence while its velocity is still very high.   This is indicated not only by the straightness of its path but also by the very small ionisation along it.   The distribution of the ionisation along the path is interesting.   Over considerable distances the ions occur mainly in pairs, but here and there 20 or 30 appear to have been liberated in a closely packed group.   (A similar distribution appears in a second approximately straight ray which crosses the first.)   The groups show a peculiarity which is also met with in the clouds condensed on the cathode rays produced by X-rays when a suitable expansion ratio is used : while the negative ions have given rise to a densely packed cluster of drops the positive ions have been drawn out by the electric field before losing their mobility, giving the appearance of a shower of drops falling from the negative cloud.

If we omit the clusters, the number of ions in the trail amounts to about 32, *i.e.* 16 pairs, per centimetre at atmospheric pressure. If we take into account the groups the number of ions per centimetre is roughly doubled, giving a number not very much lower than the estimate of 48 pairs per centimetre obtained by Eve[*] by indirect methods.

The occurrence of the groups or clusters of ions may be interpreted as indicating that in certain cases the corpuscle liberated from an atom by a β-particle of high velocity may itself have energy enough to ionise for a very short distance. The β-rays of fig. 2 are obviously of smaller velocity, producing much more ionisation per centimetre and being much more readily deviated.

A still later stage of slower velocity has been reached by the particles giving the abruptly ending coiled up trails which appear in figs. 1 and 3. These β-ray endings are indistinguishable from the cathode rays, produced in air by Röntgen rays, such as are shown in the succeeding plates.

It will be noticed that the β-rays photographed do not show abrupt deflections like the α-rays, but, except while the velocity remains very high, they show gradual bending resulting in large deviations. The scattering of the β-rays is thus mainly or entirely of the cumulative or " compound " type, being due to a large number of successive deflections, each in itself inappreciable.

Ionisation by Röntgen Rays. (Plates 8 and 9.)

The X-ray bulb was excited by a Leyden jar discharge, in most cases so timed that the rays traversed the cloud chamber immediately after the expansion, while the gas was in the supersaturated condition. The ions had thus extremely little time in which to diffuse before being fixed by the condensation of water upon them.

The terminals of the upper spark gap Q of fig. 3 (p. 281) were connected with the inner coatings of two Leyden jars, the outer coatings of which were connected to the Crookes tube. The inner coatings were also connected through glass tubes filled with water to the terminals of the Wimshurst machine. The steel ball in its fall first caused the X-ray discharge and afterwards the illuminating spark, the water tubes having a sufficiently high resistance to prevent the jars supplying the illuminating spark from discharging while the ball traversed the upper spark gap, but conducting sufficiently well

[*] ' Phil. Mag.,' 1911, vol. 22, p. 551.

to allow of both sets of jars being simultaneously charged by means of the Wimshurst machine.

The moment of occurrence of the X-ray flash relative to the expansion was adjusted by varying the length of the thread suspending the steel ball. Tests were made of the length of thread required to make the X-ray discharge simultaneous with the completion of the expansion; it was then known that with a thread shorter than this the X-rays would pass after the expansion. For the purpose of making this test the X-ray tube was removed, and the wires supplying it were connected instead to the mercury spark-gap; two illuminating sparks thus traversed the mercury vapour during the fall of the ball, the interval between them being the same as that between the X-ray flash and the illuminating spark, for the same length of thread, in the ordinary use of the apparatus. A series of photographs was taken with different lengths of thread, the camera, placed horizontally, being focussed on a pointer attached to the plunger; a single image of the pointer on the photographic plate indicated that the expansion had been completed before the passage of the first spark, a double image resulting if the first spark passed before the expansion was completed. These photographs also furnished information regarding the rapidity of the expansion; it was found to be completed within about 1/50th of a second.

The Crookes tube was fixed at a distance varying from 30 to 70 cm. from an aperture in the wall of the cloud chamber about 1·2 cm. in diameter; this was closed by a quartz plate 0·38 mm. thick. The quartz window was used as it happened to be convenient for another purpose. The rays passed through a narrow cylindrical channel, in most cases of 2 mm. bore, in a lead block about 5 cm. thick placed close to the quartz window, lead screens being also inserted to shield the rest of the cloud chamber from the rays. The camera occupied position (a) of fig. 4. A horizontal cylindrical beam of X-rays was in this way made to traverse the cloud chamber across its centre, and was at such a distance from the camera that the magnification was about 2·45 diameters. To avoid distortion by the cylindrical walls of the cloud chamber a portion of the cylinder 5 cm. in length was removed and replaced by a plane parallel glass plate.

Photographs of some typical X-ray clouds are shown in Plate 8. In all cases (with one exception, fig. 5) the rays traversed the supersaturated gas, the order of events being: (1) Production of the supersaturated condition by sudden expansion; (2) Leyden jar discharge through the Crookes tube, causing ionisation within the cloud chamber; (3) condensation of water upon the ions; (4) passage of the illuminating spark, giving a photograph of the cloud condensed on the ions.

The potential difference between the top and bottom of the cloud chamber was in some cases 40 volts, in others only 4 volts, the top being always positive.

In most cases the expansion ratio was between 1·33 and 1·36; *i.e.* it considerably exceeded the minimum (approximately 1·31) required to cause condensation on the positive as well as the negative ions (the minimum for the latter is 1·25), but less than is required to give dense clouds in the absence of ions ($v_2/v_1 = 1·38$). Under these conditions, as the photographs show, the tracks of the cathode- or β-particles produced in the gas by the X-rays are very sharply defined, the ions being fixed by condensation of water upon them before they have had time to diffuse, or travel under the action of the electric force, for any appreciable distance.

The following are among the more striking features of the photographs, of which figs. 1 to 4 of Plate 8 are a few examples out of a considerable number obtained under these conditions.

1. Cathode or β-rays are seen to start from within the track of the primary X-ray beam, many of them extending to some distance outside it.

2. There is no indication of any effect of the X-rays on the gas other than the production of the corpuscular radiation; the track of the primary X-ray beam is not distinguishable otherwise than as being the region in which the β-rays have their origin. In some photographs, it is true, there appear scattered throughout the region illuminated by the spark drops which might be taken to represent ions set free by the X-rays, but these show no concentration along the path of the primary beam, and, moreover, they appear in equal numbers in comparison photographs taken under conditions otherwise identical but without any X-ray discharge. There is no doubt, I think, that these scattered drops are condensed upon uncharged nuclei similar in nature to those produced by weak ultra-violet light and certain metals, which require a similar expansion to catch them. They appear to be due to a chemical action in which some trace of impurity plays an essential part, as they are much more numerous when the air in the apparatus has recently been renewed.

Ionisation by X-rays appears therefore to be, as Bragg has suggested, entirely a secondary process, except in so far as each cathode ray produced in the gas may be said to indicate the formation of one pair of ions by the X-radiation.

3. The number of cathode rays produced in air in a known length of a limited beam of X-rays can readily be counted by this method.

4. The X-radiation thus far used has been heterogeneous. It is to be expected therefore that the cathode rays should be of varying length. Reduced to atmospheric pressure, a frequent length, measured along the

path, was from ¾ to 1 cm., or measured in a straight line from beginning to end of the path, about half these amounts. Tracks as long as 2 cm. were, however, met with.

5. The rays show two distinct kinds of deflection as a result of their encounters with the atoms of the gas—Rutherford's "single" and "compound" scattering. The gradual or cumulative deviation due to successive deflections of very small amount is evidently, however, in this case much the more important factor in causing scattering, all the rays showing a large amount of curvature, while quite a small proportion show abrupt bends. When abrupt deflections occur they are frequently through large angles, 90° or more.

6. The rays tend to become more and more bent as the end is approached, the actual end of each cloud trail being also enlarged into a kind of head, possibly owing to the path of the corpuscle finally becoming extremely irregular in form.

7. In many of the photographs there are cloud trails sufficiently sharply in focus over at least a portion of their length to show the individual drops and, therefore, allow of the ions on which they have condensed being counted. An enlargement of one such track is shown in fig. 6 of Plate 8 ; the number per cm. of this trail amounts to about 278, the equivalent of 376 ions or 188 pairs of ions at atmospheric pressure. This number appears to be fairly typical for the middle portions of the tracks, *i.e.* about 5 mm. from the end. Out of 12 counts of this kind, the smallest number obtained is 150 pairs per cm. (at atmospheric pressure)—this is at the beginning of a ray—the largest 2160 pairs per cm. in the last ½ mm. of a ray.

8. The cathode rays appear to start in all directions. I have not yet attempted any systematic statistical study such as would be required to determine the relative frequency of different initial directions of the rays with respect to the direction of propagation of the Röntgen radiation.

When the expansion ratio is less than about 1·33, the cathode-ray cloud-trails begin to lose their sharpness, as is illustrated by the photographs in Plate 9. With expansion ratios between 1·31 and 1·33, the positive ions are spread out by the electric field before becoming fixed, giving rise to what looks like a shower of drops falling from each trail, which is still marked by the negative ions. When the expansion falls below that required to catch the positive ions, the negative ions begin to show a similar spreading out under the action of the field, and finally, while the expansion still considerably exceeds that required to catch negative ions, the clouds cease to give any picture of the original path of the corpuscle. To get the form of the path of an ionising particle as accurately as possible, the expansion ratio ought to exceed 1·33 ; but, on the other hand, for counting the ions, a smaller expansion has advantages. An expansion just too small to catch positive ions is perhaps the best for counting the ions ; it was only in photographs obtained under such conditions that the ionisation at the ends of the trails could be determined.

When the Röntgen rays are flashed through the cloud chamber before the expansion of the air, diffuse double tracks are obtained, the positive and negative ions being separated by the electric field, and a certain amount of diffusion of the ions occurring in both positive and negative trails (Plate 8, fig. 5). It would have been interesting to obtain by this very direct method a test as to whether the number of positive and negative ions set free is the same, or, in other words, whether the positive and negative ion carry equal charges—a question which has been raised by certain experiments by Townsend. Unfortunately. I have thus far only succeeded in obtaining on the negatives a few very short portions of such double tracks, which are at the same time sharply in focus and free from complications due to over-lapping with other tracks. These short portions do, however, show equality in the numbers of positive and negative ions; the positive and negative clouds, to take one example, containing each 30 to 31 drops, there being some uncertainty in one or two cases as to whether an image on the plate represents one drop or two.

These experiments have been carried out in the Cavendish Laboratory. I have to thank Mr. F. Lincoln and his assistants in the workshop for most efficient aid in the construction of the apparatus.

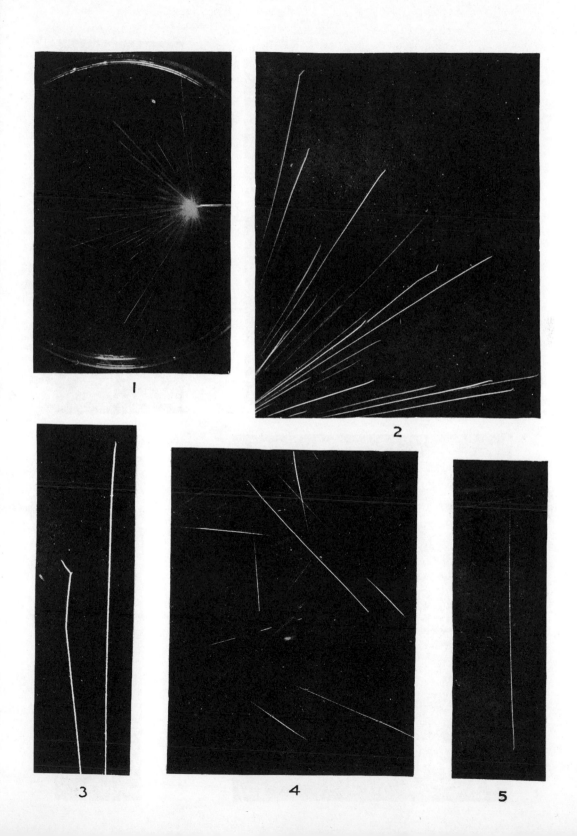

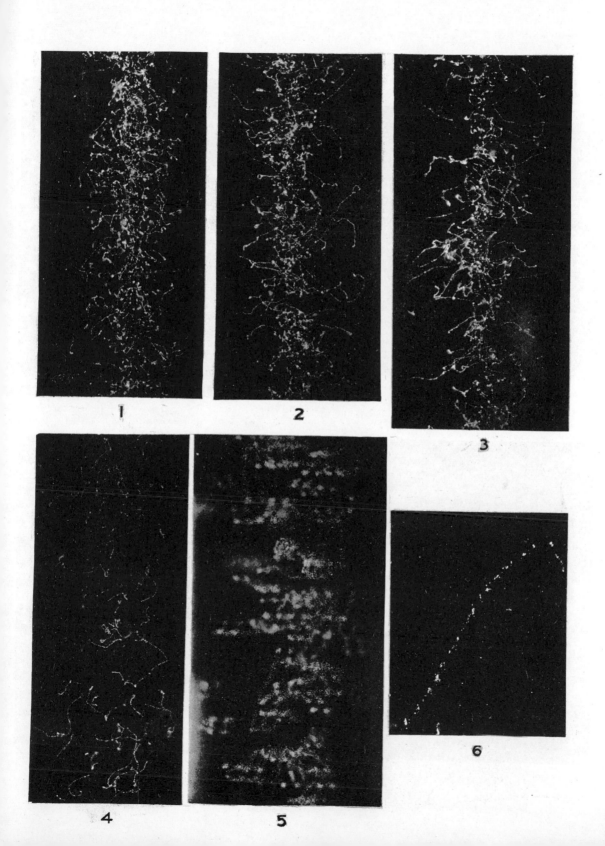

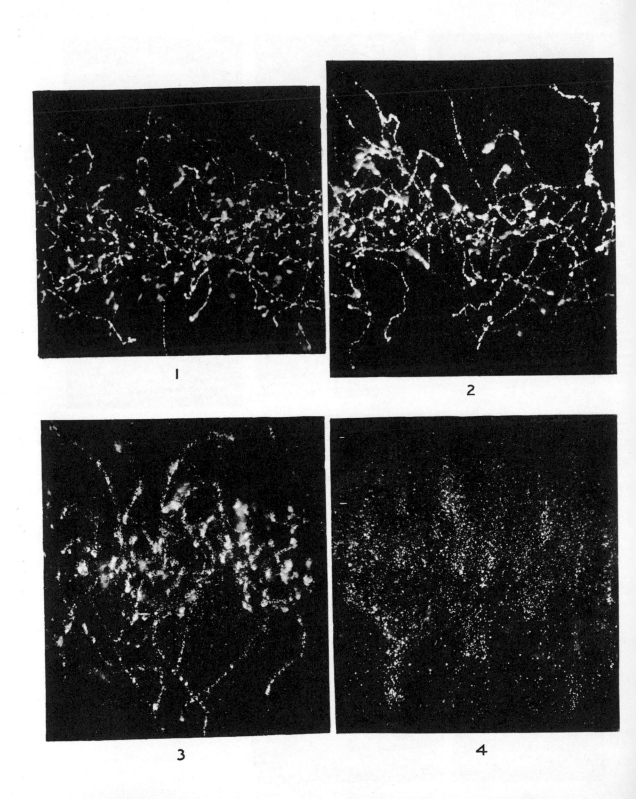

CHAPTER V

THE FIRST MASS-SPECTROGRAPH [1]

30. Limitations of the parabola method.—The parabola method of analysis of positive rays described in Chapter III, though almost ideal for a general survey of masses and velocities, has objections as a method of precision; many rays are lost by collision in the narrow canal-ray tube, the mean pressure in which must be at least half that in the discharge bulb; very fine tubes silt up by disintegration under bombardment; the total energy available for photography falls off as the fourth power of the diameter of the canal-ray tube.

The first two objections can be overcome, as will be described below, by replacing the brass or copper tube by fine apertures made in aluminium, a metal which appears to suffer little disintegration, and by exhausting the space between these apertures to the highest degree by means of a subsidiary charcoal tube or pump. The falling off in intensity of the parabolas as one attempts to make them finer is a very serious difficulty, as the accuracy and resolving power depend on the ratio of the thickness to the total magnetic deflexion; and if we increase the latter the electric deflexion must be increased to correspond and the parabolas are drawn out, resulting again in loss of intensity.

Also, the nature of the patch thrown on the plate by the use of a long circular tube will clearly be the same as that caused by the light from an evenly illuminated disc passing through a circular aperture of the same diameter, that is to say it will have a penumbra. Similarly the parabolic streak produced by an infinite series of such patches will not be particularly suitable for accurate measurements as it has no definite edges.

31. Methods of increasing the intensity of the spot.—The concentration of the stream of positive rays down the axis of the discharge bulb is very marked, but there is good evidence for assum-

---

[1] The word "mass-spectrograph" was originally intended to be used only for instruments in which the particular sequence of electric and magnetic fields here described is used to give a spectrum depending upon mass alone. As it has been found possible (*V.* p. 84) to produce photographed mass-spectra by other devices this restriction can no longer logically be insisted upon. For convenience, however, it will be retained in this book.

38

ing that the intense part of the stream occupies a considerable solid angle. This suggests the possibility of an increase of intensity by means of a device which should select the rays aimed at a particular spot on the plate, whatever direction they come from. For example, a thin gap between two coaxial equiangular cones would allow the rays to be concentrated at the vertex. The dimensions of the patch formed would be roughly those of one given by a cylindrical canal-ray tube of diameter equal to the width of the gap. The increase of intensity would therefore be considerable ; but the method is not easy to put into practice, and, in the case of deflexions through large angles, would necessitate a curved photographic surface.

Clearly the simplest way of increasing the intensity of the spot without increasing its dimensions, at any rate in one direction, is to use two parallel straight slits. In the case of the parabola method this device would only be of use in a special case such as the resolution of a close double, as the parabolas will only be sharp at points where they are parallel to the slit.

Such a slit system eliminates the difficulty of the penumbra mentioned above, at any rate so far as measurements at right angles to the line image are concerned.

32.—Possibilities of " focussing."—Beams of charged particles which are homogeneous electrically (constant mv^2/e) or magnetically (constant mv/e) can be focussed like rays of light by special devices.[1] The method of Dempster, described in the previous chapter, makes use of a form of magnetic focussing. But the rays generated by the ordinary discharge bulb are heterogeneous both in mv^2 and mv so that what is required is an arrangement which will focus all rays of constant mass, even though their velocity may vary over an appreciable range.

33. Principle of the Mass-spectrograph.—This purpose is achieved by the arrangement illustrated diagrammatically in Fig. 8. The exact mathematical analysis has been worked out by R. H. Fowler,[2] but it is proposed to give only the approximate theory here for the sake of simplicity.

The rays after arriving at the cathode face pass through two very narrow parallel slits of special construction S_1 S_2, and the resulting thin ribbon is spread out into an electric spectrum by means of the parallel plates P_1, P_2. After emerging from the electric field the rays may be taken, to a first order of approximation, as radiating from a virtual source Z half-way through the field on the line S_1 S_2. A group of these rays is now selected by means of the diaphragm D, and allowed

[1] Aston, *Phil. Mag.*, **38**, 709, 1919.
[2] Aston and Fowler, *Phil. Mag.*, **43**, 514, 1922.

to pass between the parallel poles of a magnet. For simplicity the poles are taken as circular, the field between them uniform and of such sign as to bend the rays in the opposite direction to the foregoing electric field.

If θ and φ be the angles (taken algebraically) through which the selected beam of rays is bent by passing through fields of strength X and H, then

$$\theta v^2 = lX\frac{e}{m} \text{ (1), and } \varphi v = LH\frac{e}{m} \text{ (2),}$$

where l, L are the lengths of the paths of the rays in the fields. Equation (1) is only true for small angles, but exact enough for practice.

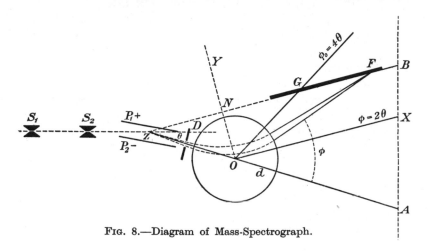

Fig. 8.—Diagram of Mass-Spectrograph.

It follows that over the small range of θ selected by the diaphragm θv^2 and φv are constant for all rays of given e/m, therefore

$$\frac{\delta\theta}{\theta} + \frac{2\delta v}{v} = 0, \text{ and } \frac{\delta\varphi}{\varphi} + \frac{\delta v}{v} = 0,$$

so that

$$\frac{\delta\theta}{\theta} = \frac{2\delta\varphi}{\varphi},$$

when the velocity varies in a group of rays of given e/m.

In order to illustrate in the simplest possible way how this relation may be used to obtain focussing, let us suppose the angles (exaggerated in the diagram) small and the magnetic field acting as if concentrated at the centre O of the pole-pieces. If the breadth ZO $= b$, the group selected will be spread out to a breadth $b\delta\theta$ at O, and at a further distance r the breadth will be

$$b\delta\theta + r(\delta\theta + \delta\varphi) \text{ or } \delta\theta \left[b + r\left(1 + \frac{\varphi}{2\theta}\right)\right] \quad . \quad . \quad . \quad (3)$$

Now as the electric and magnetic deflexions are in opposite directions, θ is a negative angle. Say $\theta = -\theta'$. Then if $\varphi > 2\theta'$, the quantity (3) will vanish at a value of r given by

$$r(\varphi - 2\theta') = b \cdot 2\theta'.$$

This equation appears correct within practical limits for large circular pole-pieces.

Referred to axes OX, OY the focus is at $r \cos (\varphi - 2\theta')$, $r \sin (\varphi - 2\theta')$, or r, $b.2\theta'$; so that to a first-order approximation, whatever the fields, so long as the position of the diaphragm is fixed, the foci will all lie on the straight line ZF drawn through Z parallel to OX. For purposes of construction G the image of Z in OY is a convenient reference point, φ being here equal to $4\theta'$. It is clear that a photographic plate, indicated by the thick line, will be in fair focus for values of e/m over a range large enough for accurate comparison of masses.

34. Optical analogue.—It may be a help to form an understanding of the principle of the apparatus if we suppose that the beam is one of white light and the electric and magnetic fields are glass prisms deflecting the light in opposite directions. The slit system acts as a collimator. If the glass of the first prism has a coefficient of dispersion double that of the second the heterogeneity of the rays of light will cause a spreading of the beam identical with that caused by heterogeneity (in respect to velocity) in the case of the positive rays. It will be clear that if we make the angle of refraction of the second prism more than double that of the first an achromatic image will appear at F.

Since it is a close analogue of the ordinary spectrograph and gives a " spectrum " depending upon mass alone the instrument is called a " mass-spectrograph " and the spectrum it produces a " mass-spectrum." It possesses one notable advantage over the optical spectrograph for, although we can never change the ratio of the dispersions, we can make the refractions whatever we will by the control of X and H, and so bring any desired range of the spectrum on to the plate.

35. The Discharge Tube.—Fig. 9 is a rough diagram of the original arrangement of the mass-spectrograph when used for analysing positive rays generated by the ordinary discharge tube method. The discharge tube B is an ordinary X-ray bulb 20 cm. in diameter. The anode A is of aluminium wire surrounded concentrically by an insulated aluminium tube to protect the glass walls, as in the Lodge valve.

The aluminium cathode C, 2·5 cm. wide, is concave, and placed just in the neck of the bulb—this shape and position having been adopted after a short preliminary research.[1] In order to protect the opposite end of the bulb, which would be immediately melted by the very concentrated beam of cathode rays, a silica bulb D is mounted as indicated. The use of silica as an anticathode has the great advantage of cutting down the production of undesirable X-rays to a minimum. The cathode was earthed.

The discharge was maintained by means of a large induction-coil actuated by a mercury coal-gas break ; about 100 to 150 watts were

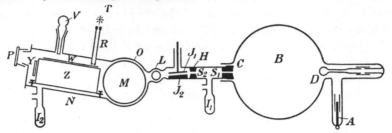

FIG. 9.—Diagram of the First Mass-Spectrograph.

passed through the primary, and the bulb arranged to take from 0·5 to 1 milliampere at potentials ranging from 20,000 to 50,000 volts. Owing to the particular shape and position of the electrodes, especially those of the anode, the bulb acts perfectly as its own rectifier.

The method of mounting the cathode will be readily seen from Fig. 10, which shows part of the apparatus in greater detail. The neck of the bulb is ground off short and cemented with wax to the

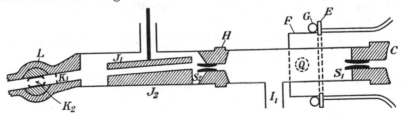

FIG. 10.—Mounting of Cathode of First Mass-Spectrograph.

flat brass collar E, which forms the mouth of an annular space between a wide outer tube F and the inner tube carrying the cathode. The concentric position of the neck is assured by three small ears of brass not shown. The wax joint was kept cool by circulating water through the copper pipe shown in section at G.

The gas to be analysed was admitted from the fine leak into the annular space and so to the discharge by means of the side-tube attached to F shown in dotted section at Q. Exhaustion was performed by a Gaede mercury-pump through a similar tube on the

[1] Aston, *Proc. Camb. Phil. Soc.*, **19**, 317, 1919.

opposite side. The reason for this arrangement is that the space behind the cathode is the only part of the discharge bulb in which the gas is not raised to an extremely high potential. If the inlet or outlet is anywhere in front of the cathode, failing special guards, the discharge is certain to strike to the pump or the gas reservoir. Such special guards have been made in the past by means of dummy cathodes in the bore of the tubes, but, notwithstanding the fact that the gas can only reach the bulb by diffusion, this arrangement is far more satisfactory and has the additional advantage of enabling the bulb to be dismounted by breaking one joint only.

36. The Slit System.—The very fine slits used in this apparatus were made with comparative ease as follows : A cylinder of pure aluminium about 10 mm. long by 5 mm. wide is carefully bored with a hole 1 mm. diameter. The resulting thick-walled tube is then cleaned and crushed with a hammer on an anvil until the circular hole becomes a slit about 0·3 mm. wide. Continuation of this treatment would result in a slit as fine as required giving the maximum resistance to the passage of gas, but its great depth would make the lining up of a pair a matter of extreme difficulty. The crushed tube is therefore now placed between two V-shaped pieces of steel and further crushed between the points of the V's at about its middle point until the required fineness is attained. Practice shows that the best way of doing this is to crush until the walls just touch, and then to open the slit to the required width by judicious tapping at right angles to that previously employed. With a little care it is possible to make slits with beautifully parallel sides to almost any degree of fineness, 0·01 mm. being easily attainable. At this stage the irregularly shaped piece of aluminium is not suited to accurate gas-tight fitting ; it is therefore filled with hard paraffin to protect it from small particles of metal, etc., which if entering cannot be dislodged owing to its shape, and turned up taper to fit the standard mountings. After turning, the paraffin is easily removed by heat and solvents.

The position of the two slits is indicated in the diagram. They were roughly 0·05 mm. wide by 2 mm. long and could be accurately adjusted parallel to each other by means of their diffraction patterns. The space between them was exhausted by the liquid-air-cooled charcoal tube I_1.

37. The Electric Field.—The spreading of the heterogeneous ribbon of rays formed by the slits into an electric spectrum took place between two parallel flat brass surfaces, J_1, J_2, 5 cm. long, held 2·8 mm. apart by glass distance-pieces, the whole system being wedged immovably in the brass containing-tube in the position shown. The lower surface was earthed. The upper surface was raised to the desired potential, 200–500 volts, by means of a set of small storage-cells. In order to have the plates as near together as possible, they were sloped at 1 in 20—i.e. half the angle of slope of the mean ray of the part of the spectrum which is to be selected by the diaphragms. Of these there are two : one, K_1, an oblong aperture in a clean brass plate, is fixed just in front of the second movable one, K_2, which is mounted in the bore of a carefully ground stopcock L. The function of the first diaphragm is to prevent any possibility of charged rays striking the greasy surface of the plug of the stopcock when the latter is in any working position. The variable diaphragm is in effect two square apertures sliding past each other as the plug of the stopcock is turned, the fact that they are not in the same plane being irrelevant. When the stopcock is fully open as sketched in Fig. 10 the angle of rays passing is a maximum, and it may be stopped down to any desired extent by rotation of the plug, becoming zero before any greasy surface is exposed to the rays. Incidentally the stopcock serves another and very convenient use, which is to cut off the camera from the discharge tube, so that the latter need not be filled with air each time the former is opened to change the plate.

38. The Magnetic Field.—After leaving the diaphragms the rays passed between the pole-pieces M of a large Du Bois magnet of 2500 turns. The faces of these are circular, 8 cm. diameter, and held 3 mm. apart by brass distance-pieces. The cylindrical pole-pieces themselves are soldered into a brass tube O, which forms part of the camera N. When the latter is built into position, the pole-pieces are drawn by screwed bolts into the arms of the magnet, and so form a structure of great weight and rigidity and provide an admirable foundation for the whole apparatus. Current for the magnet was provided by a special set of large accumulators. With a potential of 300 volts on the electric plates the hydrogen lines are brought on to the scale at about 0·2 ampere, and an increase to 5 amperes, which gives practical saturation, only just brings the singly-charged mercury lines into view. The discharge is protected from the stray field of the magnet by the usual soft iron plates, not shown.

39. The Camera.—The main body of the camera N, which is exhausted by the charcoal tube I_2, is made of stout brass tube 6·4 cm. diameter, shaped to fit on to the transverse tube O containing the pole-pieces. The construction of the plate-holder is indicated by the side view in Fig. 9 and an end-on view in Fig. 11. The rays after being magnetically deflected passed between two vertical earthed brass plates Z, Z about 3 mm. apart, and finally reached the photographic plate through a narrow slot 2 mm. wide, 11·8 cm. long, cut in the horizontal metal plate X, X. The three brass plates forming a T-shaped girder are adjusted and locked in position by a set of three levelling-screws, at each end ; the right-hand upper one is omitted in Fig. 11. The plates Z, Z serve to protect the rays completely from any stray electric field, even that caused by the photographic plate itself becoming charged, until within a few millimetres of their point of impact.

The photographic plate W, which is a 2 cm. strip cut lengthwise from a 5 × 4 plate, is supported at its ends on two narrow transverse rails which raise it just clear of the plate X, X. Normally it lies to the right of the slot as indicated, and to make an exposure it is moved parallel to itself over the slot by means of a sort of double lazy-tongs carrying wire claws which bracket the ends of the plate as shown. This mechanism, which is not shown in detail, is operated by means of a torque rod V working through a ground glass joint. Y is a small willemite screen.

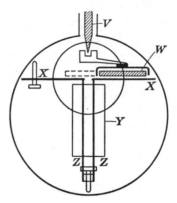

FIG. 11.—The Plateholder of the Camera.

The adjustment of the plate-holder so that the sensitized surface should be at the best focal plane was done by taking a series of exposures of the bright hydrogen lines with different magnetic fields on a large plate placed in the empty camera at a small inclination to the vertical. On developing this, the actual track of the rays could be seen and the locus of points of maximum concentration determined. The final adjustment was made by trial and error and was exceedingly tedious, as air had to be admitted and a new plate inserted after each tentative small alteration of the levelling-screws.

40. Experimental procedure.—The plate having been dried in a high vacuum overnight, the whole apparatus was exhausted as completely as possible by the pump with the stopcock L open. I_1 and I_2 were then cut off from the pump by stopcocks and immersed in liquid air for an hour or so. The electric field, which ranged from 200 to 500 volts, was then applied and a small current passed through the magnet sufficient to bring the bright hydrogen molecule spot on to the willemite screen Y, where it could be inspected through the plate-glass back of the cap P. In the meantime the leak, pump, and coil, had all been started to get the bulb into the desired state.

When this was steady, J_1 was earthed, to prevent any rays reaching the camera, and the plate moved over the slot to its first position. The magnet current having been set to the particular value desired and the diaphragm adjusted, the coil was momentarily interrupted and J_1 raised to the desired potential, after which the exposure took place. During this, preferably both at the beginning and the end, light from a lamp T was admitted for a few seconds down the tube R (Fig. 9) the ends of which are pierced with two tiny circular holes. The lower hole is very close to the plate, so that a circular dot or fiducial spot is formed from which the measurements of the lines may be made.

The exposures ranged from 20 seconds in the case of hydrogen lines to 30 minutes or more, 15 minutes being usually enough. As soon as it was complete the above procedure was repeated, and the plate moved into the second position. In this way as many as six spectra could be taken on one plate, after which L was shut, I_2 warmed up, and air admitted to the camera. The cap P, which is on a ground joint, could now be removed, and the exposed plate seized and taken out with a special pair of forceps. A fresh plate was now immediately put in, P replaced and the camera again exhausted, in which state it was left till the next operation.

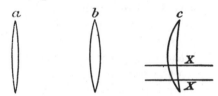

FIG. 12.—Form of the Spectrum Lines.

41. Form of the Spectrum Lines.—Owing to the form of the slits used, the shape of the spot formed when undeflected rays from such a slit system strike a photograph surface normally, is somewhat as indicated at a (Fig. 12). When they strike the plate obliquely the image would be spread out in one direction, as in b. This would be the actual form in the apparatus if the deflecting fields were unaffected by the passage of the rays. This appears to be the case in the magnetic field, but owing to an obscure polarizing effect [1] the electric field is weakened in the region of the beam, allowing rays of smaller energy to pass the diaphragm. As this effect is greatest in the centre this part of the beam will be more deflected by the magnet and the spot will take the form shown at c.

The image on the plate will therefore be the part of this figure falling on the narrow slot in X, X ; and as the apparatus is not exactly symmetrical, its shape in the spectra is the figure lying between the lines X, X in Fig. 12, c.

42. The distribution of the mass-spectrum over the photographic plate.—In order to study the positions of the focus F (Fig. 8)

[1] V. p. 77.

on the plate corresponding to different values of the effective mass m when X and H are constant, we may assume perfect focussing and only consider a single median ray. If R is the radius of curvature of the path of a ray of effective mass m while in the magnetic field, and d the radius of the field, clearly $\tan \frac{1}{2} \varphi = d/\text{R}$. But X and θ are constant, hence mv^2 must be constant so that the radius of curvature in the magnetic field varies as $\sqrt{m}$. We may therefore write

$$\tan \tfrac{1}{2} \varphi = \sqrt{(m_0/m)} \quad . \qquad . \qquad . \qquad . \quad (4)$$

where m_0 is a constant and can be interpreted as that mass which under the conditions of the experiment is bent through a right angle in the magnetic field.

Again if ON the length of the perpendicular dropped from the centre of the magnetic field upon $ZF = p$ (a constant) then

$$\text{NF} = p \cot (\varphi - 2\theta) \quad . \qquad . \qquad . \quad (5)$$

By combining (4) and (5) we get an expression for NF/p in terms of m_0 and m. This is complicated,[1] but its differential can be shown to vanish when $\tan \frac{1}{2} \varphi = \tan 2\theta$. Thus the mass-scale is approximately linear near $\varphi = 4\theta$.

This linear law was observed experimentally at the very outset and though at the time it was unexplained it added greatly to the ease and accuracy of the determinations of m.

The quantity actually measured is the distance between a fixed point on the photographic plate called the "fiducial spot"[2] and the focussed image F. Let us call this distance D. D and NF differ by a constant k—about 5·4 cm. in the apparatus—so that the relation between D and m has the form $D = f(m/m_0)$ where f is a function in which all the coefficients p, k, and $\tan 2\theta$ are geometrical constants, the fields only affect m_0. It follows directly that so long as the apparatus is rigid :—If D_1 and D_2 are the distances from the fiducial spot of any two points on the plate and m_1 and m_2 the corresponding masses for given values of D_1 and D_2, the ratio m_1/m_2 will be the same in every photograph.

43. Practical method of deducing the effective mass of a particle from the position of its line on the photograph.—The mathematical investigation described above is of interest as it explains the results obtained, but the actual determination of masses from mass-spectra was a purely empirical process, and consisted in the comparison of the positions of the lines caused by the masses in question with the positions of known reference lines. The only assumption made was that given at the end of the previous paragraph and even this was capable of verification by experiment, using such methods

[1] Aston and **Fowler**, *Phil. Mag.*, **43**, 515, 1922.   [2] *V.* p. 46.

as that described below, or even more fundamentally, in the special case of the ratio 2/1, by the known identity of the mass ratios O_2/O. O/O^{++}, and C/C^{++}.

The reference lines used at the outset of the work were lines given by particles of elements and compounds the relative masses of which were known to at least the order of accuracy aimed for. The procedure was somewhat as follows. A series of spectra were taken with say a mixture of CO_2 and CH_4 in the discharge tube. Previous experience with the parabola method of analysis led to the expectation that lines at $6-C^{++}$, $8-O^{++}$, $12-C$, $16-O$, $28-CO$, $32-O_2$, $44-CO_2$ would certainly be present, there would also be a series of hydrocarbon lines between 12 and 16, CH, CH_2, CH_3 which could be regarded as known. A spectrum was selected containing as many as possible of these known lines and their masses m_1, m_2, m_3,—were plotted against the distances of the lines from the fixed fiducial spot and a curve drawn through the points so obtained. This is our first *calibration curve*— of necessity inaccurate owing to the gaps between the points. A second spectrum was now taken in which the same lines appeared in a different place, for by altering the magnetic field we can place them wherever we please, and the new set of distances from the fiducial spot measured. These distances were now transformed into masses (no longer integral) m'_1, m'_2, m'_3,—by means of the curve previously drawn. Supposing the curve to be accurate and the ratio law to hold

$$\frac{m'_1}{m_1} = \frac{m'_2}{m_2} = \frac{m'_3}{m_3} = r$$

where r is clearly a measure of the change in m_0 in the mathematical discussion above. In practice these ratios were found to be very nearly the same, so that a mean value of r could be taken with confidence. The known masses multiplied by that mean now gave a new set of points on the original curve. By carrying on this process all the serious gaps in the curve could be bridged and its accuracy brought up to the required standard.

The calibration curve so formed renders the identification of one line sufficient to deduce the masses corresponding to all the other lines on the plate, and as in general many lines are known on each spectrum, its accuracy is continually subject to fresh test. In practice it was found perfectly reliable so long as none of the geometrical constants of the apparatus were altered.

44. Comparison of masses by the method of " coincidence." —The method of deducing the masses of particles from the position of their lines described in the foregoing paragraph is simple and straight-forward. It also has the great advantage of not requiring an accurate knowledge of the numerical values of the electric and magnetic fields. The only requisite is that these should be constant during the exposure,

and even if this constancy is not quite perfect the shift in position
will affect all the lines known and unknown alike and therefore introduce no serious error into the results obtained.   There is, however,
another method of comparing masses which requires no knowledge,
either theoretical or empirical, of the relation between effective mass
and measured displacement.   This is independent of the calibration
curve and therefore constitutes a valuable check on results obtained
by its use.   It depends upon the following considerations : Suppose
we wish to compare an unknown mass m' with a known mass m.   A
mass-spectrum is taken with fields X and H such that the mass m
gives a line at a certain position on the plate.   The fields are now
altered until the line caused by the unknown mass m' is brought to
the identical position on the plate previously occupied by the line
due to m.   The paths of the rays in the two cases must be identical,
hence if X′, H′ are the new values of the fields it follows at once from
equations (1) and (2) [1] that $m'/m = X/X' \times (H'/H)^2$.   Now it is
only necessary to measure one of the fields if we keep the other constant and therefore H, which cannot be measured or reproduced accurately, was kept constant and X was assumed to be proportional to
the potential applied to the plates P_1, P_2.   Thus the position occupied
by the line 12 due to carbon with a potential on the plates of 320
volts should be exactly coincident with that occupied by line 16 due
to oxygen with 240 volts, when the magnetic field was held constant.
All such coincidences were found to occur to the accuracy then
attainable.

Methods depending on the measured variation of X with H constant have some practical disadvantages.   The first and most obvious
of these is that any small change in the value of the magnetic field
between the two exposures will lead to a definite error, this error will
be double the percentage change in the field, since the square of the
latter is involved.   The second objection is founded on considerations
of intensity.   If the parabola method of analysis is compared with
the mass-spectrograph it will readily be observed that, in effect, the
latter focusses at a point all the rays which in the former method
form a short element of arc on a parabola.   The length of the element
of arc is determined by the angle of the electric spectrum allowed to
pass, i.e. the width of the diaphragm.   Its position on the parabola
is at our disposal, for, referring to Fig. 4, p. 26, it will be seen that
the higher we make X, that is to say the higher the energy of the
beam of rays we select at constant θ, the nearer the element of arc
will approach the axis OY, in fact its distance from that axis will
simply be inversely proportional to X.   Also, however many parabolas
we consider and however much we move them about by changing H,

E

so long as X is constant the elements of arc selected will all lie on a line parallel to OY. Now it has already been pointed out [1] that the intensity of normal parabolas is a maximum near the head p, where the energy corresponds to the full fall of potential across the discharge tube, and fades away rapidly, in some cases very rapidly indeed, at points more distant from the origin. In order to get the greatest intensity at the focussed spot we must therefore choose X so that the element of arc selected will be near the head of the parabola. This is done in practice by observing visually, by means of a willemite screen, the very bright line given by the hydrogen molecule while different potentials are applied to the plates. The best value of X so determined must also be the best value for all the other normal lines, so that in the ordinary calibration curve method, when X is kept constant, it is possible to use conditions in which all the normal lines on the mass-spectra will be at their brightest together, whatever range we bring on to the plate by altering the magnetic field.

In the coincidence method this very fortunate circumstance cannot be taken advantage of, for with H constant the selected elements of arc will now lie on a line parallel to OX. We can only arrange matters for one, the lighter, of the two masses to be compared, to be at its optimum. In the case of the heavier the selected arc must lie at a greater distance from the origin and therefore provide a much feebler intensity. The disparity in brightness, due to this effect, will be the greater the greater the ratio of the masses considered; it can be corrected to some degree by softening the discharge tube while the heavier mass is being photographed.

In spite of these drawbacks the principle of the method of coincidences has been the underlying one in the development of methods of precision. Its first notable application was in the measurements of the masses of helium and hydrogen.

45. The determination of the masses of atoms of hydrogen and helium by the method of " Bracketing."—The determination of masses so far removed as these from the ordinary reference lines offers peculiar difficulties, but, as the lines were expected to approximate to the terms of the geometrical progression 1, 2, 4, 8, etc., the higher terms of which are known, a special method was adopted by which a two to one relation could be tested with some exactness. Two sets of accumulators were selected, each giving very nearly the same potential of about 250 volts. The potentials were then made exactly equal by means of a subsidiary cell and a current-divider, the equality being tested to well within 1 in 1000 by means of a null instrument. If exposures are made with such potentials applied to

[1] P. 26.

the electric plates first in parallel and then in series, then magnetic field being kept constant, all masses having an exact two to one relation will be brought into coincidence on the plate.[1] Such coincidences cannot be detected on the same spectrum photographically ; but if we first add and then subtract a small potential from one of the large potentials, two lines will be obtained which closely bracket the third. To take an actual instance—using a gas containing hydrogen and helium, with a constant current in the magnet of $0 \cdot 2$ ampere, three exposures were made with electric fields of 250, $500 + 12$, and $500 - 12$ volts respectively. The hydrogen molecule line was found symmetrically bracketed by a pair of atomic lines (Plate III, Spectrum VII, a and c), showing within experimental error that the mass of the molecule is exactly double the mass of the atom. When after a suitable increase of the magnetic field the same procedure was applied to the helium line and that of the hydrogen molecule, the bracket was no longer symmetrical (Spectrum VII, b), nor was it when the hydrogen molecule was bracketed by two helium lines (d). Both results show in an unmistakable manner that the mass of He is less than twice that of H_2. In the same way He was compared with O^{++}, and H_3.[2] The method is discussed on p. 49. The values obtained by its use can be checked in the ordinary way by comparing He with C^{++} and H_3 with He, these pairs being close enough together for the purpose. The following table gives the range of values obtained from the most reliable plates :

Line.	Method.	Mass assumed.		Mass deduced.
He	{ Bracket	O^{++}	$= 8$	$3 \cdot 994 - 3 \cdot 996$
	{ Direct	C^{++}	$= 6$	$4 \cdot 005 - 4 \cdot 010$
H_3	{ Bracket	C^{++}	$= 6$	$3 \cdot 025 - 3 \cdot 027$
	{ Direct	He	$= 4$	$3 \cdot 021 - 3 \cdot 030$
H_2	Bracket	He	$= 4$	$2 \cdot 012 - 2 \cdot 018$

These figures led to the conclusion that hydrogen was a simple element and that the mass of its atom corresponded to the chemical atomic weight and was definitely divergent from a whole number. Incidentally they furnished conclusive proof that the body of mass 3 first observed and investigated by Sir J. J. Thomson[3] was actually a molecule consisting of three hydrogen atoms, a result independently established about the same time by the chemical work of Wendt and Landauer.[4]

[1] V. p. 48.   [2] V. p. 100.
[3] J. J. Thomson, *Rays of Positive Electricity*, p. 116, 1913.
[4] Wendt and Landauer, *Jour. Amer. Chem. Soc.*, **42**, 930, 1920.

46. The measurement of the lines.—The accurate determination of the distance of the lines from the fiducial spot is a physical problem of considerable interest. The image itself is due to a caustic of rays, the edge of which will be sharp on the side of maximum magnetic displacement, so that this, the left side in the plates, may be expected to maintain its sharpness when a large diaphragm is in use, while the other will fade away gradually. Hence very bright lines will be broadened to the right by this effect (which is analogous to spherical astigmatism in ordinary lenses), but to the left the only broadening will be that due to ordinary halation. The relative importance of these two forms of spreading can be gauged by taking photographs with a very small diaphragm, for then the first will be eliminated and the second can be estimated by comparing lines of different intensity. It is found that for ordinary diaphragm apertures the halation effect is much the smaller ; it can also be minimized by using lines of approximately equal intensity so that the most reliable measurements of lines for position are obtained from their left-hand edges. This is well illustrated in the " bracketed " lines of hydrogen *a* and *c*, Plate III. In (*a*) measurements of the left-hand side of the three lines shows this bracket to be really symmetrical though it does not appear so to the eye, on account of the astigmatic spreading of the middle line caused by the use of an open diaphragm and rather too long an exposure. In (*c*) the diaphragm was almost closed and the exposures more carefully adjusted, so that both sides of the lines are sharp and their breadths practically identical.

The most accurate measurements were made on a comparator. The spectrum was set as closely as possible parallel to the axis of the instrument, and the distances between the left-hand edge of the lines and the fiducial spot read off on a Zeiss standard scale. For faint lines it was necessary to use a very low power eyepiece of the reading microscope, and in the case of the faintest lines of all, the best results could be obtained by laying a millimetre scale on the plate and estimating the distance from the fiducial spot to the optical centre of the lines, by the unaided eye.

47. Resolving power and accuracy of mass determination.—Taking the width of the slits as 1/25 mm. and putting in the dimensions of the apparatus the theory shows that in the region $\varphi = 4\theta$ lines differing by a little less than 1 per cent. should be just separated. In actual practice a better result was obtained, for the instrument proved capable of separating the lines of xenon, which differ by 1 in 130 ; this is probably because the part of the line which falls on the strip of plate exposed is due to the narrower edges of the slits.

The numerical relation between mass and position in this part of the spectrum corresponds to a shift of 1·39 mm. for a change of mass of 1 per cent., so that even with the unaided eye an accuracy of 1 part in 1000 could be approached. Although it is sufficient in theory to know the mass of one line only to determine, with the calibration curve, the masses of all the others, in practice every effort was made to bracket any unknown line by reference lines and only to trust comparative measurements when the lines are fairly close together. Under these conditions an accuracy of 1 in 1000 was attainable.

48. Lines of the First, Second and higher Orders.—It was shown on page 27 that particles having two charges gave a parabola corresponding to an effective mass of one-half the normal mass. In the same way a particle with three charges will have an effective mass of one-third, and so on. These apparent masses will duly make their appearance on mass-spectra as lines corresponding to simple fractions of the real mass causing them. It is convenient in these cases to borrow the nomenclature of optics and refer to the lines given by singly, doubly, and multiply charged particles respectively as lines of the first, second, and higher orders. Thus the molecule of oxygen gives a first-order line at 32, and its atom first- and second-order lines at 16 and 8.

49. Molecular lines of the Second Order.—The work of Sir J. J. Thomson on multiply charged positive rays showed very definitely that molecules carrying more than one charge were at least exceedingly rare,[1] for not a single case was observed which could not be explained on other grounds. Up to the time of the experiments with the fluorine compounds the same could be said of the results with the mass-spectrograph. This absence of multiply charged molecular lines, though there is no particular theoretical reason for it, was used as confirmatory evidence on the elementary nature of doubtful lines.

The spectra obtained with BF_3 show lines for which there appears no possibility of explanation except that of doubly charged compound molecules. The two most obvious of these may be seen on Plate IV, Spectrum III, and at the extreme left-hand end of Spectrum IV. They correspond to masses 23·50 and 24·50, the first being quite a strong line. Were there no lines of lower order corresponding to these, the whole-number rule might be in question; but all doubt is removed by the fact that the lines 47 and 49 are two of the strongest on the plate. A comparison of several spectra upon which these lines occur shows a definite intensity relation which practically confirms the conclusion that the first pair of lines are true second-order lines corresponding to the first-order lines of the second pair. Now lines

[1] J. J. Thomson, *Rays of Positive Electricity*, p. 54.

47 and 49 cannot by any reasonable argument be elementary, they must in fact be due to compounds of fluorine.

50. Negative mass-spectra.—It has been mentioned that positive rays could become negatively charged by the capture of electrons by collisions in the narrow canal-ray tube of the Thomson apparatus, and so produce parabolas in the quadrant opposite to that containing the normal ones. The slit system of the mass-spectrograph is specially designed to eliminate such collisions as far as possible by exhausting the space between the slits. If the means of exhaustion of this space is deliberately cut off, and the normal electric and magnetic fields both reversed in sign it is possible, at a small cost in definition of the lines, to photograph the mass-spectra of negatively charged particles. Such negatively charged particles are only formed by elements or compounds having marked electronegative properties.

51. Mass-numbers.—The problem of nomenclature of the isotopes became serious when the complex nature of the heavy elements was proved. The plan generally adopted at present is to use the chemical symbol of the complex element with an index corresponding to its mass : e.g. Ne^{22}, Rb^{87}. This index is called the " mass-number " of the atom. It may be defined in two ways. Theoretically, it is the number of protons in the atom, practically it is the nearest whole number to its weight expressed on the ordinary chemical scale. These integers are identical in all cases so far as our knowledge extends at present.

52. Results obtained with the First Mass-spectrograph.—The original instrument, adapted from time to time to suit particular needs, was in continual use from 1919 till it was dismantled in 1925, with results which will be given in Part III. Typical spectra obtained by its means are reproduced in Plates III and IV. The first experiments were done on neon and the spectra obtained gave the first entirely satisfactory proof that this consisted of isotopes each of whole number mass.[1] As the work progressed with chlorine and other complex elements it soon became clear that all atoms had masses which were integrally related to a close approximation, the " whole number rule." Hydrogen, as theoretically expected, was found to be an exception to this. Indications were obtained that other elements such as lithium and iron would show similar but smaller variations, but the measurement of these required more powerful instruments and methods the development of which will now be described.

[1] Aston, *Phil. Mag.*, **39**, 449, 1920.

PLATE II

THE ORIGINAL MASS-SPECTROGRAPH SET UP IN THE CAVENDISH LABORATORY IN 1919;
NOW IN THE SCIENCE MUSEUM, SOUTH KENSINGTON.

B, Discharge Tube. *A*, Anode connected to high potential terminal of induction coil below table. *C*, Reservoir containing gas to be analysed. *I₁*, *I₂*, Charcoal-liquid air tubes exhausting slit-system and camera. *S*, Soft iron plates to shield discharge from stray magnetic field. *L*, Leads from high tension battery to electric plates. *M*, Du Bois electromagnet. *T*, Pea lamp for photographing fiducial spot. *V*, Vacuum-tight and light-tight control for moving photographic plate. *W*, Camera showing light-tight cap on the left. *H*, Magnet circuit ammeter. *O*, Magnet circuit control resistances. *G*, Gaede rotating mercury pump connected to the camera and the discharge tube by glass tubes and stopcocks.

PLATE III

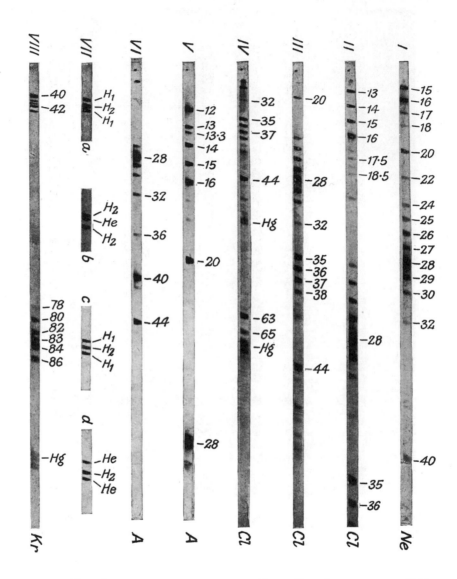

TYPICAL MASS-SPECTRA OBTAINED WITH THE FIRST MASS-SPECTROGRAPH, 1920.

PLATE IV

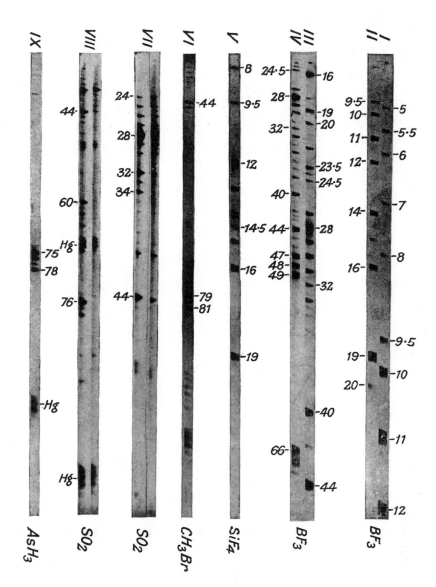

TYPICAL MASS-SPECTRA OBTAINED WITH THE FIRST MASS-SPECTROGRAPH, 1920.